MISTLETOE PROPOSAL ON THE CHILDREN'S WARD

KATE HARDY

TAMING HER HOLLYWOOD PLAYBOY

EMILY FORBES

MILLS & BOON

First Published in Great Britain 2019
by Mills & Boon, an imprint of HarperCollins*Publishers*
1 London Bridge Street, London, SE1 9GF

Mistletoe Proposal on the Children's Ward © 2019 by Pamela Brooks

Taming Her Hollywood Playboy © 2019 by Emily Forbes

ISBN: 978-0-263-26998-7

MIX
Paper from
responsible sources
FSC® C007454

This book is produced from independently certified FSC™ paper
to ensure responsible forest management.
For more information visit www.harpercollins.co.uk/green.

Printed and bound in Spain
by CPI, Barcelona

MISTLETOE PROPOSAL ON THE CHILDREN'S WARD

KATE HARDY

MILLS & BOON

To Gerard, Chris and Chloe,
who always make Christmas special to me.

CHAPTER ONE

'How are the ward Christmas things coming on, Anna?' Robert Jones asked.

'Brilliant, thanks.' Anna smiled at the head of the Children's Department. 'The Secret Santa is pretty much sorted, we've got Christmas dinner booked and most people have given me their deposits and menu choices, and the only thing I'm short of now is someone to be Father Christmas on Christmas Day.' Her smile broadened. 'Seeing as our usual Santa has let us down horribly.'

Robert held up both hands in a 'stop' gesture and laughed. 'Anna, you know why I can't do it this year. I'd have to fly back from New York. And that's more than my life is worth, on my silver wedding anniversary.'

'Even for the ward? Even for me?' she teased.

'Even for the ward and even for you,' Robert said. 'Actually, Anna, I did want to ask you a bit of a favour. Jamie Thurston—the new paediatric orthopod who's covering Nalini's maternity leave for the first three months—is joining us today.'

'And you want me to show him around and help him settle in?' Anna guessed.

'Would you?' Robert asked.

'Of course.' She smiled at him again. 'I'm in the PAU this morning. I'll leave a message with whoever is on the desk to ask him to meet me at one and I'll take him to lunch.'

'Great.' Robert patted her shoulder. 'Thank you.'

'Pleasure,' Anna said, and had a quick word with Lacey on the reception desk before she headed for the Paediatric Assessment Unit.

Her third patient of the day was a four-month-old baby who had been referred to her clinic by the health visitor, on the grounds of possible DDH—developmental dysplasia of the hip. A quick read through the notes ticked all the boxes of a higher risk: Poppy Byford was a first baby, a girl, born at thirty-six weeks and had been in the breech position. So Anna was pretty sure that the health visitor had picked up the problem.

'Good morning, Ms Byford. Do come in and let's have a look at Poppy,' Anna said. 'Hello, you gorgeous girl.' She cooed at the baby, who giggled and waved her hands. 'She's beautiful,' Anna said, and stuffed the little twinge of longing right back down out of the way. She could enjoy being an aunt and enjoy working with her young patients, and that was enough. Wanting more was greedy and pointless—and the quickest way to get her heart broken.

'Thank you.' Poppy's mum looked nervous.

'Your health visitor asked you to bring Poppy to see me because she thinks Poppy might have something called developmental dysplasia of the hip—you might hear it called DDH for short, or "clicky hip",' Anna explained. 'Usually it shows up in a newborn examination, and I can see in Poppy's notes that the doctor did a hip test at her six-week check and it seemed normal. But the health visitor's concerned and wants me to do another check.'

'Is Poppy going to be all right?' Ms Byford asked. 'I did start looking it up on the Internet, but…' She grimaced.

'The Internet is a very scary place where medical problems conditions are concerned,' Anna said. 'It's like when you're pregnant with your first child, and you always hear the horror stories about difficult labours rather than the smooth ones, even though the difficult ones are much rarer. There is a possibility that Poppy might grow out of the condition, but I'd like to examine her properly and then do an ultrasound scan to check how her hip is developing.' She smiled. 'I promise what I do isn't going to hurt her, but she might not appreciate being manipulated and might grumble a bit.'

'All right,' Ms Byford said.

'Have you noticed when you change her nappy that one hip doesn't open out quite as much as the other?' Anna asked.

Ms Byford wrinkled her nose. 'Not really. I thought everything was normal. I mean—she's my only one.'

'So you don't have anything to compare her with. That's fine.' Anna gave her a reassuring smile. 'Could you take her tights off for me, please?'

Once Ms Byford had taken the tights off the baby, Anna examined Poppy and cooed at her while she manipulated the baby's joints, blowing raspberries to make her laugh.

'So do you think she has this clicky hip thing?' Ms Byford asked.

'I felt a bit of a clunk when I moved her legs just

now, so yes,' Anna said. 'I can see that her right leg is slightly shorter than the left, and basically I think her thigh bone isn't moving properly in the socket of her pelvis. We'll do the scan, and then we can think about treatment. It might be that we do a watch-and-wait thing, or we might put her in a special harness to treat the hip dysplasia, but I'll be in a better position to know what'll work best once I've seen the scan results. And the scan's like the one you had when you were pregnant with her, so it won't hurt,' she added reassuringly.

While Poppy was having her scan, Anna saw her next patient. The scan results definitely showed a problem with Poppy's hip, but whether the harness would be enough or the baby would need treatment with traction, she wasn't sure.

'I'm going to have a word with one of my colleagues,' she said to Ms Byford. 'He's a specialist in children's bones, and I'd like to check a couple of things with him. I'm sorry, I'm afraid it means a bit more waiting about for you, but please try not to worry because this really is something we can sort out for Poppy.'

To her relief, the new paediatric orthopod was in one of the offices, reviewing notes for his operating list the next day. She rapped on the open door. 'Mr Thurston?' she asked. 'I'm Anna Maskell, one of the special regs on the ward, and I've got a baby with clicky hip. She's a borderline case and I'm not sure if she needs an op, so would you mind reviewing her scan and treatment plan with me, please?'

'Sure,' he said, looking up from his notes.

His eyes were the most piercing cornflower blue, and Anna felt her pulse leap.

How completely inappropriate.

For a start, they were at work, and her patients always came first. Secondly, given that Jamie Thurston looked to be in his mid-thirties, he was probably already involved with someone; but, even if he wasn't, Anna wasn't looking for a relationship. Love wasn't on her list of things to do, not any more. It had taken her two years to put her heart back together since Johnny's affair and the disintegration of her marriage, and she wasn't planning to risk her heart breaking ever again.

'Thank you. Robert asked me earlier if I would show you around,' she added. 'I was due in the Paediatric Assessment Unit before you arrived, so I asked Lacey to pass on a message inviting you to lunch, as it's your first day and you probably haven't had a chance to find your way around yet.'

So this was Anna Maskell, the woman who'd left him that kind message, Jamie thought.

She was taller than average with broad shoulders, a shock of dark curly hair she'd tied back at the nape of her neck, and eyes the same green as the sea on a summer day; she was more like an Artemis than a delicate nymph, though it shocked him he was even thinking that way. For a moment, his tongue felt as if it had stuck to the roof of his mouth. Then he pulled himself together. 'Yes, she did tell me. Thank you. That was kind.'

'Pleasure. My patient?' She sounded businesslike, but kind rather than snippy.

'Of course.' He logged out of his screen and shifted his chair so she could draw up the scan for her patient.

'Poppy Byford is four months old,' Anna said. 'She has all the risk factors for DDH, but her newborn and six-week checks were completely normal. The health visitor was concerned that one hip wasn't opening out properly and referred her. I definitely felt a clunk when I manipulated her legs, and I don't think watch-and-wait is the right way forward for her, but I'm not sure whether to try a Pavlik harness for a couple of months or whether traction would be a better option—I'm hoping we might be able to get away without an operation, but I could really do with an orthopod's view. As I said, she's borderline.'

Jamie liked the way she was so clear in giving him the information he needed to help him make the clinical decision—and that she'd clearly thought the treatment options through before coming to see him.

'I agree, it looks borderline,' he said. 'As she's younger than six months, I agree that it would be better to start with something less invasive than an operation. Let's try a harness for three months,' he suggested, 'and we can give an ultrasound review of how her hips are developing every month.'

'Great. Thank you.' She smiled at him.

How strange that a smile could almost make him feel warm inside.

He hadn't felt warm since Hestia had died, three years ago.

Before he realised what he was doing, Jamie found himself looking at Anna's left hand. Ridiculous. Apart from the fact that not wearing a ring didn't mean she wasn't already committed elsewhere, he wasn't looking to get involved with anyone. No way could he face the emptiness of losing someone again and having to try to put his life back together again afterwards.

Work.

This was strictly work. End of.

'Would you like me to come and talk to Poppy's mum and fit the harness?' he asked.

'Would you mind?'

'Sure. I was only reviewing tomorrow's list, and that can wait. I'll come now.'

In the assessment unit, Anna introduced him swiftly to Poppy and her mum.

'The good news is,' Jamie said, 'we're not necessarily looking at an operation to help Poppy's hips. We can fit something called a Pavlik harness; it will keep her hips in the right position so they can develop properly.'

'Will it hurt?' Ms Byford asked.

'No. It's lightweight and made of fabric,' Anna said. 'You might find it a bit upsetting to see it, and Poppy might be a bit grizzly for the first few days, but it won't hurt her and she'll soon get used to it.'

'She'll need to wear it all the time,' Jamie added. 'It will be easier for you to put her in loose clothes while she's got the harness fitted.'

'Do I take it off when she has a bath?' Ms Byford asked.

'No. Just top and tail her rather than giving her a full bath,' Jamie said. 'We'll see you every week to adjust the harness as she grows, and she can have a proper bath here when we take the harness off, before we do the adjustment.'

'So how long will she have to wear this harness?' Ms Byford asked.

'Maybe for two or three months,' Jamie said. 'We'll give Poppy an ultrasound scan every month to see how her hips are developing, and you'll see a physiotherapist with her here every week.'

Ms Byford frowned. 'What if the harness gets dirty?'

'The harness can be sponge cleaned,' Anna said. 'And some of my parents have put long socks over the baby's legs to protect the harness during nappy changes.' She smiled. 'One of my mums calls them the "poo socks".'

Ms Byford looked close to tears. 'Only a few days ago, everything was fine. And now…'

'The good news is that Poppy might not need an operation,' Jamie said gently. 'And a harness is a lot easier to manage than a plaster cast. Hopefully, wearing the harness will encourage her joints to develop as they should. I know this has been a shock to you, but she's going to be fine. The earlier we pick up something like this, the quicker it is to treat.'

'And she'll be all right?' Ms Byford asked.

'She'll be absolutely fine,' Anna reassured her. 'I know right now it feels as if you don't know anyone else going through this and it's a bit daunting, but Poppy's not the only baby I've seen with clicky hip, and all my former patients with it have gone through treatment and are just the same as their peers now. The next thing you know, Poppy will be crawling and you'll be shocked at just how fast a determined baby can move.'

Between them, Jamie and Anna fitted the harness. Poppy protested, and her mum watched them with silent tears rolling down her cheeks, looking anxious.

Anna gave her a reassuring hug. 'I know right now it feels a bit scary and overwhelming, but you'll both get used to it and she'll be back to her usual smiley self before you know it. I'll book you in with the physiotherapist and my clinic for a week's time, and in the meantime if you've got any questions just ring in.' She took a leaflet from a drawer. 'This will tell you all about the harness and what it does, if anyone asks you and it's gone all fuzzy because right now you're worrying too much about Poppy to take everything in.'

Jamie glanced at her. Anna Maskell was kind as well as professional. And he could already see the difference that kindness had made to the patient's mother; Ms Byford had stopped crying and was asking questions.

Anna, he thought, was going to be good to work with.

Not that he intended getting close to her or to any of his other colleagues in the Muswell Hill Memorial Hospital. He'd agreed to cover maternity leave here for three months, and that was all. He didn't need to make new friends. He was absolutely fine on his own.

'All the best, Ms Byford. I'll see you later, Dr Maskell,' he said. And he left the room before he was tempted to blow a raspberry at Poppy and make the baby laugh.

Babies.

How ironic that this was his vocation, the job he loved so much.

After losing Hestia and the baby, Jamie hadn't wanted to see another baby or child ever again. But he wasn't going to throw all those years of hard work and studying away and change his career. Hestia would never have forgiven him for that. But, unable to face the pity of his team at the hospital where he'd worked in south London, he'd switched to working as a locum. No involvement, no closeness, no risk of heartache. He stayed for no longer than three months in one place; as soon as his locum cover was finished, he moved on to the next job. That was how his life had been for the last two and a half years, and that was how he intended it to stay. Utterly within his comfort zone.

Anna finished writing up her notes for the last patient of her morning's clinic, then headed to the office where she'd met Jamie Thurston earlier. 'Ready?' she asked from the doorway.

'Yes.' He logged out of the files he'd been reviewing, then came to join her.

'Did Robert introduce you to everyone when you started this morning, or would you like to meet everyone now?'

'Robert introduced me,' Jamie said.

'That's great. OK. I'm assuming he also showed you the staff kitchen?'

'Yes.'

'Just the canteen, then,' she said, 'and filling you in on the social side of the ward.'

'Social side?'

Was it her imagination, or did Jamie look a bit antsy? 'We're a close team. We do a lot of things together outside work,' she said. 'And we try to do stuff that includes partners and children.'

He said nothing, simply nodded.

'Locums count as part of the team,' she said softly. But she shut up when she noticed his slight frown. Maybe he was shy. And it was his first day on the team, so she should cut him some slack.

She left it until they'd bought lunch and found a quiet table in the canteen. 'I guess it's because I have bossy tendencies,' she said, smiling to take the sting from her words, 'but I organise most of the ward's social stuff. I've had the venue for the team Christmas dinner booked since July, but I don't have to give the absolute final numbers or confirm everyone's menu choices to the pub for another week or so.'

Jamie's wrap stopped tasting like sweet chilli chicken and turned to ashes in his mouth.

Christmas.

No.

Since Hestia's death, he didn't do Christmas. There weren't tidings of comfort and joy, as far as he was concerned. Just the bleak midwinter, and the radio playing songs saying how it would be lonely at Christmas, or begging the singer's loved one to come home for Christmas, or, worse still, the song Hestia had loved and danced around the house to with him, making him sing along with her. The most popular modern song, the one that seemed to be playing all the time in December, no matter which radio station he chose.

All Hestia had wanted for Christmas was him. And their baby.

That was what he'd wanted, too.

What he'd actually got was a double funeral. All those plans, all the happiness and excitement, had sunk into a black hole. It was just over three years ago now, and everyone had expected him to move on. But he couldn't. It was too, too hard.

Which was why he worked as a locum.

And why he flatly refused social invitations from family and friends alike, since the time they'd all clearly talked about him and decided he needed help to move on, and had set him up at a dinner party with a suitably single woman. A nice, sweet woman who deserved so much more than the wreckage that had once been Jamie Thurston. He'd been polite, the first couple of times it had happened, but then he'd refused invitations so he wouldn't be put in an awkward position again. He didn't need to be fixed up with anyone. He didn't want anyone else in his life.

'Sorry. I don't think—' he began, but Anna had already fished her phone out of her pocket.

'It's very much a foodie pub, so the food's utterly amazing,' she said. 'The smoked salmon pâté is to die for.'

Die. Yeah. Jamie knew all about dying and death. Though this wasn't Anna's fault. She didn't know him, so she'd have no idea how inappropriate that phrase was.

'If you're veggie or vegan, the avocado on toast with chilli jam is fantastic. Or the spiced pumpkin soup,' she continued.

He didn't want to even think about a ward Christmas dinner, let alone go to one.

'They do the best roast potatoes in the world— better even than my mum's, which is saying a lot,' she said. 'Crispy on the outside and fluffy in the middle. And they stir-fry the Brussels sprouts with lemon and chilli. There's traditional turkey, sea bass if you prefer fish, or parsnip and chestnut Wellington for the veggie/vegan option.' She passed her phone to him so he could see the menu for himself. 'Obviously there's traditional Christmas pudding or cheese, but I guarantee the chocolate Venetian cake will ruin you for any other pudding.'

He blinked at her.

'Or I can email everything over to you, if you want to take a bit of time choosing. It's the first Friday evening in December, at half-past seven,' she said. 'And we do a Secret Santa on the ward, too—you pick a name out of the hat, leave your labelled parcel with the secretaries, and Robert puts the ward's Father Christmas outfit on and dishes them out on the night. Anyone who can't make it to the dinner gets their parcel at the start of their next shift.'

This was going way, way too fast for him.

She gave him a speculative look. 'Actually… Robert usually dresses up as Father Christmas for us on the ward on Christmas Day, but this year he's disappearing off to New York.' She smiled. 'I guess his silver wedding anniversary's a good enough excuse for him not to do it this year. But it means I need a replacement Father Christmas. You're about the same height as Robert, so the costume would fit you perfectly.'

What? Jamie could barely process this. She wanted him to dress up as Father Christmas?

He couldn't.

He just *couldn't*.

Finally, he found his voice. 'Sorry. I can't.'

Something must've shown in his eyes, because she winced. 'I'm so sorry. This is only your first day, and I'm overwhelming you. Let me backtrack a bit. I'll send you all the stuff about the ward Christmas events, but maybe you'd like to come ten-pin bowling with the team on Friday night as a starter? It'll give you a chance to meet people you might not have met on the ward yet, and we're a nice lot. Not everyone's as… um…steamrollery as me.'

Steamrollery? Yes, she was. But the woman he'd seen on the ward was also kind. She gave patients and their parents time to think about things, and made sure they had all the information they needed so they knew all the facts and could make a good decision about their healthcare plan. She tried to understand their feelings. Yes, she'd overwhelmed him a bit just now, but that was probably just because he hated Christmas.

'I haven't been ten-pin bowling in years,' he said.

'It doesn't matter if you're a bit rusty. I cheat hideously and keep the bumper bars up in my lane,' she confided, 'because I can't bowl in a straight line. Straight to the gutter every time, that's me.' She rolled her eyes. 'Sadly, being tall and built like an Amazon doesn't mean that I'm any good at sport.'

He wanted to refuse the invitation and tell her he didn't do social stuff.

But her smile disarmed him. It was warm and friendly and ever so slightly goofy, and it shocked him that she could affect him this way. He'd kept his distance from everyone for nearly three years. How could a near-stranger make him feel...?

'It's all just a bit of fun, and nobody takes things seriously,' she said. 'It's a chance for everyone to let off a bit of steam and enjoy each other's company. Thankfully nobody on the ward is one of those competitive idiots who just *have* to win all the time; everyone's really nice.'

Nice. That usually went with kindness. And if his new colleagues found out about his past they'd swamp him in pity. Jamie really, really couldn't handle that. He'd had more than enough pity to last him a lifetime. He just wanted to be left alone.

'Thanks for inviting me,' he said, fully intending to make an excuse and say that he couldn't make it.

But then the wrong words came out of his mouth, shocking him. 'I'll be there.'

What? He didn't do social stuff.

But it was too late, because she was already looking thrilled that he'd agreed to join them. 'Fantastic. We normally grab something to eat at the bowling alley, too—I'm afraid it's not the greatest nutrition because it's pretty much a choice of pizza, nachos or burger and fries, but it's edible. Our lanes are booked at seven,' she said. 'I'm assuming that you're new to the area, so I'll send you directions.'

It was definitely too late to back out now. Or maybe he could invent a last-minute emergency on Friday night and just not go.

'Let me have your number and your email,' she said, 'and I'll send you everything.'

That smile again. Its warmth melted Jamie's reluctance, and he found himself giving Anna his number and his email address. A moment or so later, his phone pinged to signify an incoming message.

'So now you have my number, and I'll send you all the rest of the stuff after work,' she said. 'Welcome to Muswell Hill Memorial Hospital, Jamie.'

CHAPTER TWO

HEADACHE? JAMIE THOUGHT on Friday night. No, because that could be easily fixed with a couple of paracetamol. Bubonic plague? Strictly speaking, that did still exist, but the last case he'd heard of had been in Colorado and that wasn't quite near enough to London to be plausible; plus if the condition was diagnosed properly it could be cured by the right antibiotic. Held up in traffic? No, because the bowling alley was within walking distance of his flat.

He didn't have a single believable excuse not to turn up to the team night out.

He did have Anna's number, so he could just call her and admit that he didn't want to go. But it felt too mean-spirited and he couldn't quite bring himself to do it.

And so he found himself outside the bowling alley at five minutes to seven. There was a group of people he recognised in the foyer; Anna detached herself from them and came over to greet him. 'Hey, Jamie! Glad you could make it.'

He'd seen her several times at work during the week, wearing a smart shirt and skirt beneath her white coat. In jeans and a long-sleeved T-shirt, and with her dark wavy hair loose, she looked very different: younger and very, very approachable. He was suddenly aware of her curves and how the faded denim clung to her.

Oh, for pity's sake. He wasn't a hormone-laden teenager. He'd seen plenty of women dressed casually.

But they didn't make him feel suddenly hot all over, the way Anna Maskell did.

Tonight was *definitely* a mistake. Even if she wasn't involved with someone, he was only here in Muswell Hill for three months, and then he'd move on. He wasn't in the market for a relationship, even a temporary one. He could never give his heart again. He'd buried his capacity to love right there in the grave with his wife and his daughter.

But he forced himself to smile back. To fake a semblance of being a normal member of the team. He let her introduce him to the people he hadn't yet met from their ward, swapped his shoes for bowling shoes, paid for his games, and chipped in his share of the food and drink order. He played the frames along with the rest of the team, sitting squarely in the middle of the scoring and being neither spectacularly good nor spectacularly bad.

Though Anna was playing on his lane, and she'd been right on the money when she'd told him that she was terrible at bowling. Without the bumper bars being put up, her ball would've gone straight into the gutter every single time; as it was, she seemed to have a strategy of zig-zagging the ball between the sides of the lane in the hope of hitting the pins in the middle, more by luck than by judgement.

'Yes! Six pins! Best roll of the night for me so far,' she whooped as the pins went down.

'Best roll of the last four years, by my count,' one of the others teased.

'I know! How cool is that?' She punched the air and then grinned. 'Go, me.'

Everyone else on the team high-fived her, so Jamie felt he had to follow suit.

But when the palm of his hand grazed briefly against hers, it felt like an electric shock.

He was pretty sure she felt it, too, because those beautiful sea-green eyes widened briefly. And for a second it felt as if it was just the two of them in a bubble: the sound of bowling balls thudding against pins on the other lanes, of the electronic scoreboard, of music playing and people laughing and talking, simply melted away.

Then he shook himself. This wasn't happening. Anna was his colleague for the next few weeks, and then he'd be moving on.

But he couldn't shift his awareness of her. The tall, energetic, human dynamo of their department. The woman who was definitely attracting him, despite his common sense.

When their food order arrived, they took a break, and Jamie found himself sitting next to Anna. His fingers accidentally brushed against hers as they reached for a piece of pizza at the same time, and again it felt like an electric shock. He was going to have to be really careful.

'So have you had a chance to look at the Christmas menu yet?' she asked.

The Christmas meal he really didn't want to go to. 'Sorry, no.'

She looked disappointed. 'Well, we've still got a bit

of time,' she said. 'And maybe I can talk you into being Father Christmas for me.'

He shook his head. 'Sorry. Absolutely not.'

'Don't tell me—you're allergic to red suits and big white beards?'

If she'd been pushy or snippy or sarcastic, it would've been easy to resist. To push back. But this, the jokiness underlain by a sweetness—this was much harder to resist.

He was going to have to tell her the truth.

'I really don't like Christmas,' he said, and waited for her to start probing.

To his surprise, she didn't.

'A lot of people find Christmas hard,' she said. 'And it's really rough on our patients and their parents. The patients who are old enough to want to be home with their families and are still young enough to believe in Father Christmas all want to know if that's what he'll give them: the chance to go home for Christmas. I hate telling them he can't do that. The ones who are too old to believe in Father Christmas—for them it's seeing their families and knowing how much it hurts them to be apart at Christmas, especially when they're trying to juggle family celebrations with hospital visits and kind of splitting themselves in two. Christmas can be horrible.'

The way she said it made him realise how she felt. 'But you don't think it is?'

'No. I love Christmas,' she said. 'I love the way it breaks down barriers and makes people kinder to each other, if only for a few hours. And I love the look of wonder in our younger patients' faces when Father Christmas strides onto the ward, saying, "Ho-ho-ho," and hands them a special gift from the Friends of the Hospital. It's nothing hugely expensive, usually a book or some art stuff or a teddy bear, but enough to show them that Christmas in hospital isn't completely bad. I bring my guitar in and we sing a few Christmassy songs; being part of that is just amazing. Despite all the worry and the fear, there's still hope and love.'

Hope and love. Things he'd lost a long time ago.

'I'm sorry for being pushy. I completely understand that you'd rather not be Father Christmas.' She gave him a wry smile. 'It's really starting to look as if it's going to be Mother Christmas this year.'

He suddenly realised what she was getting at. '*You're* going to dress up in the Santa suit?'

'I haven't been able to talk anyone else into it,' she said, 'so it's either no Father Christmas at all, or me. I guess at least I'm tall enough to get away with it.' She spread her hands and grinned. 'I might be able to borrow a voice-changer from my nephew or someone and hide it behind the beard. That, or I'm going to be channelling a Shakespearean actor and learning how to do a deep, booming voice.'

Anna Maskell was tall, yes, but there was nothing remotely masculine about her. She wouldn't convince anyone that she was Father Christmas.

Jamie knew he should be nice and offer to help. But he just couldn't get the words out.

Why did Jamie Thurston dislike Christmas so much? Anna wondered.

Maybe he'd had a difficult childhood, one where his family had rowed all the time and Christmas just made things worse—people being forced together for longer periods of time than they could stand each other. The Emergency Department was testament to how bad Christmas tensions could get. Add alcohol to the mix, and it was often explosive and painful.

But it would be rude and intrusive to ask.

She switched the conversation to something lighter. 'There's a team football thing in the park next weekend. Partners and children included, if you'd all like to come along.'

'No children and no partner,' he said, and the bleakness in his eyes shocked her.

Maybe he was divorced, and his former partner had moved away so he never got to see the children. In which case it was no wonder that he didn't like Christmas. The festive season was a time for children, and not being able to see your kids at Christmas must be like rubbing salt into a very raw wound.

'Sorry. I wasn't trying to pry. Or to come on to you,' she added, realising that he might have taken her words the wrong way.

And she really wasn't trying to come on to him. Yes, Jamie Thurston was gorgeous; he reminded her of the actor in one of her favourite historical dramas, all dark and brooding and with those amazing cornflower-blue eyes. But she wasn't risking her heart again. Johnny had made it very clear that nobody would want to tie themselves down to her, not once they knew the truth about her. She was pretty sure he'd said it to make himself feel better; the man she'd fallen in love with had been one of the good guys, but the shock of learning that they couldn't have a family without a lot of medical intervention had changed him. It had made him look elsewhere; and then the guilt of knowing how badly he'd treated Anna had pushed him into saying unforgivable things that had hurt her even more than his betrayal.

'I'm just not very good at social things,' Jamie said.

'Though the football isn't a Christmassy thing.' She winced even as the words spilled out of her mouth. Oh, for pity's sake. The poor man had made it quite clear that he didn't want to do the team thing next week. Why didn't she take the hint and just get off his case?

Thankfully then their session on the bowling lanes started again, and she had to concentrate on trying to make the ball go straight. Not that she managed it. And this time she only knocked down one pin from each end. How pathetic was that?

Jamie said to her, 'It's your follow-through.'

'Follow-through?' she asked, mystified.

'Where your hand points, that's where the ball ends up.'

She laughed wryly. 'Straight in the gutter, if I didn't have the bumper bars up. But I guess my zig-zag approach is a bit too haphazard.'

'Keep your arm straight and let the ball go when your hand's pointing to the middle of the pins,' he said. 'Watch me.'

She did. 'Wow. You got a strike.'

'Because I aimed for the middle.'

'*I* aim for the middle,' she protested.

'But you let the ball go too late,' he said. 'I take it you don't go ten-pin bowling with your partner?'

Johnny hadn't really been into ten-pin bowling. 'No partner,' she said.

He winced. 'That wasn't a come-on.'

'I know.' She smiled at him. 'You sounded like

someone who wants to help. A friend. And I appreciate that.'

He stilled, and she wondered if she'd gone too far.

But then he smiled. The kind of smile that lit up the whole room, and it transformed him utterly. It was as if he'd stepped out of the shadows he seemed to keep round him. When he smiled, Jamie Maskell was breathtakingly handsome.

'I'll help you with the next frame,' he said.

'Whatever you do, I'm still going to come last on our lane,' she warned. 'But it would be nice to actually do this right, for once.'

'I can help you do that.'

She looked at him. 'You're like me, aren't you? A fixer at heart.'

'It's kind of the definition of a surgeon, fixing things,' he said dryly.

It was more than that, she thought. He was a fixer who wasn't going to admit it.

Whatever had made Jamie Thurston put distance between himself and the world—and between himself and Christmas—maybe she could help him with that, the way he was helping her with the bowling.

She thought about it while they chatted with the others in their lane.

She stopped thinking for a little while when Jamie helped her with the bowling, standing close to her but not close enough to be sleazy or awkward. Because then he slid his arm along hers, showing her how to angle the ball correctly. The touch of his skin against his flustered her so much that she nearly forgot to let the ball go.

'You went slightly to the left,' he said when she'd

knocked six pins down. 'So this time you need to go slightly to the right.'

Again, he guided her through the procedure. And this time her ball hit the four pins in the middle, and they all went down.

'There you go. You got a half-strike.'

'That's *amazing*.' She flung her arms round him and hugged him.

When was the last time anyone had hugged him? When he'd actually *let* a woman hug him, because he'd pushed his mum and his sisters away, not to mention Hestia's family and her best friend?

Probably at the funeral.

And now Anna Maskell had ignored all his usual barriers and hugged him. Briefly, because she stepped back almost immediately and said, 'Sorry. That was a bit over the top. But I don't think I've ever managed to get all the pins down like that before and I got a bit overexcited.' She took a deep breath. 'Let me be more appropriate. Thank you for your help, Mr Thurston,' she said more formally.

'You're most welcome, Dr Maskell,' he replied, equally formally. Though he could feel himself withdrawing again. Going back into the dark little hole where he'd lived for the last three years. But that hug had made him feel odd. As if there was a little flare of light, far in the distance. A light that drew him and beckoned him—if he had the courage to go and find it.

It took enough courage for him simply to exist from day to day. Going in search of a new life still felt too hard. But now he knew it was out there, and the little light wasn't going to let itself hide again. It stayed put, telling him it would still be there when he was ready to look for it properly.

He managed to focus on the bowling for the rest of the evening. But then it was over, everyone was spilling outside, and his new colleagues all seemed to be heading off in different directions.

He'd walked a few steps when he realised that Anna was beside him. 'It looks as if we're going the same way,' she said. 'Do you mind if I walk with you?'

'That's fine.'

'Thank you for the bowling lesson,' she said.

'Pleasure.' The word was polite and automatic, but Jamie was shocked to realise that he actually meant it. He'd enjoyed helping Anna, seeing her confidence grow along with her ability.

She'd said that she thought he was a fixer at heart.

He had been, once. Before the thing had happened that he hadn't been able to fix. And he had to admit that it had been good to feel that way again, however briefly.

'I was thinking,' she said. 'Maybe I can help you.'

He frowned. 'How?'

'Christmas,' she said.

The time of year he really disliked.

'This isn't a come-on,' she added. 'Just to be clear, I'm not looking to date anyone.'

She'd said earlier that she didn't have a partner; though Jamie could imagine Anna Maskell right at the heart of a family. A large one. Why didn't she have a partner, and why didn't she want to date anyone?

Though it was none of his business and he wasn't going to ask; if he started asking personal questions, then it was tantamount to an invitation for other people to ask him the same sort of things. Things he didn't want to discuss.

'I'm not going to pry,' she said, echoing his own thoughts. 'But Christmas is a fairly big thing at Muswell Hill Memorial Hospital, so it's going to be in your face all the time. Maybe I can help show you that Christmas has its good side, so you don't feel you have to try to avoid it all the time and it makes life feel a bit less pants at work.'

Maybe he should tell her why he disliked Christmas, so she'd back off.

Then again, he didn't want to see the pity in her face once he told her what had happened.

'Show me that Christmas has its good side,' he echoed.

'Yes. And, just in case you think I'm pitying you, I will admit that I have an ulterior motive.'

He frowned. 'Doesn't that kind of ruin any scheming, if you warn me that you have an ulterior motive?'

'No,' she said, 'because I believe in what you see is what you get.'

He was going to have to ask now. 'What's your ulterior motive?'

'I help you, and you help me.'

Oh, no. He knew exactly where this was going. 'You mean, if you show me that Christmas isn't the worst time of the year, then I'll play Father Christmas for the ward?'

She grinned. 'Thank you, Jamie. That's an offer I'm very happy to accept.'

Hang on. He hadn't offered. He'd just said out loud what he was pretty sure she was thinking. 'But I—'

He couldn't finish the sentence. She'd shocked him into silence.

'Sometimes,' she said gently, 'when you avoid something, you give it more power than it deserves. Facing it head-on can cut it back down to its proper size and make it manageable again.'

He didn't have an answer to that.

'I've had days when I've had to fake it to make it,' she said. 'Days when I haven't wanted to get out of bed and face the world—days when all I've wanted to do is curl into a little ball and let it all wash over me.'

He knew exactly how that felt, and it made him look at her. *Really* look at her. And there wasn't any pity in her expression. Just empathy. Understanding. Clearly someone or something had hurt her enough that she'd been through an emotional nightmare, too.

'I'm not going to pry,' she said, 'but I think Christmas is like that for you. I'm a fixer, just like I think you are. I can't fix everything, and neither can you. But I reckon we might be able to fix a problem for each other, because we're on the same team.'

Of course she couldn't fix his problem. Nobody could bring anyone back from the dead.

He was about to say no. But then he remembered this evening. How she'd steamrollered him into joining in with the ten-pin bowling, and he'd actually ended up enjoying the evening. He'd felt part of a group of people—something he'd told himself he never wanted to do again. But that momentary closeness had managed to do what he'd thought was impossible; it had temporarily lifted the cloak of misery from round him.

If she could take the bits he hated about Christmas away, too, then maybe this was worth a shot. And if she could do that, he'd very happily wear that Father Christmas outfit to help her in return. 'So what exactly are you suggesting?' he asked.

'Doing Christmassy things together,' she said. 'It's the middle of November now. Give me a month. If I can convince you that Christmas has its good side, then you agree to be Father Christmas for the ward.'

'And if you can't convince me?'

'Then there's a bit of padding and a voice-changer in my very near future,' she said. 'And I'll also apologise for not being able to make this time of year more bearable for you.'

He could walk away now. Stay wrapped in his shroud of misery.

Or he could say yes.

Anna had made it clear that she wasn't asking him because she fancied him. The pull of attraction he felt towards her was clearly one-sided, and he had no intention of acting upon it anyway. She was merely suggesting that they could help each other.

He could almost hear Hestia's voice in his ear. *Say yes.* The petite ballet teacher he'd fallen in love with had adored Christmas. She'd loved all the snowflakes and the fairy lights and the joy that her favourite ballet brought to her students and their parents alike. He'd loved it as much as she had, because her joy had been infectious.

Without her, it had been unbearable and he'd avoided it.

He had to admit it would be good to be able to cope with Christmas again. To remember the joy Hestia had found in the festive season, instead of seeing it as a harsh reminder of everything he'd lost. And for him to stop putting a dampener on Christmas for his family, choosing to work and stay out of the way instead of spending any time with them or inflicting his misery on them during the festive season. He knew they all worried about him.

'All right,' he said. 'You're on.'

'Thank you. And you can start by texting me your menu choices for the ward's Christmas meal over the weekend,' she said. Though her smile wasn't full of triumph; instead it was a mixture of relief and gratitude. 'Maybe we can begin with something light and easy. There's a Winter Festival in the park for the next three weeks—basically it's a big Christmas market. Are you working on Sunday?'

'No.'

'Good. I'm on an early shift, so I'll meet you at four o'clock by the park gates.' She stopped outside a gate. 'This is me. I'll see you on Sunday. And thank you.'

'See you on Sunday,' he echoed.

CHAPTER THREE

FOUR NEW BRONCHIOLITIS CASES, Anna thought with a sigh on Sunday afternoon. This was peak season for the respiratory syncytial virus. In adults, it produced a spectacularly nasty cold, but in children it could be much more serious, gumming up the tiny tubes inside their lungs and making it hard for them to breathe.

Small babies often went on to develop pneumonia as a result, and Anna really felt for both her tiny patients and their parents, who were often exhausted with worry and shocked by the sight of their little ones on oxygen and being fed by a tube down their nose because the babies were too tired to suck milk from a breast or a bottle.

She finished writing up her notes, did a last check on the ward in case anyone needed emergency help before she left, then texted Jamie to let him know that she was leaving the hospital on time and would meet him at four.

Hopefully she could change his views on Christmas and take away its power to hurt him. She wasn't going to pry and ask exactly why he hated Christmas so much, but it would be good to think that she could make life a bit better for him.

Anna the Fixer. Her whole family teased her about it, but she knew they appreciated what she did. Her own problem wasn't fixable, but you couldn't have everything. She was blessed with a wonderful family and good friends, and she'd just about forgiven Johnny for the way he'd thrown their marriage away, even though part of her still thought that there were ways round her infertility; they could've given IVF a try, or fostering or adoption. But Johnny had found the pressure and the worry too much to cope with, and he'd chosen someone who could give him what he wanted without the complications.

It was just a pity that he hadn't ended their marriage before he'd found that someone else.

His betrayal had made everything feel so much worse; and for months after that Anna had felt herself not good enough for anyone. Especially when Johnny had sneered at her that nobody would want her because she wasn't a real woman and couldn't give a man the family he wanted. She knew it had probably been guilt talking, trying to justify the way he'd treated her; before she'd married him, if anyone had told her he'd ever be so cruel to her in the future she would have laughed, not believing it. She and Johnny had loved each other, and they'd been happy.

But her infertility had shattered his dreams as well as her own; the months and months of disappointment when they'd tried and failed to make a baby had made him bitter, and he just hadn't been able to cope. In turn, that had made him feel less of a man, and the anger and guilt had spilled over into spite towards the person who was causing the problem in the first place.

It had taken a long time for Anna to get her bounce

back after the split. As she'd said to Jamie earlier, she'd really had to fake it until she'd managed to make it. But she *had* made it, and she wasn't going to let herself slip back into misery.

'Don't start whining and wanting things you can't have, Anna Maskell,' she told herself firmly. 'You're really lucky and your life is as perfect as it gets. You have a family you love and who loves you all the way back, you're working in your dream job, and you have wonderful colleagues you get on really well with. You can afford to pay your rent and put food on the table. You're healthy.' Well, apart from one thing, but she wasn't actually sick with it. Infertility had just changed her options, that was all. 'You're so much more fortunate than a lot of people. And with your working hours it wouldn't be fair to have a dog, so George the Gorgeous Goldfish is enough for you.'

The line from the old song about the doggie in the window slid into her head. But it was pointless regretting that she couldn't take George for a walk in the park. There were plenty of dogs in her family that she could go and cuddle, and children she could play with. She needed to count her blessings, not dwell on the things she couldn't have.

As for dating again... She knew that not all men would think the same way that Johnny had, but she really didn't want to get close to someone and lose her heart to him, only to find out that her infertility was a problem for him and he rejected her the same way that her husband had rejected her. Then again, how could you start any kind of relationship with someone by asking them if they wanted children? It just wasn't appropriate, not at that stage. So it was easier just to duck the issue and keep everyone on a friends-only basis, rather than risk getting involved with someone she'd end up disappointing.

Jamie hadn't actually replied to her text saying that she was on her way to meet him, and Anna felt slightly antsy as she headed towards the park. Would he be there? Or had he had time to think about it over the weekend and decide that he couldn't handle any part of Christmas, after all?

He owed her nothing. They barely knew each other. If he didn't turn up, it would be her own fault for trying to steamroller him into doing something he really didn't want to do.

But she hoped that he'd let her at least try to help him.

When she reached the entrance to the park and saw him leaning against the metal railings, her heart gave a little skip. Which was completely inappropriate. They were meeting this afternoon simply as colleagues who were in the early stages of friendship; it was a kind of quid pro quo thing. If she could help him, then he would help her. This wasn't a *date* date. Yes, he was gorgeous: tall and brooding, with those enormous cornflower-blue eyes, dark hair that she suspected would be outrageously curly if it wasn't so short, and a full, sensual mouth. But he wasn't dating her. Full stop.

Her heart gave another of those ridiculous little skips when Jamie saw her and lifted a hand in acknowledgement. Oh, for pity's sake. She needed to get a grip.

'Hey. Thanks for coming,' she said as she reached him.

He inclined his head. 'How was your day?' he asked.

'Full of babies with bronchiolitis. There's a whole

bay reserved just for our RSV-positive patients, poor little loves,' she said. 'Though I feel even sorrier for the parents.'

'Because the babies can't tell them how they feel, and they're tired and not eating well, and the parents are feeling utterly helpless because they can't do anything to make their babies feel better,' he said.

'That,' she said before she could stop herself, 'sounds like personal experience.'

He wrinkled his nose. 'Observation. I did my paediatrics rotation at this time of year, and I remember what it was like.'

But she knew she'd asked something a bit too personal. She'd better switch the subject back to work. 'What made you become a surgeon?' she asked.

'I really enjoyed my surgical rotation,' he said. 'And I like working with children. Making a difference. How about you?'

'It was a toss-up between obstetrics and paediatrics,' she said. 'Helping to bring a new life into the world—that's so special and I loved every minute. And actually delivering a baby was so wonderful. But then I did my paediatrics rotation at Christmas, and that decided me. It's where I feel I can make the most difference, so that's why I chose the specialty.' She smiled at him. 'So. Shall we?' She gestured to the park.

Jamie really didn't want to do this.

But he'd had the best part of two days to come up with a reasonable excuse, and he hadn't found one. Plus, part of him wanted to be able to handle Christmas again without making his family miserable. For the last three years, he'd chosen to work over the festive season rather than join in with the family celebrations, and he used work as an excuse not to see them very often in between.

He felt guilty for not spending time with them; but whenever he was with them, it was always so obvious how much they were trying hard not to say the wrong thing. He knew they worried about him, but he found it suffocating when they wrapped him in cotton wool. Being in a family situation reminded him so much of what he'd lost, and Christmas magnified it to the point where it was too much to handle. He knew he needed to make the effort. Just… This was going to be painful. Like picking at a scab. Bit by bit.

Facing Christmas.

The time of year he dreaded.

His doubts must've shown on his face, because she said gently, 'Are you sure you want to do this?'

No. He wasn't sure at all.

She took his hand and squeezed it briefly. 'Look, we don't have to walk around the Winter Festival. We can, I dunno, go back to the high street and grab something to eat, or get a takeaway and go back to mine to chill out with some old comedies on TV—and then you can meet George.'

'George?' That got his attention. He was sure Anna had said she didn't have a partner. Or did she have a child? Was she a single mum? He hadn't heard any rumours on the ward, but then again he always closed his ears to gossip. 'Who's George?'

'George the Gorgeous Goldfish.'

He looked at her, not quite sure he'd heard that correctly. 'George is your *goldfish*?'

'Gorgeous goldfish,' she corrected. 'Yes.'

It was so incongruous that he couldn't help smiling. 'George the Gorgeous Goldfish,' he repeated.

'That's right. Obviously it's not quite like having a dog, because he doesn't stick his chin on my knee and look up at me with big brown adoring eyes, and he doesn't want to go for walks in the park or play ball. But I talk to him and he likes my singing.'

Singing to a goldfish.

That definitely wasn't what he'd expected to hear her say.

It was so surreal that he found himself smiling and walking into the park with her.

And then somehow they were right in the middle of the Christmas fair, strolling up and down the path lined by little wooden pop-up shacks selling food, drink, Christmas decorations and every kind of gift you could think of, from candles to cosmetics to jewellery to hand-knitted Christmas jumpers. There were fairy lights draped over the roofs of the shacks, and garlands of greenery.

'I hope you're hungry,' she said, 'because I'm ravenous. I didn't get time for lunch.'

'It's four in the afternoon,' he pointed out.

'Which is too early for dinner, but I need a Christmas cookie and a hot chocolate right now to keep my blood sugar level.' She grinned at him. 'Which I admit is just a terrible excuse, because I love hot chocolate and cookies.' She found a hot drink stall, tucked her arm into his and queued up. 'This one's on me,' she said.

He accepted a coffee; she dithered about having extra cream on top of her hot chocolate, but then said,

'No, because I'll have another one later, laced with cream liqueur.'

Just how long did she intend to spend at the fair? he wondered, but didn't ask.

Next was a cookie in the shape of a star, studded with chips of butterscotch. 'Perfect,' she said after the first bite. 'You have to try this, Jamie.' She broke off one of the arms of the star and handed it to him.

He had no real choice but to eat it.

When was the last time he'd eaten something and really tasted it, instead of it being simply fuel? This was delicious: buttery and sugary, zinging along his tastebuds. 'It's good,' he said. 'Thank you.'

'And now—shopping,' she said. 'I need some stocking-fillers.'

'You're not buying your Secret Santa present for the ward, are you?' he asked.

'I've already got that,' she said. 'Though you might find something here.'

'But then you'll know whose name I drew when they unwrap it,' he pointed out.

'True,' she said. 'OK. We'll do this methodically. We'll go all the way along each row and back up again, and then I'll decide what I'm getting. I have four sisters-in-law.'

He blinked. 'You're one of five?'

'The middle one,' she said. 'Two older brothers, a younger brother and a younger sister. All married, and all with children.'

Was it his imagination, or did a shadow just cross her face? He knew she wasn't married and he was pretty sure she didn't have children. But was that by choice?

'And I got to be best woman at my sister Jojo's wedding to Becky,' she said with a smile. 'Which was so cool. How about you?'

'Youngest of three. Two older sisters,' he said. 'Both married with children.'

'Being an aunt,' she said, 'is fabulous, because I get pictures drawn for me all the time and there's always someone to play games with or read stories to or cuddle.' She smiled. 'We had the best family holiday ever, this summer—we all stayed at a villa in Tuscany, with Mum and Dad. And, even though we've got very different interests between us, we've also got enough in common to get on really well together. I know they always say the middle child is the peacemaker, but fortunately I don't have to be.'

He'd guessed right from when he'd first met Anna that she was part of a huge family; she had that confidence about her, that surety of being loved by everyone and being able to talk to anyone. She clearly adored her family, and it made Jamie feel guilty for pushing his away. He did love his parents and his sisters and his nieces and nephews; but he hated how everyone seemed to alternately tread on eggshells around him or try to jolly him into moving on. So he'd reasoned that it was easier for everyone if he tucked himself out of the way and buried himself in work, and the distance between them seemed to stretch more with every day.

'Uh-huh,' he said.

'So how old are your nieces and nephews?' she asked.

'Between six and ten,' he said. And now he felt even more guilty. Anna was clearly a very hands-on aunt. Just as Hestia had been; she'd always been happy to play games with Josh, Caitlin, Dylan and Layla, and she'd had a stock of books about ballerinas that she'd read to all four of them, saying that ballet wasn't just for girls. She'd even taught them all some steps, and the kids had loved putting on performances on family Sunday afternoons. She'd taken them to performances, too, and they'd all been spellbound by *The Nutcracker*. Especially when they'd seen their auntie Hestia dancing on the stage, pirouetting and leaping.

He'd been a hands-on uncle, too, back in those days. He'd read stories, built train tracks and done pretend tea parties with teddies. Hestia's death had meant that the children had lost their uncle as well as their aunt, and he felt bad about that. For their sakes, he should've made more of an effort.

He'd start with Christmas, he decided. *This* Christmas.

He'd let Anna help him face Christmas again and get his family back; and in turn he'd help her by playing Father Christmas for the ward. OK, so he wasn't ever going to get to the stage where he could open his heart to another partner, but he knew his family deserved much better than this. He needed to change. And he needed help to do it; on his own, he knew he'd just back away again because it was too hard to face.

'Mine are a little bit younger—Will's the oldest, at eight, and Ivy's the baby. Literally, because she's six months old next week,' Anna said. 'Mum and Dad managed to space us all two years apart, and it seems to be a tradition in my generation that you get to thirty and have a baby.'

Except for her? There was a definite shadow in her eyes now, Jamie thought, but it felt like prying to ask.

He didn't want to hurt her, not when she was being so kind and sweet.

She gave him a super-bright smile. 'I've already bought and wrapped all their main presents so, as I said, I'm looking for stocking-fillers.'

'You've already bought and wrapped everything? But it's only November,' he said.

'It's December next weekend,' she corrected. 'Being organised means I get to find the perfect presents without any pressure and I also have the time to wrap them. My oldest brother refuses to go shopping until the day before Christmas Eve.' She rolled her eyes. 'That'd drive me bananas, dealing with the heaving crowds and risking having to rethink what I'm buying because what I want is out of stock.'

'So you're a planner?'

'Better believe it,' she said with a grin. 'I have spreadsheets, the lot. I keep a file of exactly what I've bought and for whom. It means I don't accidentally buy the same thing twice for one of my nieces and nephews—or buy the same book for one of the siblings, unless it's one that's been loved to bits and I'm replacing it.' She smiled. 'Perhaps you can help me look for something.'

Christmas shopping.

Hestia had loved Christmas shopping. She'd loved wrapping the presents, too, all ribbons and bows and garlands. Since her death, Jamie had bought mainly gift vouchers as presents; if he had bought an actual gift, he'd done it online and chosen the 'wrap it for me' option rather than doing it himself.

Now he realised how impersonal his actions must have seemed to his family, and he felt ashamed. They loved him and they missed Hestia, too. They'd all felt the loss of the little girl who hadn't had the chance to join them. He should've let them grieve with him instead of pushing them away.

'Perhaps you can help me, too,' he suggested.

She beamed. 'I'd love to. Buying presents is my favourite thing in the world. Right. Tell me all about your nieces and nephews.'

Uh… How did he admit that he didn't have a clue? That he'd let so much distance creep in between himself and his family that he didn't know what the kids were interested in any more? And children changed so much at their ages. 'Dylan's ten, Layla and Josh are eight, and Caitlin's six.'

'Are the girls super-girly? And do they have long hair or short?' she asked. 'Because hair ties and hair slides always go down well. Megan's six and anything heart-shaped or glittery gets pounced on with absolute glee.'

'Heart-shaped and glittery,' he said. That hadn't occurred to him. 'I think that would be good.'

'And art stuff. My nieces love paints and pens and notebooks. And books. I know they've got a fabulous bookstall here. Do Dylan and Josh like reading?'

'I think so,' he said carefully.

'Let me show you Will's favourite—he's the same age as your Josh. And the bookstall people might have a good idea for something suitable for Dylan,' she said.

Between them, they bought bangles and hair slides and scrunchies from the accessory stall, then moved on to look at the scented candles. Anna pounced on one for her mother. 'Look at this!' she said gleefully. 'Put a tealight in the middle, and the heat makes the carousel spin round with six filigree owls dangling down. My mum loves owls, so she'll *adore* this.'

He ended up with organic bath bombs and body butter for his mother and his sisters, ale from a microbrewery for his father and his brothers-in-law, books for all four nieces and nephews, a wooden duck with red Wellington boots for Caitlin, and a beautifully carved and painted wooden turtle for Layla, who he remembered loving the sea life centre when she was younger.

'What do you get an eight-year-old and a ten-year-old boy?' he asked.

'Once you get them off the games console?' she asked. 'I've already bought Will one of those mini planetarium projectors. I think I saw something similar on one of the stalls earlier.'

'I think Josh would like that, too,' he said.

'And I'm on the look-out for one of the magic science kits—the ones where you use all sorts of household objects to do tricks,' she said. 'Like adding vinegar to bicarb soda and a bit of food colouring to make lava.'

'I think that would go down well with Dylan,' Will said thoughtfully.

Once they'd finished their shopping, she looked at him. 'Wrapping paper?' she asked.

Jamie shook his head. 'I don't wrap.'

She grinned. 'Considering what you do for a living, you really can't get away with the excuse of not being neat enough.'

He couldn't help smiling back. 'There's a big difference between surgical stitching and wrapping awkward parcels.'

'Excuses, excuses, Mr Thurston,' she teased, and made him buy beautiful gift bags and tissue paper.

It was the first time in three years that he'd actually enjoyed something to do with Christmas. His family were all going to be in shock, he thought, when he handed over actual presents instead of the usual envelopes containing gift vouchers. But a good shock. And he might even brave going to see them after his shift on Christmas Day this year, instead of relying on his usual excuse of work. Thanks to Anna's advice, he was pretty sure that the kids were going to love the stocking-fillers he'd bought them.

Anna was prepared and had several foldable shopping bags in her handbag, a couple of which she lent to Jamie. The least he could do in return was offer to carry her purchases, too. And together they wandered through the fair.

There was a huge Ferris wheel at one end, all lit up, with people queueing for a ride.

'Do you want to go up on that?' she asked.

He nodded at their parcels. 'Probably not with this lot.'

But then he saw the carousel. Parents were lifting tiny children onto one of the carved wooden horses, and a fairground organ was playing Christmas songs and Christmas carols. Jamie could see the wonder on the little ones' faces as they went round and round on the horses. If life had happened the way it was supposed to, Giselle would've been nearly three and the perfect age for enjoying this.

He was coping with this. Just.

But then the song changed. To the one he couldn't avoid. 'All I Want for Christmas is You.' The song Hestia had loved so much. She'd even got her ballet class to do a special routine to it...

Cold stole through him, and it wasn't just the temperature outside now the sun had set. This was a bone-deep thing. The misery was back. Big time.

As if she noticed, she said softly, 'Time to find dinner. What would you like?'

'Anything.'

She bit her lip. 'Sorry. I've pushed you too far today, haven't I?'

'No. You've… It's helped,' he said. And it had, until he'd seen the carousel and heard that music, and loss had ripped through him again.

'When I feel low,' she said, 'I pick things that make me feel good. Decent food—not junk, something really nutritious—music, and some fresh air. Let's go get something to eat.'

Again, she hadn't pushed him to talk and she definitely wasn't prying. But the fact that she'd admitted she felt low at times made him realise that she understood how he was feeling right now. So he followed her away from the Ferris wheel and the carousel towards the food stalls.

'OK. Do you have any food allergies, and are you vegetarian?' she asked.

'No allergies, and I eat pretty much anything,' he said.

'All righty. We could have Christmas dinner in a burrito,' she said. 'Or a calzone with turkey, cranberry and cheese filling.'

'What would you prefer?' he asked, suddenly curious.

'My go-to comfort food is macaroni cheese,' she said. 'But I know it's not the best thing in the world, so I try to mix some greens and some veg in with it, to balance it out a bit.'

'I don't notice what I eat,' he admitted. Since Hestia's death, he'd seen food just as fuel and not as a pleasure.

'My best friend made me do mindfulness,' she said. 'I thought it was all hype, and I admit I've really mocked the stuff where you're supposed to eat a single raisin and take ages over it. It's so extreme. But there is a point to it. If you pay attention and notice things like colour and texture and scent, it does help to ground you a bit and it takes your mind off whatever's dragging you down. It's a kind of breathing space.' She shrugged. 'Plus I happen to know a stall here where they do really, *really* excellent macaroni cheese.'

'That,' he said, 'sounds good to me.'

'And I know this isn't the greatest nutrition, considering how I've just been banging on about healthy food,' she said, 'but last year there was a stall here that did churros covered in glitter sugar. Which I think would be perfect with a hot chocolate. And I am *so* planning to have that second one today.'

'These,' he said, 'are on me. Let's find a table.'

Anna sat thinking when Jamie left her with their shopping and queued up to get their food. That moment when he'd gone all brooding on her by the carousel, when they'd seen parents lifting their small children onto the horses, made her sure that whatever was hurting him was something to do with a child.

Yet every day he worked with sick children. How could he bear it, if it ripped his heart in two all the time?

They barely knew each other, and she knew she

shouldn't push him to talk—especially because then he might start asking awkward questions of his own. Such as why she wasn't like the rest of her siblings, happily married and having children when she got to thirty.

On the other hand, talking to a stranger and getting a different perspective on things might help him.

Or maybe she should just stop being such an interfering busybody.

'Penny for them?' Jamie asked, coming to sit opposite her and sliding a cardboard tray of macaroni cheese with spinach, complete with a wooden fork, across the table to her.

'My thoughts aren't worth a penny,' she said, not wanting to hurt him by being nosy. 'Thank you. This looks fabulous.' She took a mouthful. 'And it tastes even better.' She noticed that he'd chosen the same.

'This was a really good choice,' he said after the first mouthful.

'Though I'm buying us churros,' she said. 'And hot chocolate laced with that cream liqueur.'

'So do you come to the Christmas fair here every year?' he asked.

She nodded. 'And it's got bigger every year. Usually I do it as a girly thing, either with my best friend or my sister and sisters-in-law.' She smiled at him. 'So you could say you're an honorary girl today.'

'Hence the churros with glitter sugar,' he said dryly.

'Wait until you try them,' she said. 'I recommend the cinnamon glitter sugar. And I want to go back and get some of the Christmas candles. The ones that smell of orange and cinnamon and cloves—and they're for me, because I love candles at this time of year. Me,

Gorgeous George, a good movie, some popcorn and a candle: that's a perfect night in.'

'Thank you,' he said. 'For pushing me into doing this.'

'So you're not hating every minute of it?' she checked.

'Not *every* minute,' he said. 'I've done my Christmas shopping and the food's good.'

'So what's the hardest thing about Christmas?' she asked before she could stop herself.

He was silent for so long that she thought he wasn't going to answer, and she was about to squeeze his hand and apologise for prying when he said quietly, 'The music. Certain songs. I…' He grimaced and shook his head.

'OK. So we'll try to avoid music for the future.' At least until he was more comfortable with other aspects of the holiday season. 'Can I ask—modern or carols?'

'Modern,' he said.

'I'll try to remember,' she said. 'I don't want to make this hard for you, Jamie. I want to help make things better.'

'You are,' he said. 'And seeing how much you love Christmas—I'm beginning to understand.'

'Just wait for the glitter churros,' she said.

Clearly he thought she'd been exaggerating to tease him, because when she came back from buying their hot chocolates and churros, she saw his beautiful cornflower-blue eyes widen. 'They really *are* glittery.'

'They started doing them last year. I'm on a mission to persuade the hospital canteen to start stocking them and I don't care if they're bad for your teeth—they're so lovely and uplifting,' she said with a grin. She set the box between them, and their paper cups of hot chocolate on either side. 'Sorry. I forgot to ask if you wanted cream on top.'

'It's fine without,' he said.

And it was fine, until her fingers brushed against his while they were dipping the churros into the pot of chocolate sauce. Her skin tingled where he touched her: which was ridiculous. They were colleagues, just about starting to become friends. She knew they both had baggage that would get in the way of anything else, so she really had to get a grip instead of letting herself give in to fantasies that just couldn't ever happen.

Or she could blame her feelings on the sugar rush of the churros.

Because nothing remotely romantic was going to happen between herself and Jamie Thurston.

She hauled herself back under control and made light conversation until they'd finished eating.

'Guess it's time to go home,' she said. 'George will be wondering where I am.'

'I hate to put a downer on you, but don't goldfish have a memory of about three seconds?' Jamie asked.

'Actually, no. My nephew Will did a summer project on goldfish last year. He spent ages researching on the Internet, and then he did a flashy presentation for me. Apparently, there's a university study where goldfish learned to press a lever to dispense food. The researchers changed it so the lever would only work for one certain hour a day, and the fish learned to press the lever during that one-hour window so they'd get the food. And in another study the researchers rang a bell at feeding time for a month, released the fish into the sea, then played the sound five months later and the fish came straight back, expecting their dinner.'

'Like Pavlov's dog—Pavlov's fish?' Jamie asked.

'Exactly. George knows my routine.' She smiled. 'So I'd better make a move. Thanks for coming to the Christmas fair with me.'

'It wasn't as hard as I expected,' Jamie admitted.

'Good. So tomorrow you're going to give me your menu choices for the ward's Christmas meal,' she said. 'And are you free on Thursday evening?'

'Yes.'

'Maybe we can go skating on Thursday. Shall I book tickets for eight o'clock?'

He took a deep breath. 'OK. My aversion therapy for Christmas continues. Are you good at skating?'

'That's for me to know and you to find out,' she said, waggling her eyebrows at him.

'Better than bowling?'

She laughed. 'Don't be mean. Are you good at skating, then?'

'I'm taking the Fifth on that one.'

'You can't. You're not American,' she pointed out. 'Can you skate, or do I need to find out if they have an adult version of those penguins they use for toddlers?'

To her delight, he actually laughed. 'I am *not* going to a skating rink and holding on to a ginormous penguin.'

'Oh, good. So you *can* skate. I'll be expecting flashy moves, you know. Axle jumps, swizzles and twizzles, and camel spins.'

He looked at her. 'Did you just make those up?'

'Nope. I can assure you, they're all real moves.'

He looked horrified. 'So you're practically a professional skater.'

She took pity on him. 'More like I love watching

that show when they have celebs learning to skate with the pros, and I've picked up all the lingo from there.' Then she frowned. 'Actually, that's a point. There's going to be music at any skating rink in London, and I promised you we'd avoid music. Would you rather we did something else?'

'Yes,' he said, 'but isn't the point of aversion therapy to face the thing that makes you uncomfortable?'

'It is,' she agreed, 'but I don't want to push you so far out of your comfort zone that you run back to the centre at the speed of light and never come out again.'

'We'll go skating,' he said.

'And if it gets too much for you, then we can leave,' she said. 'Even if it's in the middle of a song.'

'That's a more than fair compromise. Thank you. I'll walk you home,' he said, and carried her parcels all the way back to her gate.

'You're very welcome to come in for a cup of coffee and to meet George,' she said.

'Another time, maybe,' he said. 'See you tomorrow.'

'See you.' And funny how his smile made her feel all warm inside.

CHAPTER FOUR

ON MONDAY EVENING Anna went straight from work to have dinner with her sister Jojo and sister-in-law Becky. She thoroughly enjoyed the chance to read a bedtime story to two-year-old Noah, even though part of her couldn't help thinking wistfully of what might have been. If her own plans had worked out, she would have done this every night with her own children, sharing stories and cuddles and laughter.

But she was lucky enough to see lots of her nephews and nieces and to share in their upbringing, so she wasn't going to let herself whine about what might have been.

Once she'd kissed her nephew goodnight and gone downstairs, Becky shooed her and Jojo into the living room, and Jojo put a glass of wine into her hand.

'Righty. Spill the beans,' Jojo said.

'I have absolutely no idea what you're talking about,' Anna said.

'*Interesting.* Because you went to the Christmas fair in the park yesterday,' Jojo said.

'How do you know?' Anna asked, surprised.

'Because Gemma at work went, too, and she saw

you.' Jojo gave a dramatic pause. 'Eating churros with a very nice-looking man, so she told me.'

'Why didn't she come and say hello, then?' Anna asked.

'Because it was obvious that you were on a date, and she didn't want to interrupt you.'

Anna rolled her eyes. 'Oh, stop fishing. It wasn't a date.'

'What was it, then?'

'Jamie's a friend.'

Jojo scoffed. 'Just good friends?' she asked, making the quote marks with her fingers. 'We all know what that really means.'

'He's my colleague.'

'There's nothing wrong with dating a colleague,' Jojo said with a smile.

'This is ridiculous.' Anna frowned. 'If you must know, he's our new orthopod, the one who's covering Nalini's maternity leave. I'm trying to talk him into being Father Christmas for me on the ward—except at the moment he's saying no because he hates Christmas.'

'Why does he hate Christmas?' Jojo asked.

'I don't know,' Anna admitted, 'but I can't really ask him, because it'd be unkind to pry.'

'True. But, if you don't know what the problem is, then you might inadvertently stamp on a sore spot,' Jojo pointed out.

'You have a point. I think it might be something to do with kids, because he went a bit brooding on me when we were near the carousel,' Anna said thoughtfully. 'On the other hand, he's an orthopaedic surgeon specialising in children's medicine, so he's around children all day. Maybe I was misreading it.'

'You'll have to find a tactful way to ask him,' Jojo said.

Anna shrugged. 'He'll tell me when he's ready.'

Jojo frowned. 'What I don't get is, if he hates Christmas, then why would he go to a Christmas fair with you?'

'Because we've come to an agreement. If I can help him to feel that Christmas is bearable, then he'll wear the red suit and beard and play Father Christmas on the ward for me on Christmas Day, in Robert's absence,' Anna explained.

'So what do *you* get out of it?' Jojo asked.

'What it is to have a lawyer for a sister. I should've guessed you'd interrogate me,' Anna said lightly. 'I've already told you the deal. I'm helping Jamie to face Christmas, and then he'll help me by being Santa.'

'That's work,' Jojo pointed out. 'I mean, what do you personally get out of it?'

'Being Anna the Fixer?' Anna suggested.

'Not enough.' Jojo looked at her. 'If you're helping him get over his hatred of Christmas, then I reckon in return he needs to help you get over Johnny.'

'I'm already over Johnny,' Anna protested. 'So I don't need any help.'

'Yes, you do. You haven't dated anyone since your divorce,' Jojo said. 'Which suggests to me that either you're still in love with Johnny—'

'Absolutely not,' Anna cut in.

'—or,' Jojo continued, unfazed, 'that Johnny's left you feeling that you're not enough for anyone.'

Trust her sister to hit the nail right on the head. Jojo was the most clear-sighted person she knew.

'And that isn't fair or true. You're wonderful, and

any decent bloke would be lucky to have you. You need to get back out there and find someone who loves you for who you are. Someone who deserves you,' Jojo declared.

'I don't need anyone,' Anna said. 'Remember, I have Gorgeous George.'

'A goldfish,' Jojo said firmly, 'is not the same as having a partner.'

'Actually, George is better. He doesn't talk back to me and annoy me.' Anna gave Jojo a pointed look. 'Unlike interfering little sisters.'

Jojo hugged her. 'I'm not interfering, Anna-Banana. Really. I just worry that you're lonely.'

'How can I be lonely when I have the best family in the world and a ton of really good friends?' Anna asked.

'You come home to an empty house every night.'

Anna spread her hands. 'So do lots of people.'

'I think Johnny and his selfishness really chipped away at your self-confidence,' Jojo said. 'You don't bother dating anyone, because you don't believe a man will give you a second look as soon as they find out that you can't have children.'

Anna sighed. 'I'm fine, Jojo. Really. And I know not everyone shares Johnny's views about infertility. Not everyone even wants children in the first place.'

'I'm still not sure you've really come to terms with the situation yourself,' Jojo said gently.

'Honestly, I have,' Anna said. 'And you'd be the first person I'd talk to if I was upset about anything.'

Jojo still looked worried. 'I hope you know I'll always be here for you. And I hope you don't think Becky and I rub Noah in your face.'

'You don't. At all.' Anna was very definite about that. 'I love him. I love the fact you both asked me to be his godmother. And I love that you and Becky let me come and read him stories and play with him whenever I want to.'

'Because we love you, too.' Jojo still looked worried. 'So do you like this Jamie guy?'

'As a colleague and potentially a friend, yes.'

Jojo raised her eyebrows.

Anna sighed. 'All right. Yes, I admit he's attractive. He reminds me of the actor in that Scottish historical drama everyone moons over.'

'*Nice*,' Jojo said approvingly. 'Does he like you?'

'I have absolutely no idea! I've only known the guy for a week. And this isn't about relationships, anyway. Though I suppose I should think myself lucky you didn't arrange for a suitable someone to partner me at dinner tonight,' Anna added ruefully.

'I wouldn't do that to you.'

It was Anna's turn to raise her eyebrows at her sister.

'Not without warning you first,' Jojo amended. 'But, if you like this Jamie guy, there's no reason not to make this Christmas deal of yours into a proper date.' She grinned. 'As he's a surgeon, at least you know he's going to be good with his hands.

'Joanna Maskell, you really are just too much, sometimes!' But Anna couldn't help laughing. 'Now, please can we drop the subject?'

To her relief, Jojo agreed; Becky called through that dinner was ready, and they kept the conversation light for the rest of the evening.

When Anna left, Jojo hugged her at the door. 'Sorry

for nagging. I do love you, Anna, and I worry about you. So does Becky.'

'I'm fine. And I love you both, too. And Noah.' Anna hugged her back. 'See you soon.'

Anna didn't see Jamie on the ward and wasn't in clinic with him during the rest of the week, but on Thursday evening she met him at the Tube station as they'd arranged, and they went to the skating rink at Somerset House. There was a massive Christmas tree at either end of the skating rink, both of them covered in twinkling lights. Spotlights dappled the surface of the rink with different colours, and the rink was already packed with people, some looking nervous and sticking very close to the edge where they could grab the sides for safety, and others almost dancing on the ice. There was a pop-up Christmas shop selling gifts, and a stall selling hot drinks and snacks.

The music was all modern and Christmassy, and Anna could see that Jamie looked antsy; she remembered him telling her that he found Christmas music difficult.

'If you'd rather not do this, we don't have to,' she said.

Jamie looked awkward. 'But we're here now and you've already bought the tickets. It'd be a waste not to use them. Which reminds me, I still owe you the money for my ticket.'

'We'll sort that out later. Let's just go round the rink for one song,' she said. 'Then we can review the situation and see if it's too much or if you want to keep going for a bit longer.'

'OK.' He took her hand and squeezed it briefly. 'Thank you. You're being very patient with me.'

'I'm a doctor, not a patient,' she quipped lightly. 'And, for that matter, so are you.'

He groaned. 'That's terrible, but you know what I meant. I appreciate what you're doing for me.'

'You're doing just as much for me, actually. This means I have someone different to drag out to all the Christmassy things I love doing and my family and friends have had more than enough of,' she said with a smile. 'Plus I have my eye on the big prize.'

'What prize?' He looked mystified.

'You wearing that red suit on Christmas Day— because, apart from the fact that I haven't managed to source a voice-changer yet, what if it fell off while I was walking through the ward, or my beard fell off to reveal it? I really don't want to be responsible for making a whole ward of sick children find out the hard way that Father Christmas isn't real.'

And then she regretted it when he looked even more panicky.

'Sorry. I'm bulldozing you again. Ignore me. Let's skate.'

They queued up to hire skates, changed into them, and started to make their way round the rink.

'You're much better at skating than you are at bowling,' Jamie said to her.

She laughed. 'That's not exactly hard! But skating is just sliding one foot in front of the other. It's easier than having to aim for something and trying to hit it. And if you think I'm bad at bowling, you should see me at archery. Everyone dives for cover.' She rolled her eyes. 'So are you going to start doing all these spins and jumps and things?'

'Two letters. That's N and O, in exactly that order,' he said.

But at least he was smiling and starting to relax, she thought.

Skating on an ice rink.

Jamie hadn't done this in years. Hestia had always avoided skating, not wanting to risk slipping over on the ice and breaking an ankle; teaching ballet wasn't exactly something you could do easily while wearing a fracture boot. So he hadn't bothered either. But once he was used to the motion again, he found himself enjoying it.

Part of him was on edge, waiting for Hestia's favourite song to start playing and haunt him, but he forced himself to smile because he didn't want Anna to feel bad. She was trying so hard to help him, and he appreciated that she was trying to take the sting out of the festive season for him. And she clearly loved being out here on the rink, in the middle of the crowd among all the lights and with cheerful Christmas pop songs belting out.

All they needed now was for it to snow. Not the stuff that would settle and make all the pavements slippery enough to cause mayhem, but a few light, fluffy flakes that melted when they touched the ground, making the rink magical. And how weird was it that the idea actually appealed to him?

Then he realised that a child just in front of them was down on the ice, crying. He took Anna's hand and gestured over to the little boy. 'I think we should go and offer some help.'

She nodded, and they skated over.

'I'm Jamie and this is Anna. Can we help?' Jamie asked the little boy's mother.

She looked grateful. 'Thank you. I need to get him back on his feet before someone skates into him.'

Jamie helped her pick him up, but the little boy wouldn't stop crying. He was holding his arm, not letting anyone touch it. And Jamie had the strongest feeling he knew what had just happened.

'I'm a doctor,' he said gently. 'Can I have a look at your arm?'

The little boy shook his head.

'What's his name?' Anna asked.

'Adeoye—Ade for short,' the boy's mum said.

'Ade, does it hurt here?' Jamie asked, pointing to his own wrist.

Ade nodded, still sobbing.

'When you slipped over,' Jamie said, 'did you put your hands down first to stop yourself falling flat on your face?'

Ade nodded, but this time he spoke, his voice almost hiccupping through the tears. 'It really hurts.'

Jamie could see that the boy's wrist was an odd shape and, given what Ade had just told him, he was pretty sure it was a Colles' fracture. 'Does it feel tingly or numb?

Ade shook his head.

That was a good sign. 'Do you feel dizzy or sick?'

'A bit,' Ade admitted.

'OK. That's probably the shock of falling.' Jamie turned to Ade's mother. 'I think he's broken his wrist—it's a special kind of fracture called a Colles' fracture.'

'It's really common when someone falls over onto

an outstretched hand,' Anna said. 'We see a lot of them at the hospital when it's icy.'

'I can't do anything to help you here, because Ade will need an X-ray to check whether any of the bones need manipulating back into place before they put the cast on,' Jamie said. 'If you take him to the emergency department now, they'll do an X-ray and put a back slab on to keep his wrist stable overnight, then they'll probably put a lightweight cast on tomorrow morning.' He smiled at her. 'I'm an orthopaedic surgeon, for children, so I do a lot of this sort of thing.'

Ade's mother bit her lip. 'Will he be in a cast for long? He's got the school Christmas concert in a couple of weeks.'

'I'm sure they won't mind him being in a cast,' Anna said, 'and at least you'll have time to alter any costumes around the cast, if you need to.'

'If it's a straightforward fracture,' Jamie said, 'he'll have a cast on for four to six weeks, and then he'll need to do exercises every day to get his wrist properly mobile again.'

'I'd better get him to hospital,' she said.

'St Thomas' is the nearest emergency department to here,' Jamie said. 'I worked there for a bit. They're really nice. It's about ten minutes from here in a taxi and twenty on foot.'

Ade's mother looked at her son, who was still guarding his arm. 'I'll call a taxi now.'

'We'll help Ade with his skates while you make the call,' Anna said, 'and we'll wait with you until the taxi gets here.'

She was a natural with children, Jamie thought, telling the boy a stream of terrible jokes to distract him from the pain and even managing to make him laugh. Ade's mother thanked them when the taxi arrived, and then Anna looked at Jamie. 'Review time, then. Stop now, or have another skate?'

There was a hopeful look on her face, and he was pretty sure which one she'd choose. 'Another skate,' he said. 'And then I'm guessing it's hot chocolate?'

'That sounds utterly perfect,' she said, smiling at him.

And how crazy was it that his heart suddenly felt as if it had done a backflip?

This wasn't supposed to happen. It wasn't part of their deal. They were colleagues, sort of on the way to becoming temporary friends. They weren't supposed to get close and personal.

She was the first woman since Hestia to make him feel like that. Her warmth and her huge, huge heart just drew him. Yet, at the same time, he was pretty sure that Anna was hiding some deep sadness in her own past. She deserved more than he could give her. So he forced himself to keep things light.

Until the moment when she stumbled and he caught her so she didn't fall.

She looked up at him, those beautiful sea-green eyes wide and her lips very slightly parted.

And he knew then that it would be, oh, so easy to dip his head slightly. Brush his mouth against hers. Wrap his arms round her, and then deepen the kiss until they were both dizzy...

Was it his imagination, or was she staring at his lips, the way he was staring at hers? Did she feel the same thing? Did she want him to kiss her?

His tongue felt as if it had been glued to the roof of

his mouth. He couldn't say anything, do anything but try to resist this insane urge to kiss her.

But if he didn't resist… What then? Would she kiss him back?

He could hardly breathe.

Could he?

Should he?

And then she said, 'Thank you for saving me.'

Her voice broke the spell and brought his common sense back into play. No. Of course he shouldn't kiss her. He needed to be sensible.

'You're welcome,' he said. 'More skating?'

At least if he had to concentrate on putting one foot in front of the other, he wouldn't be thinking about how it would feel to kiss her. How her skin would feel against his. How she was tall enough to be a perfect fit in his arms…

'More skating,' she said.

He didn't dare glance at her expression to find out if she looked relieved or disappointed. Kissing was absolutely not an option. This wasn't a date.

He just needed to concentrate on his footwork and the music. So far, he'd been lucky and they hadn't played That Song. Hopefully they'd already played it enough times earlier in the evening. Two more songs, and he'd suggest they get hot chocolate and leave.

Anna knew she was really making an idiot of herself. Fancy almost falling at Jamie's feet, like the poor little boy who'd slipped over earlier.

And then, when he'd grabbed her to steady her, it had felt as if she'd been galvanised.

Propinquity, that was what it was. Or maybe the

bright lights dazzling her, the magical feel of the skating rink taking her out of the real world and letting her see the possibilities. Tempting her to do something that really wouldn't be sensible in real life.

For a moment, she'd found herself staring at his mouth and wondering what it would be like if he kissed her. How soft and teasing and inviting his mouth would be. How it would feel to have his arms wrapped round her, holding her close to him.

But that wasn't the deal.

She was supposed to be making him feel better about Christmas, showing him the good side of the season and taking the sting out of whatever had hurt him in the past, not flinging herself at the poor man and embarrassing both of them. He'd made it perfectly clear that he wasn't in the market for a relationship, and neither was she. She needed to focus on skating. Skating, not kissing. She repeated the mantra to herself half a dozen times, hoping that somehow it would stick in her head. Skating, not kissing. Skating, not kissing...

But all the time she found herself very aware of him. The space he took up. His height. His dark good looks, those gorgeous cornflower-blue eyes, that shy and so-rare smile.

Get a grip, Anna, she told herself crossly. This isn't a date. Stop thinking about the what-ifs, because there aren't any.

Two more songs and they'd leave.

They went round and round the skating rink, and she couldn't help noticing how the other couples there were skating hand in hand, how the more confident ones stopped and spun their partner round into their arms and kissed them despite no mistletoe being in evidence.

She wasn't meant to be noticing the kissing.

Concentrate on the skating, she told herself fiercely. Even if it was driving her slightly crazy.

Maybe she needed some hot chocolate, a sugar rush to stop her thinking about the sweetness of his mouth. So, when the second song ended, she said, 'I'm done. Time for hot chocolate, I think.'

'Great idea,' he said.

Except, when they were in the queue, someone bumped into them and Jamie ended up with his arms around her to protect her.

And all of a sudden there wasn't enough air. Despite the fact that they were outside and had the whole of London around them, there just wasn't enough air to suck into her lungs.

She made the mistake of looking into his eyes, and it looked as if it was the same for him because his pupils were absolutely enormous.

It isn't because of you, she told herself sharply. It's a physiological reaction to a low light area, that's all.

Except the lights weren't really that low. It was actually really, really bright in the courtyard, so anatomically speaking his pupils should be tiny.

The fact that they weren't made her heart skip a beat.

Was he going to kiss her?

On the skating rink, it would've been much too dangerous. Too easy for either or both of them to slip and fall. But here—here, they were on solid, unslippery ground.

Except it felt way more slippery than the rink.

If he kissed her, and she kissed him back... What then?

Right at that moment, she couldn't move. They were in the queue, pressed together, with his arms around her and his face really close to hers. Had she been five inches shorter, it wouldn't have been an issue. But their lips were well within kissing distance, and Anna really didn't know what to do.

It was the first time she'd actually wanted to kiss anyone since Johnny.

And, OK, she knew that kissing didn't necessarily *mean* anything. But she had a nasty feeling that, if she let him, Jamie Thurston could steal her heart. And she dared not risk that. It had taken her too long to put herself back together after Johnny. She wasn't looking for another relationship. Not even a temporary fling. Anna Maskell wasn't a fling kind of girl.

How could she move out of his arms without making a fuss and embarrassing both of them? Worse still, would he guess that she was moving away from him precisely because she wanted him to kiss her and this whole thing was driving her crazy?

She was saved by the waitress at the hatch asking, 'What can I get you?'

The people in front of them took their own drinks from the counter and left, giving her space to move away from Jamie, and he said, 'Two hot chocolates, please.' He sounded cool and calm, not as if they'd been seconds away from kissing each other dizzy *in public*.

The space helped, but it wasn't quite enough to stop Anna feeling like a teenager standing next to her crush at a high school disco. And she wasn't wearing ice skates any more, so she couldn't use her *skating, not kissing* mantra.

Somehow she managed to make light, fluffy conversation about skating and Christmas trees and decorations while they sat on one of the benches and drank their hot chocolate and watched the skaters, and then they headed back to Muswell Hill. The tube was too noisy for them to talk, giving her time to think, and on the way home Anna came to a decision. She knew how to neutralise the attraction now: she'd treat him in exactly the same way that she did her other male friends, so at the station she'd kiss him on the cheek, smile and say goodbye.

Except then Jamie offered to walk her home. She thought it would be a bit churlish to refuse, given that they were going the same way.

At her garden gate, she took a deep breath. Polite, she reminded herself. Pretend he's just like any other male colleague. 'You're very welcome to come in for a coffee or a glass of wine or something.'

Something? Oh, no. Please don't let him interpret that as her being like a teenager and talking in code for 'come in and snog me witless'.

To her relief—mingled with disappointment, if she was honest with herself—he said, 'Thanks, but I'd better be going.'

'OK. Thanks for coming skating tonight.' She paused. 'I hope it wasn't too difficult.' This whole thing was meant to be about helping him, not about her making a fool of herself and starting to want things she couldn't have.

'No. It was fun.' He looked surprised, as if he hadn't expected to enjoy it. 'Thank you for organising it.'

'No problem. See you at work tomorrow.' She stepped forward, intending to kiss him on the cheek; but somehow everything got a bit tangled and she ended up kissing him on the mouth instead. And her lips tingled, every nerve-end reacting to the touch of his skin.

Anna Maskell had a huge heart. She was warm and affectionate, the sort of person who kissed everyone, and it didn't mean anything, Jamie reminded himself.

Except he'd messed it up and, instead of kissing him on the cheek the way she'd obviously intended to, she'd kissed his mouth. And it was as if someone had just lit touchpaper and blown up some of the walls he'd built over the last three years, letting him *feel* again.

Dared he let himself want this? Dared he risk his heart with Anna?

They said that lightning didn't strike twice in the same place...

Which was an unfortunate metaphor, given what had happened to Hestia. Eclampsia, from the Greek for 'light burst'.

No. He couldn't do this. He couldn't offer Anna an uncomplicated relationship. So he needed to back off.

Now.

Before either of them got hurt.

'See you at work tomorrow,' he muttered, and left without looking back.

CHAPTER FIVE

'THE WAY I feel right now, anyone would think I was fourteen, not thirty-four,' Anna told George, dropping a blanched pea with the skin taken off into his tank. 'A fourteen-year-old who's just snogged a boy outside the school disco—the one she's secretly fancied for months—except it was really embarrassing instead of romantic because their braces clashed, and now she thinks he's going to tell his mates and everyone's going to laugh at her at school tomorrow.'

George swam up and ate the pea.

'Except obviously neither of us was actually wearing a dental brace. I know Jamie's not going to say anything at work, and neither am I. And I don't fancy him.'

George waggled his tail, as if to say, *Who are you trying to kid?*

'But it's just as embarrassing as a fourteen-year-old's brace-clash. There was me, thinking I could be all cool and calm and just kiss him on the cheek and treat him in exactly the same way that I treat every male in my life, and what do I do? I go straight in and kiss him on the mouth. How stupid am I?' She dropped a small piece of blanched broccoli into the tank. 'Eat your greens, Georgie-boy, because they're good for you.'

The goldfish did her bidding.

'Just as well it happened after I asked him in for a drink and he said no. Otherwise… Oh, for pity's sake.' She gave George another pea. 'Right, that's the end of your treats for today. I don't want to overfeed you and give you swim bladder.' She sighed and put the box of goldfish treats back in the fridge. 'I'm such an idiot,' she told the fish when she came back. 'I haven't dated anyone since Johnny, and I don't need to. I'm quite happy with my life as it is, and coming home to just you. But when I nearly fell over and Jamie caught me… We were quite close to kissing, right in the middle of the skating rink. He was definitely looking at my mouth.'

She plugged her phone into her speaker dock. 'I was just as bad. I did all that staring-at-the-mouth thing right back at him, and I actually wanted him to kiss me. And now I feel such a fool, and I hope I haven't wrecked our working relationship.' She grimaced. 'I'll just have to apologise to him tomorrow, tell him I don't know what on earth came over me, and explain that I'm really not looking for a relationship and he'll be perfectly safe with me in future. And I hope he'll still let me teach him about the magic of Christmas, or I really am going to have to practise a deep, booming voice and wear the red suit and beard myself. I hate to think I might be letting the kids down.'

George swam up and down his tank, as if in sympathy.

'Righty. There's only one way to get rid of feeling stupid and miserable,' she said, hit 'play', and started singing and dancing along to her favourite Wham! songs.

* * *

On Friday morning, she walked into work, wondering just how she was going to face Jamie on the ward. Maybe he'd be in Theatre today. Or maybe she'd get some good ideas after a cup of coffee.

But when she checked her clinic list, she knew she wasn't going to get away with it. Eleven-year-old Lily Brown had been one of Nalini's favourite patients, and she was a favourite with Anna, too. Lily had scoliosis, and they'd worked with her for years, first with a plaster cast to help straighten her spine and then with a brace.

Now Lily was facing surgery, because despite the brace the curve in her spine was getting worse. She'd had the MRI scan last week, and a pre-op assessment a couple of days before to check her blood pressure and her pulse, and an ECG to check that her heart was fine. There weren't any contra-indications, so surgery looked like the best option.

Just as Anna was working through her checklist, there was a knock on her open door. She glanced up to see Jamie standing there.

In a suit rather than scrubs, he looked absolutely delicious.

And that was the most inappropriate thought she'd had all morning. It had to stop. Now. Because they were absolutely not getting together.

'Hi,' he said. 'I see you already have coffee. I was going to offer to make you one.'

'Thanks, but I'm fine.'

'I was wondering if we could have a chat about Lily Brown before her appointment,' he said, 'and if you can get me up to speed. I saw from the notes that you've been working with her for years.'

And, just like that, it was easy again. They could focus on work. On their patient. They could ignore anything personal between them and simply concentrate on making a difference to the people who really mattered. She could almost have kissed him—if it wasn't for the fact that a kiss had caused all the awkwardness between them in the first place.

'Sure,' she said. 'Go grab yourself a coffee and I'll meet you in the consulting room with her scans.'

By the time she'd finished getting him up to speed with Lily's case, it was time to start clinic and she called Lily and her mother in.

'Lily, Heather,' she said, 'this is Mr Thurston, who's covering Nalini's maternity leave and is going to do the operation next week.'

'I'm Jamie,' he said, shaking their hands in turn. 'It's good to meet you, Lily and Mrs Brown.'

'Call me Heather,' Lily's mum said. 'We're practically permanent fixtures here and I prefer first names.'

'Heather,' Jamie said with a smile. 'OK. I've reviewed your MRI scan, Lily, from the base of your brain to the bottom of your spine, and there aren't any other problems we need to worry about. The special X-rays you had taken last week have shown me the flexibility of your spine and where I need to operate, and you passed your pre-op assessment with flying colours.'

Lily bit her lip. 'I wish Santa really existed,' she said, 'and that he'd bring me a new back so I didn't have to have an operation and make Mum worry so much about me.'

'This is the next best thing to a new back,' Jamie said, 'and I've done this operation a few times now, so I promise your mum doesn't have to worry. The team here is great, so you'll be in safe hands.'

'Is it going to hurt?' Lily asked.

'You'll be asleep while I operate, so you definitely won't feel any pain then,' Jamie said. 'Has anyone talked you through exactly what's going to happen?'

Lily shook her head.

'OK. I'll talk you through it, and then if there's anything I haven't covered you can ask me. On Sunday night, you'll come in to the hospital and stay here overnight. I'm afraid you won't be able to have anything to eat after about seven o'clock, which means no breakfast on Monday. Then you'll come to Theatre and I'll be there to meet you,' he said. 'We'll give you a pre-med to make you sleepy, put some special cream on the back of your hand so you won't feel the needle going in for the anaesthetic, and then we'll give you the anaesthetic so you won't be awake during the surgery. And there will be a whole team of us looking after you in Theatre.'

He ticked off the team roles on his fingers. 'There will be the anaesthetist, who makes sure you stay asleep; the radiographer, who takes X-rays of your spine while you're asleep; a neurologist, who will be looking after your spinal cord during the surgery; and a team of nurses and another surgeon to help me.'

Lily looked thoughtful. 'Will you be there, Anna?'

'No, I'll be on the ward,' Anna said, 'but I'll come to see you afterwards.'

'Though Anna is very welcome to come into Theatre to see what I'm doing, if she has time between seeing her other patients,' Jamie said. 'The operation

I'm going to do is something called a spinal fusion.' He took the model of a spine from the corner of the room. 'You probably already know these bones here are called vertebrae. I'm going to put wires and screws into your vertebrae and connect them to a rod so the curved bones will grow straighter, and then I'll put a bone graft over the wires and screws. Over the next year, the bone graft will grow with the existing bone in your spine and your spine will be straighter.'

Lily nodded.

'Is there anything you'd like to know?' he asked.

'Will it hurt?'

'You'll feel a bit sore after the surgery,' he said, 'but in a few months' time your back won't hurt as much as it does now. Yes, you will still get back pain every so often, but it won't be anywhere near as bad as it is now, and everyone gets a bit of back pain from time to time.'

'And I'll get taller?'

'You'll get taller,' he confirmed. 'Actually, you'll get taller during the operation. If you get your mum to measure you on the day of the op and mark it on your bedroom doorframe, then do the same when you're back home after the op, you'll be able to see exactly how much difference it's made.'

'And my back will be straight?'

'Straighter,' he said. 'You'll still have a little bit of a curve, but it'll be much less noticeable.'

'What happens after the surgery?' Heather asked.

'The anaesthetist will wake Lily up,' he said, 'and then you can see her. She'll go to the High Dependency Unit for a day or so, but then we can move her to the ward.' He smiled at Lily. 'You might feel a bit sick after the anaesthetic, but it will pass. And we'll give you painkillers so you won't be too sore.'

'How long will I have to stay in hospital?' Lily asked.

'Probably for about a week after your surgery,' he said. 'You'll gradually get more mobile. Walk a little bit every day and listen to what your physio says, because keeping moving will help you recover better. You'll be back at school probably about six weeks after your surgery.'

'So I'm not going to miss much?'

'No. And your friends can visit you on the ward, if you want.'

'It's a good idea to have a rota,' Anna said, 'so you get lots of people coming in to see you. And definitely have music and your phone, so you've got something to do. Having a headphone splitter would be good, because then you and your friends can listen to the same thing.

'We'll get one over the weekend,' Heather said. 'Is there anything else?'

'Pyjamas that button up the front, because they're easier to get on after the operation,' Anna said. 'Loose tops are best because they'll be more comfortable on the dressing. And you might find your lips and your face get a bit dry, Lily, so bring some moisturiser and lip balm.' She smiled. 'Your hair is lovely, but you might find it gets knotty, so I'd recommend having it in a plait rather than a ponytail or a bun.'

'And make sure you drink lots of fluids,' Jamie added. 'You might find in the first couple of days that light foods are easier to deal with—things like jelly, custard and yoghurts.'

'Pineapple,' Lily said with a smile. 'I love pineapple.'

'Me, too,' Jamie said. 'Does that answer all your questions, Lily, or is there anything else? And nothing's too small or too silly. You can ask me whatever you like. I want you to feel comfortable coming in for the operation.'

Lily thought about it. 'No. Though I'm a bit scared.' She looked at her mother. 'In case I don't wake up.'

'You'll wake up,' Jamie reassured her. 'There are support groups. Maybe you can go onto one of the forums and talk to the people there; you'll meet lots of people who had the same operation at your age. They can tell you all sorts of tips and what it feels like after the operation, so it won't be so scary for you.' He quickly looked something up on the Internet, scribbled the website address down on a page of a reporter's notebook, then tore off the page and gave it to her. 'This is a good place to start. I'll see you on Monday morning, then, and if you've got anything else you're worrying about, just tell me.'

The rest of the clinic flew by, and then it was time for their break.

'Want to join me for lunch?' Jamie asked.

As colleagues? She could do that. 'Thanks. That'd be good.'

They headed for the canteen, bought lunch and found a quiet table.

'You were really good with Lily this morning, especially with those practical suggestions. I wouldn't have thought of them.'

She shrugged. 'You're a surgeon, and I work on the

ward. I know what the aftercare's like, that's all. In my shoes you'd do the same.'

'But I saw your face in that consultation. Her case has really got to you, hasn't it?'

She nodded. 'That bit where she said she wished Father Christmas would bring her a new back for Christmas. I really wish I had a magic wand, sometimes, so I could really fix things.'

'We do the best we can,' Jamie said quietly. 'And that's the key thing. We do make a difference, Anna.'

'I know.' And she needed to finish clearing the air between them. 'Jamie, I want to apologise for last night.'

'No apology necessary.'

She rather thought he was just being nice. 'I want us to be able to work together, so I need to be honest with you. I'm not looking for a relationship. Last night, I think all the romance of the skating rink got to me— the tree, the lights and the music.'

'Uh-huh.' He didn't look convinced.

And now for the rest of it. 'I'm going to tell you something now, but I want you to promise me first that you're not going to pity me.'

That got his attention. He looked straight at her. 'I promise, but you don't have to tell me anything.'

'No, I need to explain why I'm sticking just to friendships with people in future.' She swallowed hard. 'You know I said everyone in my family seems to hit thirty and have a baby?'

He nodded.

'That was the plan for me, too. My biological clock was ticking madly when I was twenty-eight, and over the next year my husband and I agreed I'd stop taking the Pill. The idea was that we'd wait three months to clear all the drugs from my system, then start trying for a baby.' And that was the sticky bit.

'Except my periods didn't actually come back. I did a couple of pregnancy tests, in case we'd slipped up and I was actually already pregnant—that happened to one of my friends—but the tests were all negative.' The disappointment had almost choked her. 'And then, when my period still didn't turn up, I started to wonder if something might be wrong with me. I spent a fortune on ovulation kits to see if my periods were just so super-light that I wasn't noticing them, but the tests all said I wasn't even ovulating.

'That's when I went to see my doctor, and he suggested we start by testing levels of my follicle-stimulating hormone. You're supposed to do the test on the fourth day of your cycle but, because we hadn't got a clue when my cycle actually was, he suggested doing a couple of tests six weeks apart. They both showed raised levels of FSH, and that confirmed that my ovaries had stopped working. My doctor diagnosed premature ovarian insufficiency. Fortunately I didn't have any of the other symptoms of menopause—no hot flushes, no mood swings, no night sweats—but the only way I was going to have a baby was with IVF and a donor egg. Which my husband didn't want to do.'

Jamie frowned. 'He didn't want to consider adoption or fostering?'

'He wanted an uncomplicated, very average pregnancy with a baby at the end of it. Which I couldn't give him. So he found someone who could.' She shrugged. 'It would've been nice if he'd ended our marriage first, but there you go.'

Jamie blinked. 'Your husband had an affair?'

'Yes. He knew he'd behaved badly, and that kind of made him worse—he was trying to justify himself.' She grimaced. 'And he did that by making me feel that no reasonable man would ever want to be with me because I wasn't able to have kids.'

'That's horrible, and it's also untrue.'

'I know, but it did mess with my head a bit for a while,' she admitted. 'But I've come to terms with it, now. And I'm really lucky. I have six nieces and nephews, and I've got a feeling that Jojo and Becky are getting broody again now that Noah's turned two. So there are lots of children in my life and I'm very happy to be a hands-on aunt. My brothers and sister all include me in family days out, and so do my friends, so I get to do all the things I would've done with my own kids. I just don't get all the broken nights and the tantrums and the super-evil nappies to go with them, and I won't get all the teenage angst and slammed doors and being told that I've ruined someone's life.' She smiled. 'There has to be an upside, right?'

Jamie rather thought that smile was forced; he could see there was still a kernel of hurt in her eyes. But now he understood what made her tick.

'Thank you for being so honest with me.'

'I just wanted you to know why I'm really not looking for a relationship. I've come to terms with my condition and I'm fine about it.'

'Your ex is a piece of...' He bit the words back.

'Yeah. His photograph ended up on a dartboard or two,' she said, 'and my brothers and my sister all wanted to go and punch him.'

'I think I want to punch him, too, right now.'

She shook her head. 'Violence doesn't solve anything. He was as hurt as I was by the situation, but he just didn't deal with it very well.'

'Which makes you a very noble person for not hating him for what he did.'

'I'm not that noble—I'm the one who put his photo on the dartboard,' she said. 'But actually I do feel a bit sorry for him. He really wanted a baby, and I think he kind of rushed into that relationship. They're not together any more and his ex is being a bit awkward about letting him see his daughter.'

Jamie stared at her in surprise. 'What? He told you all about that and expected you to be sympathetic?'

'No, his mum told me.' She smiled. 'I know there's this stereotype of the awful, interfering mother-in-law, but Maggie's lovely and we always got on really well. We stayed friends after the divorce and we have a catch-up lunch every so often. We just tend to avoid the subject of her son. I mean, it's not her fault that Johnny turned into a selfish toad. She didn't bring him up to be that way and she was so angry with him for the way he treated me. And the only reason I know about his situation now is because he's been living back with his parents since his ex dumped him. His mum had to re-arrange one of our lunch dates so we could avoid me having to see him, and that's when it all came out.'

He thought about it. Despite the pain her ex had caused her, Anna had stayed in touch with his family. Whereas Jamie barely saw Hestia's parents or her sister, thinking it would be too painful for all of them; he would simply be a physical reminder of their loss. If Anna hadn't married him and fallen pregnant with

Giselle, she wouldn't have had eclampsia, wouldn't have had that fatal haemorrhage, and she'd still be alive. But now, hearing Anna talk about her former in-laws, he could see a different side. Maybe they were lonely. Maybe seeing him would've given them a chance to talk about their daughter and sister, keep her alive in their heads. Guilt flooded through him. He should have made more effort with them; and he definitely shouldn't have shut his own family out.

'You're an amazing woman, Anna Maskell,' he said. 'It's impressive that you can have such a positive attitude towards something so painful and difficult.'

She shrugged. 'It isn't all me. I had counselling, and my counsellor showed me that all the "why me" pity-party stuff isn't at all helpful. She taught me to spin it round and think, "someone has to have this happen to them, so why *not* me?"'

Jamie didn't have an answer to that. He'd done the 'why me' himself so many times. And he'd refused counselling, despite being offered it. Maybe that had been a mistake. Maybe that was something he needed to do to move on. Or maybe not—because Anna was really helping him see a different side to things.

'So are you on any treatment?' he asked. Then he grimaced. 'Sorry. That's intrusive. Ignore it. I was being nosy and rude. You don't have to answer.'

'No, I'm fine talking about it, and actually that's one of the reasons I don't hide it away. I'm not the only woman in the world who's gone through a super-early menopause, and maybe I can pay things forward a bit and help someone who's struggling to deal with a similar situation, the way other people have helped me. Obviously at thirty-four I'm a couple of decades younger than most women with the menopause.' She smiled at him. 'So, yes, I'm having treatment. I'm on hormone replacement therapy to help keep up my bone density and avoid the risks of cardiovascular disease.'

'But doesn't HRT...?' He stopped.

'Put me at higher risk of breast cancer? No, actually, because of my age. It's fine. I need to be careful with my calcium intake, which is why I drink hot chocolate rather than tea and I take my coffee very milky, and I do a five-kilometre run twice a week because it's good weight-bearing exercise and helps with bone density. I have a DEXA scan every year to keep an eye on my bone density. So, as far as I'm concerned, everyone's looking after me. And I'm not letting my premature menopause or my infertility define me.'

'You're the sort of person who makes lemonade when life gives you lemons.'

'No—I make lemon drizzle cake and lemon meringue pie, actually. They're much nicer and slightly better for my teeth,' she said with a grin, making him laugh.

Even though she made him feel so light of spirit, at the same time Jamie felt guilty. Anna had been through a lot and she'd pushed herself to move on, whereas he was still wallowing in what had happened to him.

Then again, she was helping him move on now. Maybe he should tell her about Hestia and Giselle, explain why he found Christmas so hard. He opened his mouth to start that conversation, but the words stuck in his throat and refused to come out.

'So, anyway, now you know that you're totally safe with me,' she said. 'We can be friends.'

'Friends,' he agreed.

'And I hope you'll continue our Christmas bargain, because I really do want you as our ward's Father Christmas.'

'OK,' he said. 'What do you suggest next?'

'Maybe we could try a Christmas movie,' she said.

'That's fine. When?'

He was half expecting her to suggest watching a DVD at either his place or hers, but then she said, 'There's a special screening at the Alexandra Palace theatre on Monday night. First come, first served for seating, so if we get there early enough we'll get a decent seat. We could maybe go and get a pizza somewhere first.'

'Sounds good,' he said. 'OK. Let me buy the tickets.'

'How about I buy the tickets and you buy the pizza?' she suggested.

'That works for me,' he said. 'Thank you. Monday night it is. And it'll be a good way to decompress after Lily's surgery. I meant what I said earlier, by the way. If you want to observe any part of the operation, you're very welcome—as is anyone on our team who might find it useful.'

'I might just take you up on that.'

Weird how her sea-green eyes made his heart skip a beat. But, after what she'd just told him, Jamie knew how inappropriate the reaction was. Anna had made it very clear that she wasn't interested in anything more than friendship. So he'd stuff the feelings back inside rather than let them out to bloom.

CHAPTER SIX

ON MONDAY MORNING Jamie met Lily Brown outside the operating theatre.

'All ready?' he asked.

'I think so.' She gave him a nervous smile.

'Good.' He smiled at her; he noticed that her mother looked just as nervous, and patted Heather's arm. 'She'll be fine. I'm going to take my time over this so I get it right and Lily gets the best possible outcome.'

Heather nodded. 'I know. I just…'

He knew what she wasn't saying. 'Of course you're going to worry. You're her mum. Have you got someone who can wait with you during the op?'

'My friend's coming as soon as she's dropped her daughter off at school,' Heather said.

'Great. You can stay with Lily while she's having the anaesthetic, until she goes to sleep, but then I'm afraid we'll have to send you out for a cup of tea.' He smiled at her again. 'I'm going to go and scrub in—which means washing my hands super-thoroughly—and I'll see you on the other side, OK?' He turned to Lily. 'And I'll see you in Theatre, Miss Brown.'

The operating theatre was just how he liked it: quiet, with a Bach piano piece playing softly. He'd already managed to establish a good working relationship with his team, and thankfully they were happy with his choice of music to operate to.

'Good morning, everyone. I'll just run through what we're doing this morning and make sure everyone's happy with their roles,' he said.

Once that was done, he settled down to make the first incision and to make a huge difference to Lily Brown's spinal column.

Anna knew that Lily's operation was complex and would take at least four hours. She managed to get enough time to go and observe the operation during her lunch break, and saw for herself that despite the gentle teasing of her sister Jamie Thurston *was* really good with his hands.

He was also really nice with the rest of the team, just like Nalini was, treating everyone as a valued colleague; it was the total opposite of the arrogant surgeons who had been around when Anna had been a student. They'd viewed themselves as superior beings and considered any questions to be a personal attack on their abilities. She noticed that Jamie explained exactly what he was doing as he went along and why he'd chosen to use one particular method over another, and he was clearly happy to use any questions as a teaching point.

She really hoped that he'd agree to stay at Muswell Hill Memorial Hospital for a bit longer than his scheduled three months and cover the rest of Nalini's maternity leave, because he was a real asset to the team. And also, if she was honest with herself, because she liked him being around—even though she knew it was ridiculous and there was absolutely no possibility of a relationship between them. She was doing just fine on her own, and Jamie clearly wasn't ready to move on from whatever had broken his heart.

She lingered in Theatre for as long as she could, enjoying watching the procedure, then headed back to her clinic.

At the end of the day, she popped into the High Dependency Unit to see Lily. 'How are you doing?' she asked.

'OK.' But Lily's lower lip was wobbly, she noticed.

'I brought you something,' she said, and handed over a tube of lip salve. 'Just in case you forgot yours or you might like a different flavour for a change. This one's cocoa butter and it's really nice.'

'That's so kind of you.' Lily started to cry and scrubbed the tears away with the back of her hand. 'Sorry. I don't know why I'm crying. I should be happy because my back is going to be better and that means they're going to stop calling me Quasimodo at school.'

'You, honey, are an Esmeralda if ever I saw one, not Quasimodo,' Anna said, sitting on the side of her bed and exchanging a glance with Heather that told her Lily's mother had had no idea how bad the teasing had been and was horrified to learn what had been said to her daughter. 'You've been worrying about the opera-tion and now it's all over and you're filled with relief, so that's probably why you're feeling a bit weepy—plus sometimes people react like that to the anaesthetic. It's absolutely fine and it's perfectly normal, so you don't need to apologise. The good news is that after a night's sleep you'll feel an awful lot better.'

Lily didn't look convinced, and Anna hated to think

how terrible the poor girl had been feeling at school. But maybe there was something she could do to help. 'Actually, there are a lot of really kick-ass people with scoliosis. You know Usain Bolt?'

'No way,' Lily said, her eyes widening in surprise. 'But he's a famous sprinter.'

'Yup. The fastest man in the world has scoliosis—and it hasn't stopped him, has it?'

'That's incredible,' Heather said. 'I had no idea either.'

Anna went on to list half a dozen actresses and singers who had scoliosis—some of the most famous and beautiful people in the business, all of whom she hoped Lily might have looked up to.

'And they all have scoliosis?' Lily asked. 'Really?'

'Really,' Anna confirmed. 'Not all of them needed an op—some had a brace like the one you used to wear and that worked for them. But they all have scoliosis. So, next time anyone says anything horrible to you, just tell them those names. Show them that scoliosis is simply one part of you and it doesn't define you. You're awesome, Lily Brown, and don't let anyone ever tell you otherwise.'

'Anna's absolutely right,' Jamie said from the doorway. 'Though I didn't know that about Usain Bolt.'

'You do now,' Anna said with a smile. 'He's a great ambassador for the condition. And Princess Eugenie. She was a year older than you are when she was diagnosed, Lily.'

Lily nodded. 'I remember seeing the pictures in the paper. Her wedding dress was low at the back so you could see her scar. I thought she was so brave.'

'So are you. It's who you are inside that counts, and how you deal with life,' Anna said.

Who you are inside... How you deal with life.

And Anna herself was brave, Jamie thought. She had no scars on the outside to show how her life had been turned upside down by a medical diagnosis, but there were definitely scars on the inside. Yet she carried on and made the best of things. He rather thought he could learn a lot from her.

More visitors arrived to see Lily, and Anna smiled. 'We'll go now and let you catch up with everyone. I'll see you on the ward tomorrow.'

'Yes, and I want to see you on your feet—even if it's only for two steps,' Jamie said. 'You're doing brilliantly. It's good to see you smiling.'

'Thank you. Thank you so much for everything you did for me,' Lily said.

'Pleasure. That's why I do this job—so I can make people better,' he said.

Anna and Jamie headed for the high street to grab a pizza before the show started at the cinema.

'So how do you know all that stuff about famous people with scoliosis?' he asked.

'I looked it up,' she said. 'Actually, I do the same for some of the conditions I know really get our patients down, and it kind of makes the kids feel a bit better that someone famous, someone whose name they actually recognise, has managed to deal with having that same condition. And I guess it makes them feel a little bit less alone.'

'It's a really good idea,' he said.

'I managed to observe the op for a few minutes

during my lunch break,' she said, 'and it was fascinating. I don't often get to see surgeons at work.'

'Maybe we could look at some kind of formal enrichment process on the ward,' Jamie said. 'Your team can see what we do and ask us whatever you like, and we can learn from you about the kind of things our patients face post-op and see if there's anything we can tweak to make their recovery easier for them.'

'Good idea,' Anna agreed. 'Let's talk to Robert about it.'

When they'd eaten, they walked together up the hill to the Alexandra Palace; the massive building with its iconic transmission mast loomed up from the far side of the park.

'I really didn't expect to see so much of the City of London from here,' Jamie said when they were at the top of the hill next to the palace. 'It's a bit like Primrose Hill—the skyline's instantly recognisable, with the Shard and the Walkie-Talkie. It's gorgeous.'

'It's a great view. It's also brilliant for watching fireworks,' she said.

They went into the complex and took their seats in the theatre.

'This is amazing,' Jamie said, looking around the room. 'Is it as old as it looks, or is it a clever modern interpretation of something that used to be here?'

'It's an original Victorian theatre,' she explained. 'It was closed to the public for eighty years and it's only just been restored and reopened. They do all sorts of things here—stage plays, the odd pop-up cinema, concerts. During the restoration, my parents made a donation for each of us for Christmas, so our names are all on a board in the foyer.' She smiled. 'It's so nice to feel we've been part of that.'

'Does your family live locally?' he asked.

She nodded. 'My parents still live in the house where we grew up, though we're trying to persuade them to move to something a little bit smaller and easier to manage. We all love it around here, so we all ended up moving back after we'd finished uni. I trained at the London Victoria, but I've worked at Muswell Hill Memorial Hospital ever since I qualified.'

The more Jamie heard about Anna's family, the more he liked the sound of them; and the more guilty he felt for pushing his own family away. His parents and sisters would love this place, he knew.

He looked up at the ceiling. 'That's stunning. I had no idea this was even here. Thanks for organising this.'

'My pleasure.' She looked slightly awkward. 'Um, I hope you don't mind that the film's a bit on the girly side.'

Love, Actually. He'd seen the posters for it in the foyer. 'I haven't actually seen it in full,' he admitted, 'though it's my sisters' favourite Christmas film.'

'Mine, too. I had a massive crush on Hugh Grant and years ago my best friend made me a life-sized cardboard cut-out of him,' she said with a smile. Then her smile faded. 'It got damaged when I moved in with Johnny and it couldn't be repaired. Looking back, I think the damage probably wasn't an accident. It should've made me see then that Johnny might not have been a keeper.'

Her ex had broken her cardboard cut-out—a gift from her best friend that had been a bit of fun to make Anna smile? How mean-spirited, Jamie thought. 'You weren't tempted to name your goldfish after Hugh?' he asked. 'Or even Grant the Goldfish, if you wanted to keep the alliteration.'

'Nope. George is named after my first love.'

'You named him after your ex-boyfriend?' Jamie asked, surprised.

'First love,' she corrected. 'George Michael. Mum used to play Wham! all the time when we were kids. I listen to Wham! now if I'm in a bad mood. Dancing around the kitchen and singing into my hairbrush is the quickest way to get me smiling again. And it's even better if I've got a niece or nephew with me. We all love singing and bopping around the room together, hairbrushes in hand.'

He could just imagine it. Anna Maskell would throw herself into the singing whole-heartedly—just as she did with everything else. And he could just see her with her nieces and nephews, encouraging them and spending time having fun with them.

She would've made a brilliant mother. What a shame she hadn't had the chance.

He was sitting very close to her and it would be, oh, so easy to reach out and take her hand. To hold her hand throughout the film. Every nerve in his body told him to do it.

But he remembered what she'd told him: she wasn't looking for a relationship. So it wouldn't be fair to put that kind of pressure on her. Even though he thought her ex had been utterly selfish, and her infertility wasn't a problem for Jamie in the way it clearly had been for her ex. In an odd way, it kind of made her safe to date, because it meant there was absolutely no way he could lose her in the way that he'd lost Hestia—but he rather thought that made him just as selfish as Anna's ex. And that wasn't who he was.

Anna was really family-orientated; although on the surface she seemed to have come to terms with her infertility, Jamie had a feeling that underneath maybe it wasn't so clear-cut and she still really wanted a family of her own. In his experience, pregnancy meant taking a huge risk. It had cost him everything—the love of his life, his baby, his peace of mind—and he wasn't sure he had the courage to take that kind of risk again. So he really wasn't the right one for Anna. Even though he wanted her, he needed to be unselfish about this.

He tried to concentrate on the film, but he found himself glancing at Anna every so often. He could see her face clearly in the light from the screen, and she was obviously enjoying the film hugely. He thought it was a bit daft, and it was probably more the sort of film she would've enjoyed more with her female friends, but he didn't really mind it.

Until they got to the scenes with the school Christmas concert.

Until the girl came on the stage and sang That Song. The one that always broke his heart. Although the young actress's performance was brilliant, the song just brought back so many memories for him that he felt as if he was drowning.

He glanced to the side; thankfully, Anna hadn't noticed. And he'd make damn sure that he was absolutely fine before the lights went up in the theatre so she didn't notice and feel guilty. He'd smile his head off, even though right at that moment he wanted to howl.

* * *

As they filed out into the foyer, Anna said, 'I think the school concert's my favourite bit in the film—well, that and when Colin Firth's character tries to speak Portuguese and is endearingly pants at it.' She grinned. 'But the Christmas lobster—that's genius. Which reminds me, I was going to ask you: would you like to come to the Christmas concert at my nieces' and nephew's school next week? The three middle ones are performing. They've done rehearsals at my parents' place and I can't wait to see them in costume. Aria's a shepherd in the Reception class nativity, Charlie's a robin in his class's special dance, and Megan's got the board for the partridge in the pear tree for her class's song, so she'll be leading the line on the front of the stage.'

'Thank you for inviting me, but I'm afraid I can't make it.'

How did he know? She hadn't given him a date. Anna really hadn't expected him to balk at a school Christmas concert. But something in his eyes warned her it wasn't because he was busy. 'What's wrong?' she asked quietly.

He shook his head again, clearly not wanting to discuss it in public.

'Let's go back to mine for a hot drink,' she said, and shepherded him through the park and back to her flat. She didn't push him to make conversation, because she could see he was struggling.

He stopped at her gate. 'Thank you for this evening,' he said politely. 'I'll see you tomorrow.'

'No, you'll come in and have a mug of tea or something with me,' she said, 'because I have a feeling that right now you could do with some company.'

'I...'

'Jamie, I'm not going to hurt you,' she said gently. 'I want to help. And sometimes it's easier to cope with something that's upset you if you share it with someone else.' Her counsellor had taught her that. 'Whatever you say won't go any further than me.'

Thankfully, that made him walk through her gate.

She ushered him into the kitchen. 'What can I get you? Tea? Coffee?'

'I don't mind. Anything,' he said.

It was so obvious that he was trying not to be difficult. And he was struggling. She'd had days like that herself. She made them both a mug of hot chocolate, then led him through to the living room.

'Let me introduce you. This is George the Gorgeous Goldfish. George, this is my friend from work, Jamie.'

'Hi, George,' Jamie said, but his voice was a flat monotone, worrying her even more; she'd hoped that the sheer incongruity of being introduced to a goldfish might at least make him smile and put a crack in the wall he seemed to be building round himself.

Clearly not. So how was she going to break through to him?

She thought about it. He'd chatted to her before the film, and she was fairly sure he'd enjoyed the film itself—but he'd gone really quiet when she'd asked him to the concert. That had to be the problem. She didn't know how to make this better; and she was scared that whatever she said might make things worse. On the other hand, she couldn't just leave him to the thoughts that were clearly ripping him to shreds.

She gestured to him to sit on the sofa, and sat down next to him. 'Jamie, I'm really sorry if I'm treading on a sore spot, because that's not my intention,' she said, 'but the school Christmas concert seems to be the thing that's really upset you and I don't understand why. I don't want to make things worse, so please can you help me understand what it is?'

She'd been honest with him, Jamie thought. So now it was time for him to be honest with her.

'It wasn't the concert, exactly. It was the film,' he said. 'That song. "All I Want for Christmas is You". It was Hestia's—my wife's—favourite song, and she'd sing it all round the house in December.' He took a deep breath. 'She died. So did our baby. Just over three years ago.' The anniversary had been the week before he'd started at the Muswell Hill Memorial Hospital. 'If they'd still been alive, this year would've been the first year we'd have gone to nursery school for a Christmas concert.'

It was the first time he'd actually said it out loud for a long, long time. Usually it was like a bruise in his soul, there all the time, aching and never reaching the surface.

And now he'd actually said it out loud, he didn't know what to do. What to say next.

Every instinct told him to run.

And he couldn't look at Anna. He couldn't bear to see the pity on her face.

As if she'd guessed what he was thinking—or, more likely, it was written all over his expression—she took his hand and squeezed it briefly, before letting it go. 'The last thing you need right now is pity, and I'm not pitying you at all, but I do sympathise. It's hard enough to lose people you love, but Christmas has to be the worst time of all for it to happen.'

Yeah. She could say that again. Everyone else seemed to be celebrating, talking about love and peace and happiness, and all that had been around him that year had been death and sadness. And he got sucked into it every year. Christmas was supposed to be a time of joy, but for him it was a time of shadows and he didn't know how to break the cycle.

'I understand now why you don't like Christmas,' she said quietly, 'and I'm so sorry I've been insensitive. I'm your colleague and I hope I'm becoming your friend. If you want to talk, I'm here—and, just in case you're worrying, I have absolutely no intention of betraying your confidence and making you the hot topic on the hospital grapevine.'

He knew that. She wasn't the type to spread gossip.

'In my experience,' she said, 'talking about difficult things kind of cuts them down to size and stops them being overwhelming. When I found out about my infertility, I was devastated. It felt as if my life didn't have any point, if I couldn't have children. I didn't feel as if I was a real woman, because I couldn't do what every other woman in the world seemed to be able to do. But you know Jenna Conti on our ward? Her twin sister Lucy had a serious accident a few years ago that meant she couldn't have children, and Jenna was her surrogate mum and had a baby for her. Jenna introduced me to Lucy, so I had someone to talk to who actually understood what it was like to have your choices taken away. Lucy and Jenna both really helped me.'

Someone who understood. Someone who'd been in her shoes.

Jamie didn't know anyone who'd been in his shoes. Nobody who'd been a widower or a widow in their early thirties; nobody who'd lost their partner and their baby to eclampsia.

'And you've lost someone?' He knew it was bitter and he hated himself for it, but he couldn't call the words back now.

'My grandparents,' she said, 'and I've been lucky because they had a long and happy life and, even though I'm sad they're no longer around, it felt as if it was in the natural order of things. But my best friend lost her mum to breast cancer, so I understand how people feel when they lose someone too soon. It's not the things you did or said, it's the things you didn't have time to do or say.'

Her words resonated with him. He hadn't even had the chance to say goodbye to Hestia. And it wasn't the same, sitting in a hospital morgue with someone you knew for definite couldn't hear you saying goodbye, someone who couldn't squeeze your hand one last time. It wasn't at all like being with someone right at the end, holding them and telling them you loved them, making sure they weren't alone as they slid into unconsciousness and then death.

He'd let Hestia down because he hadn't been there when she'd died.

He looked at Anna then, and there wasn't a trace of pity on her face. Fellow-feeling, sympathy and kindness, yes, but not pity. He opened his mouth, and suddenly the words blurted out. 'Hestia had eclampsia.'

She looked sad, but said nothing. Though she did take his hand again. She wasn't holding his hand like a lover; she was holding his hand like someone who cared what he said, who was going to give him the space to think about what he said, and who wasn't going anywhere until he'd talked.

So he talked.

'She was seven months pregnant and she'd just gone on maternity leave. Our baby was due the week before Christmas. Hestia was on her way to the corner shop to get a pint of milk. She collapsed in the middle of the street and had a seizure. And I often think, maybe if I'd checked the cupboards before I went to work and got some milk so she hadn't had to go out...' He shook his head.

'Which I know is ridiculous, because obviously it would've happened anyway. Just she would've been at home instead of outside. And nobody would've called an ambulance, because nobody would've known she'd collapsed or was having a seizure, so in a way that would've been even worse. At least she wasn't alone at the very end—there were people nearby who helped her.' He raked a hand through his hair.

'The ambulance came quickly, but she'd had a cerebral haemorrhage and she died in the ambulance on the way to the emergency department. Our daughter Giselle died, too. It was too late to do a C-section to save the baby.'

'Your worst nightmare,' she said softly.

One he'd never woken up from.

'I'm sorry that something so terrible happened to your wife and baby,' she said.

'And I wasn't there with them at the end. That's the worst bit,' Jamie said. 'I know Hestia loved me, and I loved her, but I can't help feeling I let her down.'

'Were you at work when it happened?'

He nodded. 'I was in the operating theatre. She was even brought into the hospital where I worked—but it was another three hours until I got the message from the Emergency Department.'

'That's not your fault,' she said. 'And even if you'd got the message in Theatre, you could hardly have dropped everything and left your patient on the table.'

'Leaving my junior to carry on with an operation that was outside his experience and putting unfair pressure on the whole team, and letting the patient down as well. In my head, I know that,' he said. 'But another part of me still feels I failed my wife. I'm a *doctor*, for pity's sake. I should've noticed that something was wrong before I left for work that morning.'

'You're an orthopaedic surgeon, not an obstetrician,' she reminded him. 'OK, yes, as a doctor you would either know the symptoms of the really scary pregnancy complications or you would've looked them up—but you can't know everything about everyone else's specialties. Nobody can.'

Technically, that was true. He knew that. Emotionally, he still felt he'd let Hestia down.

'Did she have any symptoms of pre-eclampsia, or was she at high risk?' Anna asked.

Jamie shook his head. 'She wasn't diabetic, she didn't have kidney problems or high blood pressure or anything else that would make her more susceptible to pre-eclampsia, and there wasn't a family history of pre-eclampsia or any difficulties at all during pregnancy. Her blood pressure was fine; there was a tiny bit of protein in her urine at her last appointment, but the midwife wasn't overly concerned and was going to do a check at her next appointment.' The appointment two days after her death. 'Hestia hadn't mentioned any headaches either.'

'Then you're really not being very fair to yourself,' Anna said. 'You can't possibly diagnose a condition if there aren't any symptoms. And remember eclampsia's called that for a reason: it's a lightning strike.'

From the Greek. He remembered.

'It's something that you simply can't predict.'

'One in four thousand pregnancies.' He knew every horrible statistic. Death in pregnancy or childbirth was so much less common nowadays; but shockingly one in fifty women with eclampsia died, and of the babies one in fourteen died.

Hestia and Giselle had both been on the wrong side of the statistics.

'I'm sorry,' she said. 'And it must be hard for you, working in paediatrics and seeing children who are the same age as your daughter would've been now.'

'Weirdly, it's easier at work,' he said. 'Because the children we see are ill and we're making them better. I can cope with that. It's…' He blew out a breath. 'It's seeing children outside. That's hard. All the might-have-beens.'

'Then I won't push you to come to my nieces' and nephew's Christmas concert,' she said. 'That'll be too much for you.'

'Isn't it hard for you, too?' he asked. 'Seeing people with babies and toddlers? All the might-have-beens?'

'It was, at one point,' she said. 'But I'm lucky that my family and friends are really generous. I'm god-mother to several of my friends' children. They all in-clude me in things they do with the kids, so I get to do most of what I would've done with my own children, if I'd been that lucky. I go to swimming class or to toddler music class, I get invites to all the nursery and school shows, I get to do bedtime stories and all the fun bits of parenting like afternoons at the park, days at the beach or trips to the sea life centres.' She gave him a wry smile. 'Not just the fun bits, though. I've had my share of changing poomageddon nappies, too.'

'Poomageddon?' he asked, mystified.

'That was my nephew Noah, when he had gastric flu last year and Jojo and Becky went down with it as well. I looked after the three of them, dispensing lots of drinks, paracetamol and cool flannels. The nappies were, you might say, a bit on the challenging side. But we managed.'

And Jamie had had longer to come to terms with his wife and baby's death than Anna had had to come to terms with her infertility and a husband who'd had an affair and a baby with someone else, letting her down.

Then he realised he'd spoken aloud. 'I'm s—'

'Shh.' She pressed her forefinger lightly against his lips. 'Don't apologise. There isn't a time limit on grief, and we're not in a competition over who's had the toughest deal. Things are as they are. And maybe I've had more support than you have. I'm really lucky with my family.'

'Mine are good, too,' he said. And that was something else he felt guilty about. 'Except I've pushed them away. I use work as an excuse not to see them very often, and I always make sure I'm on duty on Christmas Day so I don't have to face them—they're all so kind and so careful not to say anything that might upset me, and I hate the fact they feel they have to tread on eggshells around me. They wrap me in so much cotton wool that it suffocates me. I know it looks as if I'm being self-ish, abandoning them and wallowing in misery—but, the way I see it, if I'm not there, then they can have fun without worrying about accidentally upsetting me.'

'Then maybe,' she said, 'we should carry on with our Christmas deal. Take the sting out of it for you so you can cope with it again and make things up with your family so you can enjoy each other's company.'

'That's what I want to do,' he said. 'Just…' It was so hard. As if he'd put an unscaleable wall around himself and he didn't know how to get out again.

'And we'll make sure we avoid that song. Though,' she pointed out, 'it's the one song that probably gets the most airplay at this time of year, so it's really not going to be easy to avoid it.'

'I know.'

'It's not the same as my situation with Johnny,' she said. 'But, if he'd been the man I thought he was when I married him, and he was the one who'd been left behind, I would've wanted him to find happiness again. To meet someone who could give him the love I didn't have time to give. And I'm guessing that Hestia would've hated the idea of you cutting yourself off from everyone and being lonely for the rest of your life.'

'She would,' he admitted. 'And I think that's why I agreed to your Christmas bargain. Because I really do want to move on from the past and make things right again with my family—and hers—but I just don't know where to start.'

'With my family,' she said, 'a text would do. All I'd have to say is "I'm having a bit of trouble dealing with this, but please bear with me because I love you and

I'm trying to find my way back somehow", and they'd understand. They'd give me space for a while and then try to meet me halfway. Though I also know not every family's like mine.'

'I think mine are. But it's been so long,' he said. 'It's too late.'

'It's never too late. Call them. Text them or write to them if you don't think you'll be able to say the words,' she said. 'Because my guess is they've tried to give you space and now they don't know how to reach you either, and they're as scared of that huge gulf as you are. They're worried that if they reach out they'll accidentally push you further away. So don't let that gap get any bigger. You don't have to reach the whole way across, just some of the way. And, from what you've just told me, I'm pretty sure they'll reach right back to meet you.'

He had no idea how Anna had got so wise, but he was grateful.

'You could,' she said, 'text them now.'

He glanced at his watch. 'It's a bit late. I wouldn't want them to think it was an emergency and start worrying.'

'Do it tomorrow, then. Before you go to work. Then you'll have a valid reason not to look at your phone all day, because you're operating. It gives you all a bit of space.'

'Thank you,' he said. 'For listening. For talking sense into me. For putting up with me being such a mess.'

'That's what friends are for,' she said. 'And I think you'd do the same for me if our positions were reversed.'

He thought about it. 'Yes. I would. I don't think I'm as good with people as you are… But I'd try.'

'Well, then.' She smiled at him. 'Go home.'

'And plan what I'm going to say, right?'

'Right. Just keep it simple and honest,' she said, and released his hand.

Which was probably just as well, because he was very tempted to wrap his arms round her. To hold her. And it wasn't just gratitude. It was other feelings prompting him, things he wasn't used to feeling and which scared him and thrilled him in equal measure.

And then there was the guilt. How could he even be noticing another woman like this, when he'd just spilled out his heart about losing Hestia? Even though he knew Hestia wouldn't have wanted him to spend the rest of his life grieving for her and he needed to move on, it still felt like a betrayal of sorts.

He needed to get his head together. Be cool, logical and unflappable, like the surgeon he was at work. 'OK. I'll see you tomorrow.'

'You bet.'

He walked back to his flat, and her words echoed in his head all the way.

If he'd been the man I thought he was when I married him, and he was the one who'd been left behind, I would've wanted him to find happiness again. To meet someone who could give him the love I didn't have time to give.

Jamie knew that was what Hestia would've wanted for him, too. She would've been furious that he'd wallowed in despair for three years.

Find happiness.

Meet someone.

All the breath suddenly left his lungs when he realised that he *had* met someone. Someone who was changing the way he was seeing the world and was teaching him to find happiness. Someone who'd been through the mill herself. Anna Maskell was bringing light back into his life; and maybe, just maybe, he could be the one who did the same for her.

He thought about that all the rest of the way home.

And then it was easy to write those texts to his family. Keeping the words simple and heartfelt and honest.

Hi. I'm sorry I've shut you out for the last three years. I've been finding it hard coming to terms with Hestia and Giselle dying. But I want you to know I love you and I'm trying to find my way back to some kind of normal. Please don't give up on me.

He waited until the morning to send them, not wanting to worry anyone with a late-night message.

What he hadn't expected was how quickly the replies came, his phone pinging almost immediately after he'd sent them. His mother, his sisters, his mother-in-law, Hestia's sister. And they were all variations on a theme.

I love you too and I'm here whenever you're ready to talk.

Tears filled his eyes. Anna had been right. His family were all ready to reach out over that gulf, to meet him halfway. But, without her pushing him, he would never have been able to make that first step and reach out to them.

Anna Maskell, he decided, was getting the biggest bouquet of flowers ever.

He didn't manage to see her during the day, because she was busy with clinic and ward rounds and he was in Theatre, so instead he texted her during a break.

You busy tonight?

The reply came back.

Sorry. Going to Zumba with my sister-in-law and then a family dinner.

So he couldn't call round to her place tonight with the flowers, then.

His phone pinged again with another message from Anna.

Am free tomorrow, if you want to do something.

This was his chance to move on. Instead of leaving all the Christmas stuff to her, he could make an effort. Suggest something. Meet her halfway.

Maybe we can go and see some Christmas lights?

The Regent Street angels?

That's fine. I'll meet you at your flat at seven. Maybe we can grab dinner, before or after.

Love to.

It wasn't a date, he reminded himself. It was just part of their Christmas bargain. Except maybe now he could start to move forward and do things for her, too. Help her move past the hurt Johnny had inflicted and see just what an amazing woman she was.

Any man would be lucky to have Anna Maskell as his partner.

Could he be that man?

Although part of him was terrified at the idea of opening himself up to another relationship and risking the possibility of loss, another part of him wanted to be that man. Because the alternative was Anna meeting someone else and settling down with him. Jamie wanted Anna to be happy, but the thought of it being with someone who wasn't him made him feel miserable.

He needed to do the right thing by her. Help her see how wonderful she was, give her the courage to move past Johnny's betrayal and give her heart to someone who deserved her. A man who could give her the family she wanted, deep down.

And he wanted to be the man who deserved her. Did he have the courage to take that risk? Given her infertility, any pregnancy would be extremely high risk—if the treatment even worked in the first place. IVF had no guarantees. Even suggesting it was like offering false hope, something he might not be able to deliver. But there were other options. Surrogacy. Fostering. Adoption,

Could he move on and risk loving again?
Could he make Anna happy?
Or should he put her first and just back off?

CHAPTER SEVEN

ON WEDNESDAY MORNING Anna saw Lily during her ward rounds, then called back in later to see her with a sudoku magazine.

Lily beamed. 'That's really nerdy—and really kind. Thank you. I love these sorts of puzzles.'

'Pleasure.' Anna smiled back at her. 'Well, hey, I was wondering what a maths wizard might like to do to pass the time between visitors—and hopefully you'll make some friends on the ward, too, so you can chat to people here.'

'Jamie came to see me earlier,' Lily said. 'Mum helped me get out of bed and I took two whole steps in front of him, and he was really pleased.'

'I bet he was. Keep up the good work. The physio's coming back to see you this afternoon,' Anna said with a smile.

Jamie.

She still couldn't quite believe that he'd actually suggested doing a Christmas thing rather than leaving all the plans to her. Was this a sign that he was starting to heal and getting ready to move on? Was Christmas finally losing its sting for him?

She really hoped that he'd contacted his family; and

she hoped even more that they'd reacted the same way her family would have reacted, reaching back out to him.

Though she was going to have to be careful. Jamie had lost his wife and child; so it was a fair bet that, when he was ready to move on again, he'd want someone who could give him a family without complications. Which meant moving on with someone other than her. She couldn't afford to think of Jamie Thurston as anything other than a friend and a colleague—no matter how tempting his gorgeous blue eyes and shy smile were.

Her life was full and it was good. Plenty of people struggled on with far more problems than she had. Wanting more was simply greedy, and she'd count her blessings.

At five to seven that evening, Jamie stood outside Anna's front door, holding an enormous bouquet of flowers. He'd ordered them from a local florist the previous day, asking for something pretty and Christmassy. The florist had made an arrangement with deep red roses, cream-coloured freesias, and then eryngium that had been sprayed silver, teamed with the silvery green foliage of eucalyptus and the deeper green leaves of laurel.

He rang the bell; a few moments later, she opened the door, smiling a welcome at him. 'Hey. Perfect timing. I'm just about to put my boots on and find wherever I put my gloves.'

'These are for you,' he said, and handed her the bouquet. 'I hope you like them.'

'For me? Thank you. They're absolutely gorgeous.

I love them.' Her eyes widened. 'But it's not my birthday or anything.'

'It's because you've really helped me and I wanted to say thank you.'

'Oh.' Her cheeks flushed, making her look incredibly pretty. He really wanted to kiss her, right there and then, but he held himself back.

'So does that mean we've done enough festive things now to make this time of year easier for you, and you're going to be my Father Christmas on the ward?' she asked.

'I'm still thinking about it. I'm not *quite* ready to say yes,' he said.

Though what he wasn't admitting, even to himself, was that he didn't want his Christmassy trips with Anna to end. He was starting to look forward to them, and it wasn't just that she was taking the sting out of Christmas for him. It was because he enjoyed her company. Being with her made the world feel like a much warmer, sweeter place. He liked who he was when he was with her. But was he being selfish? Should he step aside and let her find someone who really could bring her happiness, someone without all the emotional baggage and complications that came with him? Or, with her help, could he become the man who'd bring her the joy she deserved?

'OK. I need to put these in water before we go out. Come in while I grab a vase.'

In her kitchen, Jamie noticed all the children's paintings held onto the door of her fridge with magnets. He hadn't noticed them on Monday night, when he'd still been numb and despairing; but now he could see how much she was loved by her nieces and nephews, and how much she clearly loved them.

'These flowers really are spectacular,' she said, filling a vase and putting the bouquet into water. 'I still don't think I've done anything special to deserve them, but I really appreciate them.'

'Actually, you've done way more than you think,' he said. 'I texted my mum, my sisters and Hestia's mum and sister yesterday morning just before I left for work. Like you suggested, I kept it simple and honest. I apologised for pushing them away and said I was finding it hard to deal with what happened, but I wanted to let them know that I loved them.'

'Good,' she said. Then she met his gaze head-on. 'Did they reply?'

'All of them. Before I'd even got halfway to the hospital.' He could still hardly believe it, and shook his head in wonderment. 'All of them said they loved me, too, and would be there whenever I wanted to see them or talk. They understood and they'd wait until I was ready.'

'I'm glad,' she said.

So was he.

They headed out to see the Christmas lights in Regent Street: angels with enormous wings and draping skirts made from twinkly lights. Jamie couldn't help thinking of Hestia, and the times he'd seen her on stage wearing an ankle-length gauzy skirt; how often he'd thought she'd danced like an angel. Looking up at the lights, he almost felt as if she approved of what he was doing. That he was looking to rejoin the world and find happiness again.

'They're glorious. Apparently it's a nod to the very

first Christmas lights that were put up here in the nine-teen-fifties,' she said, 'because they were angels, too.'

As they walked down towards Bond Street, their hands brushed against each other. Once, twice; the third time, Jamie couldn't help catching Anna's fingers loosely in his. She didn't pull away; and gradually, as they walked, he let his fingers mesh more closely with hers until they were really holding hands.

This was how Anna remembered feeling as a teen, with her skin tingling with nerves and excitement as she held her boyfriend's hand for the very first time.

Except she was thirty-four, not fourteen. And Jamie Thurston wasn't a skinny boy with terrible skin and greasy hair. They'd both had their hearts broken and were at different stages of putting the pieces back together.

If she had any sense, she'd make some excuse to drop his hand—fake-sneezing into a tissue or something like that—and she'd chatter brightly to him and keep him at a distance. Firmly in the friend zone. This wasn't a date.

But, for the life of her, right at that moment she couldn't help holding his hand just as tightly as he was holding hers.

They strolled down to Bond Street to see the peacock-inspired lights, the beautiful fan-shaped display spanning the whole street at one end, and then individual peacock feathers peeking out from behind them in silver and gold, the 'eye' of the feather gradually changing colour.

Speaking would break the spell, she thought, so she

said nothing until they turned into a side street and found a pop-up Christmas street food market.

'Shall we?' Jamie asked—though he didn't let go of her hand.

Food. He meant food. He wasn't talking about kissing her under non-existent mistletoe, Anna reminded herself, even though her lips were tingling slightly in anticipation.

'Dinner sounds good,' she said, hearing the huskiness in her own voice and wincing slightly.

He was still holding her hand as they chose dinner—Christmas spiced turkey empanadas with cranberry chilli salsa, which tasted even better than they sounded, and then rich squares of Christmas pudding brownie, sprayed gold and with a swirl of cinnamon cream and a glacé cherry on top.

He held her hand again all the way back to the Tube station, all the way back on the train, and all the way from the station to her front door.

'Thank you for a lovely evening,' he said.

'I enjoyed it, too.' She paused. 'Do you want to come in for coffee?'

Her hair was loose, and he tucked a strand behind her ear. 'Yes. And no.'

She frowned. 'Is that some weird kind of surgical puzzle?'

'It's me saying I want to spend time with you, but it's complicated and it's probably fairer to both of us if I don't.'

She looked down at their joined hands. 'I see.' Which was totally untrue. She was more confused than ever. Was this a thing, or wasn't it? Were they friends, or finding their way towards something else?

He kissed her cheek. 'This scares the hell out of me. You're the first person who's made me feel anything at all since Hestia died. Which is a good thing—but it's also something I need to get my head around.'

'I haven't dated anyone since Johnny,' she admitted. And in some ways Jamie was the worst man she could date. Being with him was a huge risk. He'd already lost so much. Would she be enough for him? What if he decided further down the line that he wanted a child of his own? That would put her right back in the same place she'd been with Johnny, unable to give her man the one thing he really wanted: a baby. And, although she didn't think Jamie would deliberately hurt her, she'd once believed that about Johnny. Could she really trust her judgement?

Or maybe she was overthinking this. 'Though tonight wasn't a date.'

'Agreed. It was part of our Christmas bargain. But if you drew a Venn diagram I think there would be quite a crossover.' This time, Jamie kissed the corner of her mouth.

She rested her palm against his cheek. 'So we're going to take this slowly. See where it goes. Just between you and me. No pushing, no rushing, no pressure.' Less risk, though she wasn't quite brave enough to admit that.

'That works for me.' He took a deep breath. 'You're going indoors now and I'm going back to my own place. As you said, no rushing. Just...' He wrapped his free arm around her and held her close. 'See you tomorrow.'

She wrapped her free arm around him, still holding his hand and enjoying the closeness. 'See you tomorrow.'

And funny how the world seemed different, the colours brighter.

On Friday morning, Anna and Jamie were in clinic with Michael Jeffries, a teenager who'd been caught up in a bad tackle during a football game and had torn his anterior cruciate ligament.

'I saw the other doctor,' he said, 'and she said I'd torn my ACL but there was a lot of swelling, so I had to wait for that to go down and a full range of movement to return before she could even think of operating.' He grimaced. 'I couldn't even turn on the spot. She said I could do swimming and have physio for the last month to keep my quads and my hams strong, but I wasn't allowed to do anything where I'd turn, jump or twist.'

'Which must've made you a bit stir-crazy,' Anna said sympathetically.

'Yeah. I hated it. I couldn't wait for today. Football's my life,' Michael said. 'Please tell me you're going to be able to fix my knee. I've got a place at the football academy. If I can't play, they'll give it to someone else and I'll be out. I'll have lost...' He shook his head, clearly close to tears.

Anna glanced at Jamie, willing him to give the boy some hope.

'The good news is I can fix your knee,' Jamie said, 'but the bad news is that you're not going to recover overnight. It'll take at least six months, and realistically it could be as much as a year before you can return to full training.'

'A whole *year*?' Michael looked horrified.

'A year,' Jamie said. 'And let's be very clear about this—if you go back to training before you're ready, you could do more damage to your knee, to the point where I wouldn't be able to fix it next time.'

Michael stared at them, his eyes wide. 'If I can't play football, my life might as well be over. I've never wanted to do anything else. I…' He blew out a breath. 'I have to play. I *have* to.'

'You'll be able to play again,' Jamie said, 'provided you give yourself proper recovery time.'

'Do you want your dad to come in?' Anna asked gently.

Michael shook his head. 'He'll be so disappointed in me.'

'It's not your fault you got hurt in a tackle,' Jamie reminded him. He brought the scan image up onto the screen of his computer and tilted the screen so Michael could see it. 'You can see the damage for yourself. The ligament's torn very badly.'

'So what are you going to do? Sew it back together?' Michael asked.

Jamie shook his head. 'I'll need to graft new tissue. What I'll do is remove the torn ligament and replace it with a bit of your patellar tendon—that's the tendon that attaches the bottom of your kneecap to the top of your shinbone.'

'And that will definitely fix it?'

'Provided you don't have damage to the cartilage that I can't see on the scan—I'll only be able to see that when I look inside your knee,' Jamie said.

Michael took a deep breath. 'All right. Will I have to stay in hospital?'

'Overnight, yes,' Jamie said. 'I'm going to do key-hole surgery. It'll take about an hour and a half, maybe a bit more, depending on how much damage I need to fix. And it's up to you whether you'd rather have a general anaesthetic so you're asleep throughout the whole thing, or if you want a spinal block so you'll be conscious during the actual operation and you'll know what's going on around you but you won't feel any pain.'

Michael looked nervous. 'I... Can I choose on the day?'

'The day before might be better,' Jamie said. 'And I think your dad needs to come in now, so I can talk you both through exactly what I'm going to do.'

'He's going to be so disappointed in me,' Michael said again.

'More like he's going to be worrying himself sick out there, wanting to know if you'll be all right,' Anna said gently.

Michael shook his head. 'If I wasn't any good at football, he wouldn't bother with me. He doesn't bother with my sister. All he cares about is—' He stopped abruptly.

Football? Anna wondered. But it wasn't her place to judge. 'OK,' she said, then went to the door and called Michael's father in.

'So when can he play again?' Mr Jeffries asked.

Nothing about whether Michael would be out of pain or what he could do to help his son, Anna noticed. This was a man whose priorities were very different from what her own would've been.

'He can play again when he's recovered properly,' Jamie said crisply, 'and that depends on how much damage there is to the cartilage, which I'll only be able to see when I operate. The important thing is that he's going to be out of pain.'

Mr Jeffries's eyes narrowed. 'Yes.'

Had Michael not let slip that comment about his sister, Anna would've thought that maybe his father was worried about how Michael would cope with having to wait until he could play again, because football was the boy's big passion. But now she wondered how much Michael really loved football for its own sake, and how much of it was a way of trying to connect with his father.

'We asked you to come in,' she said, 'so Mr Thurston could explain the operation to you both. If you have any questions about the best way to support your son's recovery, we'll be very happy to help.'

Mr Jeffries looked at her as if she was merely a decoration.

This wasn't about her, but she didn't appreciate his attitude. If he treated any of her team like that, she'd be having a stern word with him about the hospital's zero tolerance policy.

'I'm going to use a thin, flexible tube called an arthroscope,' Jamie explained. 'It has fibre optic cables inside so it acts as both a camera and a light, to show me your knee joint. I'll examine the inside of your knee and repair any damage to the cartilage. It'll confirm that your ACL is torn, Michael, so then I'll remove the graft tissue and cut it to the right size.'

'Where does the graft tissue come from?' Mr Jeffries asked.

'From the tendon that attaches his shinbone to his kneecap,' Jamie said.

'Why can't he just have physiotherapy? Surgery means he's going to be out of the team for months.' Mr Jeffries started at Jamie. 'He might lose his place at the football academy.'

'Physiotherapy on its own isn't enough. Michael's anterior cruciate ligament is badly torn, and that means he needs surgery to stabilise his knee,' Jamie explained patiently. 'Without it he'll be in considerable pain—and playing football will be completely out of the question.'

Mr Jeffries didn't look happy, but said nothing.

'Once I've removed your torn ligament, Michael, I'll make a tunnel in your bone to pass the new tissue through, and then I'll screw the graft tissue in place—it'll act as a scaffold for the new ligament to grow across, and will stay in your knee permanently. Once I'm happy it's strong enough to hold your knee together, it's stable and you've got the full range of movement in your knee, then I'll sew you up, put on a dressing and let you recover. And then, if you've chosen to have a general anaesthetic rather than a spinal block, we'll wake you up.'

'I think,' Michael said, 'I'd rather be asleep during the operation.'

'That's fine. And it's fine to change your mind if you think about it and then decide you'd rather be awake,' Jamie said. 'I'll use dissolvable stitches, so they'll disappear after about three weeks and you won't have to come back to have them removed.' He flicked a glance at Mr Jeffries, who remained utterly silent.

'Your knee will be a bit swollen and bruised for the first week and it will hurt,' Jamie continued, 'but we'll give you painkillers to help with that, and give you a special bandage that has iced water inside so it will help with the swelling. We'll give you some exercises to start off your recovery, and it's a good idea to use crutches for the first couple of weeks. Then you'll need to keep up with your physio for the next six months.'

'And then he can start playing?' Mr Jeffries demanded.

'That,' Jamie said, 'depends on how he heals. Everyone's different. I'd be guided by what the physio says.'

Mr Jeffries rolled his eyes. 'A couple of sports massages will sort it out.'

'I think you'll find,' Anna said, 'that any coach and any therapist will take the same view as the surgeon. Michael's health comes first. If he goes back too early, he'll set his progress back and risk never being able to play again.'

Mr Jeffries gave her a look of contempt. 'And you know much about sport, do you?'

'I know a little bit about medicine,' Anna said lightly. She wasn't giving this rude, arrogant man the satisfaction of arguing with him.

'Just to reassure you, Mr Jeffries,' Jamie said, 'Dr Maskell is a highly experienced senior doctor. She's one step down from being a consultant.'

'But if you'd rather have a second opinion on Michael's treatment from the head of the department,' Anna said, 'I'm very happy to go and find him for you.' Robert would be all charm—but he'd also put this man totally in his place and make it clear that their patient's needs came way, way before anything else. And Anna really regretted her impulse to call Mr Jeffries in to support Michael. She understood now why Michael hadn't wanted his father there. The man wasn't in the least bit supportive.

'That won't be necessary,' Mr Jeffries snapped.

'Good,' Jamie said coolly. 'Michael, I can get you on my list for Wednesday.'

'Thank you.'

Once they'd gone, Anna turned to Jamie. 'Thanks for sticking up for me.'

'It was the least I could do. What an idiot.' He rolled his eyes. 'If he gives anyone on the ward any trouble, let me know.'

'Thanks. Though I think we'd all just ignore him and concentrate on Michael.'

'Good idea,' he said. 'I'll just finish my notes, then we'll see the next patient on our list.'

The rest of the day flew by. Anna was late getting home but had just enough time to put on a red velvet skater dress, high heels and make-up before heading to the pub where the department's Christmas meal was being held. She had a quiet word with the manager about the music, checked that everything else was ready for them, and then they were good to go.

Once everyone was sitting down—Jamie was next to her—and had pulled their cracker, put on their paper hat and read out the terrible jokes, the meal was served. And once everyone had eaten and was enjoying coffee and petits fours, Robert excused himself for a moment and returned wearing the Father Christmas outfit and holding a large sack marked 'Swag'. 'Ho-ho-ho,' he boomed. 'This is the moment you've all been waiting for. Have you all been good, boys and girls?'

Jamie was surprised at how much he was enjoying the evening. The food was as good as Anna had promised, and he was relieved to discover it was just a meal with no dancing. There was Christmas music playing in the background, but the chatter blocked it out, and he had a feeling that Anna might just have had a word with whoever was in charge of the music because he'd been on tenterhooks, waiting for That Song, and it didn't arrive.

He'd made the effort to chat to the rest of the people he was sitting with, and it really felt as if he fitted in. Somehow, in only three short weeks, he'd managed to become as much a part of the team as he had at the hospital in south London where he'd trained and worked until three years ago. Though he had a feeling that the reason he felt so much part of it was because Anna was there.

Robert took the parcels from the sack and dished them out in turn, waiting for the recipient to open it before moving on to the next one. Jamie had drawn Keely's name; because he didn't know her well, he'd played it safe with a set of shower gel and body butter, which had been beautifully wrapped by the shop where he'd bought it. He'd been given what he recognised as a safe gift, too: a box of mixed milk, dark and white chocolates, which he intended to share.

Other people were given more personal gifts. Whoever had drawn Anna's name had bought her a clipboard and customised it with 'Ward Social Organiser Supremo' in sparkly letters on one side, and a picture of George Michael and a goldfish on the other, which had her in fits of laughter; though it also came with a jar of very posh chocolate flakes to stir into hot milk, which he knew she'd love. Jamie thoroughly enjoyed watching everyone's reactions to their gifts, and then the hubbub of chatter afterwards.

At the end of the evening, he walked Anna home. 'Thank you for nagging me into doing this tonight,' he said. 'You're right. It was a lot of fun.' And he really hadn't expected to have such a good time.

'I'm glad you enjoyed it,' she said with a smile.

'And also I wanted to tell you I'm meeting up with my family tomorrow,' he told her.

She blinked. 'So you've talked to them since you texted them, the other day?'

He nodded. 'Shelley—my oldest sister—called me and invited me to dinner tomorrow night. It's nothing fancy, just spaghetti and garlic bread and ice cream, and my niece Layla's going to make choc-chip cookies. And on Sunday I'm going to see Hestia's family for lunch.'

'That's fabulous,' she said, looking pleased.

He almost—*almost*—asked her to go with him.

But that wouldn't be fair. He needed to fix things with his family and Hestia's first. Plus he and Anna had agreed to take things slowly. He couldn't rush her into making their Christmas deal more than just friendship.

Baby steps, he reminded himself.

Though he could still kiss her goodnight on her doorstep. And funny how right it felt to have her in his arms, her mouth soft and sweet against his. He almost wished there had been dancing at the ward's Christmas meal so he could hold her close and sway with her.

'Goodnight,' he said softly. 'I'll see you later.'

'Have a good time with your family,' she said.

'Thank you. What about you—what are you up to at the weekend?' he asked.

'Sunday lunch at my parents' place,' she said, 'and no doubt a dress rehearsal for next week's Christmas concert.' Her face was full of glee. 'I can't wait. Though I'll be working for it tomorrow, with a whole week's worth of laundry and ironing to do...'

Seeing his sister wasn't as awkward as Jamie had expected. There were no recriminations, no over-the-top reunion to make him feel like the prodigal brother: just a hug and dinner. He caught up with his brother-in-law Alex, and had long conversations with Dylan and Layla, who shyly talked to him about their love of space and baking respectively.

'I'm so sorry,' Jamie said to Shelley in the kitchen when he was helping her clear away after dinner. 'I've missed out on so much of their growing up. Dylan and Layla have changed massively over last three years. I really haven't been fair to you.'

'Don't beat yourself up about the past, just go forward,' Shelley said gently. 'The main thing is that you're getting to a better place now.'

'I am.' He told her all about his job at Muswell Hill Memorial Hospital.

'It sounds as if you've really settled in.'

He nodded. 'I could be tempted to stay for the whole of Nalini's maternity leave, not just the three months we agreed to.'

'Do it, if you're happy,' Shelley said.

At the end of the evening, they agreed to do it again the following weekend—but this time with their parents and their middle sister there as well.

Back at his flat, Jamie looked at the photograph of Hestia on his screen-saver. It was his favourite photograph of her, a shot taken by a magazine of her performing as the Sugar Plum Fairy at Covent Garden, mid-pirouette with her arms gracefully above her head.

'I'm starting to move on, Hes,' he said softly. 'It doesn't mean I'm cutting you out of my life or pretending you never existed, but I know how cross you'd be with me for locking myself out of the world.' He paused. 'You'd like Anna. She's bright and sparkly, like the star on the top of the Christmas tree. I think she and I might be good for each other.'

Seeing Hestia's family on the Sunday, too, went better than he'd expected. It felt as if finally the misery of the last three years was starting to lose its sting and there was a light at the end of the tunnel.

Anna Maskell had made a huge difference to his life.

He hoped that he might be able to make the same kind of difference to hers.

CHAPTER EIGHT

JAMIE AND ANNA were on different shifts on Monday, so he didn't get to see her. But on Tuesday morning they were in clinic together, and their first patient was a week-old baby with talipes, a congenital condition where both feet pointed downwards and inwards with the soles of the feet facing each other.

'We've never had anything like this in either of our families,' Kirsty Peters, the mum, said. She bit her lip. 'The obstetrician said it wasn't anything I did wrong when I was pregnant, but I can't help thinking I must've done, and I hate it that Willow's in pain.'

'She's not in pain,' Anna reassured her, 'and you definitely didn't do anything wrong—in most cases we don't know what causes it.'

'The obstetrician said Willow would have to have an operation,' Kirsty said.

'It's not quite as scary as it sounds,' Jamie said. 'Years ago, surgeons used to operate to correct talipes, but it wasn't that effective and it led to problems when the babies grew up. Nowadays we use something called the Ponseti method. What that means is that we'll move and stretch Willow's feet until they're in a better position, then put her feet in plaster casts—that gives her muscles and ligaments a chance to relax and it means the bones grow into the right position. We'll see her every week to soak the casts off in a bath, move her feet again, and redo the casts. It usually takes about six changes of cast until her feet will be in the right position, and then we'll do the operation to release her Achilles tendons. It's really minor—we'll do it under a local anaesthetic so she'll be awake and you won't have to worry quite so much. Then we'll put the last casts on, and three weeks later we'll take them off.'

'Casts.' Kirsty looked anxious. 'She's a week old today.'

'And she's beautiful,' Jamie said. 'I know it's daunting, but this is the best way to help her.'

'You need to keep the casts dry,' Anna said, 'so you'll need to top-and-tail her rather than bath her while the casts are on. But other than that, the casts won't affect Willow's development in any way. You can do everything else that people normally do with babies.'

'Once we've taken off the final casts,' Jamie said, 'we'll give her special boots to wear. They're joined together with a bar, and she'll need to wear them all the time for the next three months, except when she's in the bath, to make sure her feet stay in the right position.'

'And she won't have to wear them any more after that?' Kirsty asked.

'Not all day,' Anna explained, 'but she will need to wear them at night until she's four.'

'Until she's *four*?' Kirsty looked horrified.

'It'll be normal for her, because she won't remember anything else,' Jamie reassured her. 'But it's really effective and it means her feet will develop completely normally—she won't need an operation.'

'I never even had a broken arm as a kid,' Kirsty said. 'To be honest, this whole thing…' She grimaced. 'I wish I'd asked my mum to come with me.'

'The first time's all going to be new for you,' Anna said, 'and the unknown is always scary. Next time, you'll know what to expect from the appointment, so it won't be so bad. You can keep cuddling Willow while we do the casts, and sometimes it helps to feed a baby while we're doing the manipulation, to distract them a bit.' She smiled. 'Talk to her, sing her a song—I'll sing with you, if that will help.'

Jamie discovered that not only did Anna sing beautifully, she knew a lot of lullabies. Clearly she'd practised them on her nieces, nephews and godchildren. He remembered then she'd said that she brought her guitar in to sing Christmas songs on the ward.

Once Willow's casts had been sorted out and they'd seen their patients on the rest of the list for the morning's clinic, they popped in to see Lily Brown before she went home—and Jamie was as thrilled by her progress as Lily herself was—and then grabbed sandwiches in the hospital canteen.

'So how did you get on at the weekend?' she asked.

'Really well,' Jamie said. 'I'm seeing my other sister and my parents next weekend. And it feels good to be properly back in touch with them—all thanks to you.'

'Hey, I'm not the one who actually *did* something,' she said with a smile. 'That's all you.'

But she'd given him the confidence to make that move.

He took a deep breath. 'You know you asked me to

the Christmas concert with your nieces and nephews tomorrow—I was wondering, is the offer still open, or is it too late to change my mind?'

'Absolutely the offer's still open,' she said, looking pleased. 'I can get one of my sisters-in-law to organise a seat.'

'Then thank you, I'd like to take you up on that.'

'Are you sure?' she asked, looking slightly worried.

No, he wasn't. But he wanted to make the effort. 'Sure,' he fibbed. And he'd fake it until he made it, if it meant that she'd smile at him like that.

'We're all going back to my parents' afterwards,' she said, 'so I hope you'll come with us. Mum will have jacket potatoes baking in the oven, salad prepared in the fridge and chilli in the slow-cooker, and she'll grill chipolatas and vegetarian nuggets for the kids.'

'That sounds lovely,' he said, meaning it. 'Can I bring anything?'

'No, just yourself,' she said. 'We can go straight from work.'

'OK. That's fine.'

Jamie spent Wednesday in Theatre. His final operation of the day was sorting out Michael Jeffries's knee—and thankfully it was Michael's mum who was waiting for him, rather than his dad.

'I'm pleased to say the operation was a success,' he said, when Michael was in the recovery room, 'and he's coming round now.'

'That's great. Thank you so much. What can I do to make things easier for him now he's had the operation?' she asked.

'Keep him topped up with pain medication and get

him to be sensible about physio—enough to get him mobile, but not so much that he sets himself back,' Jamie said.

She nodded. 'Football's his life. Sometimes I think it's because my ex—' She paused. 'Sorry. You don't need to know about that.'

'It's fine,' Jamie said. 'Relationships can be tricky. We did wonder if Michael was pushing himself because he loves football or for another reason.'

'He loves football, but mainly because he thinks it'll make his father love him. Whereas my ex just likes to be in control and he changes the goalposts all the time.' She sighed. 'He insisted on taking Michael to that appointment—I was called into work on an emergency and I was hoping Michael's gran would go with him, but unfortunately his father chose to go. I'm sorry if he wasn't very nice to your colleague.'

'Michael told you?'

She shook her head. 'My ex made a few comments about uppity women when he dropped Michael home.'

'Anna's very professional,' Jamie said with a smile, 'but outside the hospital I really wouldn't fancy his chances in a battle of wits against her.'

Michael's mum grimaced. 'Please apologise to her for me.'

'No apology needed,' Jamie said. 'I'm going to be completely unprofessional now. She'll be very glad to learn that Michael's with you and that you put his needs first.'

'I get what you're not saying,' Michael's mum said. 'And you're right. Thank God Michael lives with me and not his dad.'

'With you on his side,' Jamie said, 'he's going to be

just fine. Give it another ten minutes, and you should be able to see him and then we'll settle him onto the ward.'

At the end of his shift, he went in search of Anna. 'I'm ready when you are,' he said.

'Great. How did your ACL repair go?'

'Fine.' He paused. 'Michael's mum is really nice. The first thing she asked me was how she could make things easier for him post-op.'

'Stick gaffer tape over his father's mouth before he says something obnoxious?' Anna suggested.

Jamie laughed. 'And there was me telling her how professional you are.'

She gave him a speaking look. 'I just hope that man doesn't push Michael into undoing all the good work you put into his knee.'

'He won't,' Jamie said. 'Something tells me Michael's mother will be very careful about his visitors.'

'Ah,' Anna said, clearly picking up the subtext.

'She asked me to apologise to you. For Michael's dad.'

'No apology needed. But that's nice of her.' Anna rolled her eyes. 'Right. Let's go and do something really Christmassy.'

'I'm looking forward to it,' Jamie said.

She glanced at him when she'd collected her stuff from the staffroom. 'What's in that bag?'

'That's for me to know, and you to find out later,' he said with a grin.

'Just so you know,' she said on the way to the concert, 'I haven't told my family much about you. Just that you're my colleague and my friend.'

Not a widower they needed to pity and tiptoe round;

that was good. But did that mean he wasn't going to get to hold her hand?

Maybe he'd accidentally said it aloud, because she slipped her fingers into his. 'They're all nice, and they won't be nosy,' she said.

'Thank you.'

Her phone pinged on the way there. 'Everyone else is already there and they've saved us two seats,' she said when she checked the message.

'That's kind of them,' he said. 'So how long does the concert last?'

'Maybe an hour. Each class does one piece, and it's just lovely. You always get children singing out of key, forgetting their lines or going off at a tangent, but that's all part of the charm. They all work so hard. What I like is going back year after year and seeing them grow up and change. I've been to all of the school Christmas concerts since Will was in the Reception year and was an angel in the nativity—and his halo fell off.' She grinned. 'We've all learned a lot more about tinsel and sticky tape since then.'

When they walked into the school hall, Anna scanned the rows. 'There they are. Second row on the left. We're right at the end.'

She quickly introduced him to everyone: her parents Tony and Alison; her brothers Mark, Luke and Philip and their wives Susan, Barb and Gemma; her sister Jojo and her wife Becky; and the children who weren't performing that evening, eight-year-old Will, two-year-old Noah, and six-month-old Ivy.

'Nice to meet you all,' he said politely.

'And you, Jamie.' Alison passed him a folded A4 sheet. 'This is the running order,' she said.

'Thank you,' he said.

'Aria's up first,' Anna said, glancing over the sheet with him.

The headmistress began by welcoming them all to the First School's Christmas concert and praising the children for working so hard as a team. 'And now, presenting the Nativity, is our Reception year group,' she said.

'Aria's the third shepherd on the left,' Anna whispered as the children filed onto the stage, slipping her hand into Jamie's.

And it was charming, the story of the nativity told from the donkey's point of view. Jamie couldn't help smiling as the children sang 'Little Donkey' and 'Twinkle, Twinkle, Little Star'; he glanced at Anna and saw she had tears in her eyes. Was she thinking about what might have been, the same way he was?

'OK?' he whispered.

She nodded. 'This is just so lovely. I'm so proud of her.'

Tears of joy rather than tears of pain, then. Reassured, he sat back to enjoy the show.

Two of the Reception children came to the front of the stage while the others filed off.

'I say, I say, I say,' the little girl said. 'What do Santa's helpers learn at school?'

The little boy looked at her. 'I don't know. What do Santa's helpers learn at school?'

'The Elf-a-bet!' she said, and they both giggled.

Jamie couldn't help laughing, too, because their giggles were so infectious.

'And now we have class 1C, singing "The Twelve Days of Christmas",' the headmistress said.

'Megan's class,' Anna whispered. 'She's the partridge.'

Twelve children sat cross-legged on the front of the stage; one little girl stood in the centre of the stage; and the rest stood at the back. The girl in the centre sang the first line about her true love sending her a gift on the first day. Then, as the rest of the children sang what the gift was, Megan lifted a large card showing a hand-drawn partridge in a pear tree.

As the song continued, each child held up their card in turn and lowered it again as the rest of the class sang their way through the gifts, in a kind of Mexican wave. There was a moment of confusion when the geese and swans went up at the same time, but the children recovered themselves quickly and kept singing.

There was another joke during the class changeover—where Jamie learned that lions sang 'Jungle Bells' at Christmas, and then the next class sang 'Jingle Bells', complete with jingling bells; Jamie found his foot tapping along in time. Anna clearly noticed, because she squeezed his hand and grinned at him.

Just as with the previous class, while most of the children filed off the stage two came forward to tell a joke. Jamie stored it away for future reference on the ward: Who says *Oh-oh-oh*? Father Christmas, walking backwards!

'That's so going to be you,' Anna whispered.

Yes. He rather thought it might be heading that way.

The next class sang 'When Santa Got Stuck Up the Chimney,' complete with exaggerated sneezes, and there was another joke before Charlie's class came onto the stage. Most of the class were standing at the back and the sides of the stage, but six of the children were dressed in brown leggings with red tops; they each sported home-made brown cardboard wings, with orange cardboard 'feet' stuck to their plimsolls, and were wearing an orange beak held on with thin elastic.

'Charlie's the one on the far right,' Anna whispered.

While most of the class sang the song about robins, the six 'robins' did a dance in the centre of the stage.

Disaster struck halfway through, when the elastic on the beak of the robin next to Charlie snapped and the beak fell to the floor. The little girl burst into tears, but Charlie was quick to take his beak off and put it on her, then held his hand up to his face to make it look like a beak and improvised.

The little girl stopped crying, everyone cheered, and the dance and song continued.

And that was when Jamie could see exactly where Anna fitted into her family: they were clearly all the same, people who cared about others and helped and made the world of everyone around them a better place.

'Your nephew is amazing,' he whispered.

'I know,' she whispered back.

And Charlie's parents looked so proud of him; Jamie, who didn't even know him, felt proud of him, too.

Jamie learned that Frosty the Snowman went to school on an icicle. And he didn't even need to look at the programme to guess what the next performance was: a rendition of 'Frosty the Snowman'.

The last performance from the Year Two classes was 'The Little Drummer Boy'; the first class from Year Three recited a number of poems about snow, with some of them using triangles and jingle bells as sound effects.

Hestia, Jamie thought, would probably have suggested some snowflakes dancing on the stage, and given up her free time to coach them.

'That's my new favourite joke,' he whispered to Anna after the next one. 'Why is it so cold at Christmas? Because it's in Decem-*brrr*!' He grinned. 'That's genius.'

The second Year Three class sang 'In the Bleak Midwinter', and followed it up with a joke: 'What do reindeers hang on their tree? Horn-aments!'

'I'm so telling that one in the staffroom tomorrow,' Anna whispered. 'Don't you dare steal the punch line.'

The final class in Year Three sang 'Rudolph the Red-Nosed Reindeer', and Jamie was surprised and impressed to see that the class used sign language as they sang.

The headmistress brought the evening to a close and the whole school sang 'Away in a Manger'; when he glanced round, Jamie could see that most of the parents were close to tears. He had a lump in his throat, too.

Would Giselle's first Christmas concert have been like this?

He could imagine how proud Hestia would have been, how his parents and hers would both have had tears in their eyes for that final carol. And, even though it hadn't turned out that way for him, he was glad he'd shared tonight with Anna and her family. This was something special.

Anna was special, too.

Though he didn't quite know how to tell her.

Once the children had all joined their parents and they'd worked out who was going in whose car, Anna pointed out that there wasn't actually enough room for her and Jamie to squeeze in. 'We'll walk,' she said.

'And, with all this traffic, I bet we beat you home.' She smiled at Jamie. 'It's not raining, so it's actually quite a nice walk from here.'

'Fine by me,' he said, and let her lead him away from the school.

'So what did you think of the concert?' she asked.

'It was lovely,' he said. 'And your nephew—what an amazingly big-hearted boy he is.'

'Yeah. Charlie's pretty special,' she said. 'But I guarantee you all of them would've done the same in his shoes.'

'Because that's who your family is,' he said softly. 'You're all fixers. Which is just lovely.'

'I did tell you that my family's nice.'

He noticed she'd gone pink with pleasure, and he couldn't resist stealing a kiss.

'It was lovely how inclusive the concert was, too,' he said. 'I was amazed by them using sign language for that last song.'

'One of the girls in that class is deaf,' she said. 'Her sister is in Megan's class. And it's really nice because all the others look out for her and they make sure she hasn't missed anything.' She smiled. 'The school's got a really positive attitude when it comes to inclusion and diversity. Although all the children have the option not to take part in something that isn't to do with their particular religion, everyone ends up doing everything because they all want to share. Everyone's included. So as well as the Christmas concert, they learn about Hanukkah, Eid, Diwali and the Chinese New Year, and there are all kinds of activities everyone can take part in.'

'Tolerance, kindness and understanding are all good things. They stop fear and hatred building,' he said.

'Agreed,' she said fervently.

They reached Anna's parents' house almost at the same time as her brother's car pulled outside and her dad hopped out to open the front door.

'Told you it'd be as quick to walk home,' Anna teased.

'Indeed, Anna-Banana.' Her father gave her a hug.

What seemed like only seconds later, the house was full of people chattering and children laughing, and Jamie was swept right into the middle of it.

'For us?' Alison said when he handed her the large bag he'd been carrying.

'My contribution to tonight,' Jamie said.

She opened it, drew out the enormous tub of chocolates and gave him a hug. 'Thank you, sweetheart. These will go down really well later.'

And, just like that, he realised that they'd accepted him as Anna's friend and he was more than welcome to be part of them. He felt another crack open in the mortar of the wall he'd spent years building around him; and he was shocked to realise that, rather than making him want to build that wall higher, it made him want to start dismantling it.

Just as Anna had told him, there was an assortment of jacket potatoes, chilli, chipolatas, vegetarian nuggets and salad for dinner, followed by fruit, trifle, mince pies and chocolate cake for pudding.

And then the children annexed him. 'We need to teach you the robin dance,' Charlie said, and Jamie found himself hopping about like a robin, flapping his wings and dancing with them all as they sang the song.

After that, the games began in earnest.

'Can we play Simon Says next?' Megan asked.

'Except at this time of year we call it Santa Says,' Will added. 'Will you be Santa, Jamie? Please?'

'I'll *pretend* to be Santa,' Jamie said, 'because the real Santa's obviously really busy right now, getting everything ready to be loaded onto his sleigh.' He glanced at Anna and saw that her eyes were bright with approval. 'Though Santa always needs helpers,' he added, giving her a pointed look.

'Auntie Anna-Banana!' the children chorused.

'Come and help, Auntie Anna,' Will said. 'Please.'

'All right. Santa's helper, that's me,' she said, and came to stand beside him.

'Santa says,' Jamie announced, 'hop like a robin.'

The children all hopped delightedly, whooping and giggling, while all the adults perched on chairs and sofas, watching them.

Anna coughed. 'Oi, you lot. The only ones who get a free pass on this are Mum and Dad. The rest of you— on your feet, right now,' she demanded.

With much mock-grumbling, Anna's brothers and sisters joined the children, and everything got rowdier and funnier. Anna joined Jamie with suggestions of things that Santa would do: delivering a present, sliding down the chimney, feeding a carrot to the reindeer, eating a mince pie. The adults were caught out, one by one; in the end, Megan won the game, and Anna presented her with a sparkly reindeer headband.

'Where did you magic that from?' Jamie whispered.

'Christmas fair,' she whispered back.

Alison brought in her whiteboard from the kitchen, Becky drew a very impressive reindeer in about ten seconds flat, and someone else produced a scarf to be tied round the contestant's eyes in a game of Put the nose—a round red magnet—on Rudolph.

This time, Aria won, and was thrilled with her prize of a cuddly snowman.

Anna had felt slightly guilty about not warning Jamie what family evenings turned into at her parents' house; she should've given him the chance to back out of dinner, in case all the games and closeness with the children were too much for him. But he really seemed to be enjoying it, taking part in all the games. In the Who am I? game, where you had a picture of your character stuck on your reindeer antlers and asked questions to help you guess what you were—when the answers could only be 'yes' or 'no'—Jamie cheated horrendously by mouthing questions to Charlie, who won triumphantly. To her surprise, Jamie was the one to suggest boys versus girls for a game where paper cups were stacked in a pyramid and you had to knock them over with a ball made out of socks, where Will won and everyone commented on how many times Anna could miss the entire stack and speculated on whether she'd be able to hit the enormous Christmas tree with the ball if she was standing right next to it. And he sat down and cuddled Ivy and Noah, finishing off by reading one of Aria's favourite stories with all the children gathered round him.

'He's a keeper,' Jojo said quietly to her. 'We all think so.'

'We're not dating,' Anna whispered back.

'Liar,' Jojo said. 'But we really like him. So do the kids. And I love the fact that he makes you smile.'

'It's very early days,' Anna warned.

'Even so. Be happy, my lovely big sister,' Jojo said. 'You deserve this.'

When Jamie had finished the story, he closed the book. 'And that's it, I'm afraid. I have to go now because I need an early night. I'm doing operations at the hospital tomorrow morning.'

'At Auntie Anna-Banana's hospital?' Charlie queried.

'Yes,' Jamie said with a smile. 'We work on the same ward.'

'Will you come back and play with us again?' Aria asked.

'Yes, if you'll have me,' Jamie said.

'Or we could come to your house and play *your* games,' Megan said with a wide, wide smile.

'Meggie, you're supposed to wait to be invited to someone's house,' Will intervened.

'But Jamie's our friend now,' Megan argued, 'and you're allowed to ask to go to a friend's house.'

'We'll sort something out,' Jamie said. 'Soon.'

'Pinkie-swear?' Megan asked.

'Pinkie-swear,' he said.

Oh, how easy it would be to fall in love with Jamie Thurston, Anna thought. And the way he'd been with her family tonight, chatting easily to all of them and not minding the kids taking over...

He caught her eye. 'Shall I walk you home?'

'That'd be good,' she said.

Once they'd said goodbye to her family and had walked a few steps down the street, Jamie took her hand.

'I'm sorry,' she said. 'I should've warned you that the kids can be a bit full on.'

'Let's just say I can see exactly who their aunt is,' he said.

She winced. 'Sorry.'

'Don't apologise. They're nice. And, yes, it was very full on. But it meant I didn't get a chance to… Well, brood, I suppose, and think of what might have been. It was good for me to go with the flow.'

'And how. I can't believe how badly you cheated at Who Am I?—putting questions in Charlie's mouth.'

'Your dad was doing the same with Megan,' he pointed out, 'and Aria had her dad *and* your sister coaching her.'

She laughed. 'Yeah.'

'I enjoyed it,' he said. 'Your family's lovely. I really appreciate the way they just accepted me for who I am, not asking any questions.'

'They liked you,' she admitted.

He met her gaze. 'Good,' he said softly.

He led her down the next road.

'This isn't the way back to my flat,' she said.

'I know. It's the way to mine. Come in for a coffee,' he said.

She really hadn't expected that. He was actually letting her into his inner sanctum. 'Thank you. I'd like that.'

His flat was incredibly tidy—and incredibly impersonal, she thought. Unlike hers, his fridge was unadorned by magnets holding up children's drawings or photographs; the only thing out on the kitchen worktops was a kettle. It was worse than a show home, because it didn't even pretend to be a home: it was simply somewhere to exist.

'You'd put one of those decluttering experts to shame,' she said lightly.

'It's a short-term let.' He shrugged. 'So it makes sense to keep things tidy.'

It was a very clear warning that Jamie was planning to move on in a few weeks. She shouldn't let herself fall for him, no matter how lovely he'd been with her family or how much she liked him. They didn't have a future—and wishing wouldn't make things different.

'Uh-huh,' she said.

Once he'd made them both a mug of coffee, he ushered her through to the living room. There were no pictures, no books, no music, she noticed. The only personal thing in evidence was a silver picture frame on the mantelpiece containing a wedding photograph. Unable to stop herself, she went over for a closer look.

Jamie was wearing a traditional tailcoat and a top hat, and Hestia was wearing a timeless and very elegant white dress; they were standing in front of the doors of an ancient country church. It was the sort of photograph you saw illustrating bridal magazines, she thought. The perfect couple at their perfect wedding.

'Hestia was very beautiful,' Anna said. And her total opposite: slender, petite and blonde.

Both Jamie and Hestia were practically shining with happiness, clearly deeply in love with each other, and she felt a pang for him. For what should have been.

'It's a gorgeous photo,' she said, and replaced it on the mantelpiece. 'Sorry. I shouldn't have been prying.'

He smiled at her. 'Don't apologise. You weren't prying. Given that I don't keep knick-knacks around, I guess it makes the photo a bit of a focal point.' He paused. 'Would you rather I turned it to the wall?'

'No, of course not. Hestia was your wife and you loved her.'

He nodded. 'We were together for ten years.'

'It's a long time to love someone, and whatever happens in your future she'll always be part of your life.'

'I don't have any regrets about our time together. Just for the stuff we didn't get a chance to do,' he said. 'For you, it must be harder.'

'Sometimes, but I try to remember the good times with Johnny,' Anna said. 'Because there were a lot, especially in the early years. It's just a shame that...' She shrugged. 'Well, life isn't perfect. You need to make the best of what you have, whether that means making a big change or finding a compromise. Look for the happiness.'

'Come and sit with me,' he said softly. 'If it doesn't make you feel awkward.'

She appreciated the fact that he was so sensitive. 'No, I don't feel awkward.' She joined him on the sofa. 'You said this was a temporary place.'

'I've rented it for the length of my contract at the hospital,' he said.

So was that what he did? Rented somewhere temporarily while he was a locum, and then moved on?

'Nalini's maternity leave is going to be for longer than three months,' she said. 'Would you consider staying for a bit more of it?'

'Maybe,' he said.

She winced. 'Sorry. I'm being pushy again.'

'Being direct,' he said with a smile. 'Which is good for me. It stops me ducking the issue.'

Though he rather had ducked the issue, she thought. He hadn't actually said he'd consider staying for longer. And he'd mourned Hestia and their daughter for three years now. Would he ever be ready to move on? And, if so, would he choose to move on with her? Or was she hoping for too much?

The one thing that really troubled her was the issue of children. Even if Jamie was ready to move on, would her infertility mean that she wasn't going to be enough for him? Because there were no guarantees that IVF would work. She might not be able to offer him the future he really wanted, if that was a future with children.

So did that mean she'd be a stepping stone for him—just as he could be a stepping stone for her, to help her move on from Johnny's betrayal? Maybe that would work; they could be each other's transitional partner, easing each other from the pain of the past so they were ready for happiness in the future. Except in that case she'd have to keep some emotional distance between them and not let herself fall in love with him, because it was way too much of a risk to let herself fall in love with a man who wouldn't want a future with her. It would be setting herself up for even more heartbreak.

But was a temporary relationship, one with all her barriers up, enough? Would she be able to stop herself falling in love with Jamie? Had she already started to fall in love with him?

She didn't have a clue.

So all she could do was make the most of the moment, and enjoy being curled up on the sofa with him.

CHAPTER NINE

ON FRIDAY MORNING a case came in that made Anna worry and go to Jamie's office.

'Everything all right?' he asked when she knocked on his door.

'I need your input,' she said. 'The Emergency Department's sending up a six-month-old baby with a femoral shaft fracture.'

He went very still. 'Are we looking at a safeguarding issue?'

'Not sure,' she said. 'Before we see Zac and his parents, can we take a quick look at the X-rays?'

'Sure.'

She pulled up the X-rays on his screen and he peered at them.

'It's not the only fracture,' he said. 'There are others that have healed.'

She took a deep breath. 'So is it safeguarding?'

'Possibly not,' Jamie said. 'His bones seem quite short. How much does he weigh?'

'He's right on the fiftieth centile—eight kilos.'

'That's a pity,' he said. 'I was hoping we could send him for a DEXA scan, but he needs to weigh ten kilos before we can do that.'

She looked at him. 'DEXA scan? You're thinking OI? But there isn't a family history. The Emergency Department already asked about that.'

'A quarter of cases of osteogenesis imperfecta are new ones,' Jamie said. 'Do you want me to come with you?'

'Yes, please,' she said.

She introduced them both to Zac's parents, who were both white-faced and looking anxious.

'I can't believe he's got a broken leg,' Zac's mum said. 'He hasn't rolled off anything—I never leave him on the baby-changer unsupervised. How can he have broken his leg?' She bit her lip. 'I thought it might be a tummy thing because he wasn't feeding properly. That's why I took him to see the doctor. He hasn't been crying or anything.'

'And we haven't done anything to him.' Zac's dad looked panicky. 'We'd never hurt him. And we haven't left him with anyone who'd hurt him. I don't understand.'

'I know they've already asked you downstairs,' Anna said gently. 'We have guidelines and protocols. Our duty is to our patients.'

'We get that,' Zac's mum said. 'But it's not very nice, people thinking we've hurt him.'

'His X-rays show other fractures that have healed,' Jamie said.

'Other fractures?' Zac's dad looked horrified. 'How?'

'Oh, my God. This whole time I thought he was a fussy eater, but he's been in pain and we didn't know. He's not a crier. I…' Zac's mum was close to tears.

'Can we examine Zac?' Jamie asked.

She nodded.

'Hello, little man.' Jamie's voice was calm and soft. 'Let's have a look at you.' He blew a raspberry at the baby, undressed him down to his nappy, and gently moved his arms and legs. There was no sign of bruising, Anna noticed, but his movements were slightly different from those of most of the babies she saw. And the whites of Zac's eyes were bluer than normal. Both symptoms supported Jamie's suggestion of a diagnosis of osteogenesis imperfecta.

'Let's get you wrapped up again,' Jamie said gently, 'so your mum and dad can give you a cuddle.'

'You don't think we're hurting our boy?' Zac's dad asked, his voice cracking.

'No. I think,' he said, 'that Zac has a condition called osteogenesis imperfecta, or OI for short. You might also have heard it called brittle bone disease.'

'But—nobody on either side of our family has anything like that. They asked us downstairs,' Zac's mum said. 'And when we told them it couldn't be, they started looking worried and...'

'...and that's why they sent you up to see us,' Jamie said. 'A quarter of people we see with OI don't have a family history. What it means is that the collagen— that's the protein responsible for bone structure—is of lower quality than average, so it can't support the minerals in the bone and that means the bones fracture a lot more easily than usual.'

'So that's what's caused his broken leg? It's nothing we've done wrong?' Zac's mum asked.

'It's nothing you've done wrong,' Jamie confirmed. 'Why I wanted to examine Zac just now was to see how his joints moved. They're very flexible—something we call hypermobility—and I noticed on the X-rays that his bones seem shorter than usual.'

'The whites of his eyes are bluer than average, too, which is another sign of the condition,' Anna said.

'Is it…? Will he…?'

Jamie clearly guessed what Zac's father was struggling to ask. 'It's a serious condition and Zac will need extra support,' he said, 'but it doesn't mean he's going to die young.'

Zac's parents were both pale with relief.

'Can it be treated?' Zac's mum asked.

'Yes. We'll give him some Vitamin D supplements because it helps the body to absorb calcium and make bone. We'll also give him a special drug to help his bone density,' Jamie explained, 'and we'll measure his bone density regularly with something called a DEXA scan. It doesn't hurt, though he'll need to lie still for a minute or so during the scan and it's a good idea not to have metal fastenings on his clothes.'

'We'll remember,' Zac's dad said.

'The main thing is to manage fractures and manage the risk. We'll be able to sort out the fractures with casts, splints and a brace, but we also need to make sure he's still mobile. If he doesn't move enough, it will weaken his bones and muscles and lead to further fractures,' Jamie said. 'When he's older we might put metal rods in his long bones for support. You can get expandable ones that we lengthen with magnets, so he won't need an operation to replace the rods.'

'Swimming and water therapy will be really good exercises for him, as they lower the risk of getting a fracture,' Anna added.

Zac's mum smiled wryly. 'So he's not going to do

what his dad hoped and become a prop forward for the Welsh rugby team.'

'He's still going to be able to wave a flag and sing the songs,' Zac's father said. He stroked Zac's cheek. 'But basically anything we do might hurt him. That's absolutely terrifying. We don't want him to get any more broken bones or be in pain. We want to keep him safe.' He bit his lip, shaking his head in obvious anguish. 'How do we manage things so we don't accidentally hurt him?'

'Slow, gentle movements so you don't startle him,' Anna said, 'because if he moves suddenly he could end up with a fracture. But you can rock him, cuddle him, talk to him and sing to him just like you do with any other baby—just be gentle and support him as much as you can.'

'When you lift him, make sure his limbs and his fingers aren't caught in a blanket,' Jamie said. 'Make sure your hands are wide when you lift him: one under his buttocks and lower back, and the other behind his head and neck.'

'You might need to change your nappy-changing technique a little bit, too,' Anna said. 'Don't lift him by his ankles.'

'Is that how we broke his leg?' Zac's mum asked.

'It could've been several things,' Jamie said. 'A baby doesn't always cry when a fracture happens. You might just notice a bit of swelling around a limb—or, as you did when you took him to be checked over, that he's not feeding well. The main thing is to remember that it isn't your fault. No matter how careful you are, a fracture can still happen.'

'So when you change his nappy,' Anna said, 'slide

your hand under his buttocks to lift him. You might find it's useful to put a clean nappy under him first and then remove the dirty one, so you only have to lift him once.'

'Do you feed him by breast or bottle?' Jamie asked.

Zac's mum grimaced. 'Bottle. I know breast is meant to be better, but...'

'It's fine,' Jamie reassured her. 'You might find it helpful to put him on a pillow when you feed him, and make sure you change sides each time you feed him so he gets used to turning his head both sides.'

'What about winding?' Zac's dad asked. 'Oh, my God. My mum pats him on the back. That's going to damage his spine, isn't it?'

'It could cause problems, yes,' Jamie said. 'Colic drops are a better way of managing wind for Zac.'

'And drying him after a bath. Mum says you have to pat a baby dry,' Zac's mum said. 'So we might've broken his leg that way. Oh, my God.'

'Use a support sponge in the bath,' Anna said. 'And you could try drying his creases with a hairdryer on a cool setting rather than by patting him dry.'

'And dressing him. Those sleep suits. You have to wrangle him into them, sometimes.' Zac's dad looked horrified. 'I might've broken his arm. Or that might be how his leg broke.'

'It's worth looking for clothes that open wide so you can put Zac on the clothes, then fasten the outfit around him,' Anna said.

'Maybe Mum can make him something,' Zac's dad said.

'It's a lot to take in.' Zac's mum bit her lip. 'I'm going to be terrified to touch my boy in case I hurt

him. But not being cuddled isn't good either. I just…
I don't know how to deal with this.'

'We can put you in touch with a support group,' Jamie
said. 'Talking to other parents who've been in your situation will reassure you much more than we can.'

'But we do have leaflets as well,' Anna said. 'The
main thing is we have a diagnosis so we can make
sure everyone supports you—your health visitor, your
family doctor, and information for nursery and school
as he gets older.'

'Because of the brittle bones, Zac's more likely to
have some hearing loss, so he'll need his hearing tested
before he starts school and then every three years,'
Jamie said. 'We'll get a cast sorted out for his leg now,
and you can get in touch with us at any time if you're
worried.'

Once they'd finished treating Zac and his parents
had taken him home, Anna turned to Jamie. 'Thank
you.'

'Hey, you would've had to call me in for the fracture anyway,' he pointed out.

'But you were so good with the parents.'

'I hope so. It's our job.' He smiled at her. 'Are you
free for lunch?'

She wrinkled her nose. 'Sadly, I have a hot date with
acres of paperwork and a very big mug of coffee. But
if you're free this evening, I have an idea.'

'A Christmassy idea?'

'Wait and see.' She tapped her nose.

It was incredibly Christmassy—a carol service at Tem-
ple Church, the round Crusader church in the middle
of London.

'This is one of my favourite places in the city,' Anna said. 'I love the Crusader effigies here and the little lions and dragon at their feet, and the grotesques in the nave. It's worth looking at them after the service.'

'I've lived in London for most of my life, but I've never been here before,' Jamie admitted.

'It's not open at the weekend, so you'd have to take a day off to visit,' she said. 'But with my oldest brother being an architect, I've been taken to all kinds of incredible buildings. This one survived the Great Fire of London but it was really badly damaged in the Second World War. But they've done a fabulous job of the restorations.'

'And how,' Jamie said, looking up at the incredible vaulted ceiling. There was a huge Christmas tree in front of the Norman doorway beneath the rose window, scattered with white lights and huge baubles; enormous pillar candles in wrought-iron and glass lanterns lit the choir stalls. The church was absolutely packed, and there was something both peaceful and moving in the sound of the congregation singing carols along with the choir.

It was fine until they got to 'Silent Night'; it had been Hestia's favourite carol and Jamie's throat closed up to the point where he just couldn't sing the first verse.

He sensed Anna glancing anxiously towards him. He really needed to be fair to her. She'd brought him here because it was something she loved and wanted to share with him. So he needed to see the joy in this— to do what she did. He thought of her words to him on Wednesday night. *'You need to make the best of what you have... Look for the happiness.'*

Look for the happiness and be the man he wanted to be instead of letting himself get mired in regrets. In the third verse, he found his voice again and sang along. The words that stuck in his head were 'love's pure light': that was what he could see right here, right now, in the church.

After the service, Anna showed him her favourite grotesques in the nave; and then they filed out with the rest of the congregation.

'Was it…?' Anna's sea-green eyes were wide with worry.

'It was perfect,' he said softly. 'Thank you. And I'm glad I shared it with you. I can't think of anyone else I would rather be with, right now.'

Her eyes filled with tears, and one spilled over.

He wiped it away with the pad of his thumb. 'Anna. Don't cry. I didn't mean to hurt you.'

'You haven't. Just… You looked a bit upset earlier.'

'"Silent Night". It was Hestia's favourite carol.'

'It's mine, too. She had good taste.'

'Yeah.' He took her hand. 'Shall we walk along the river to London Bridge?'

'I'd like that,' she said.

They wandered hand in hand along the Embankment, and all felt right in Jamie's world: as if something had tilted and everything had slid into place. Right here, right now, with this woman, he realised that he was actually happy. That he could see a future, for the first time in a very long while. It wasn't going to be easy, and they'd have to be painfully honest with each other over the question of having a family, but he really wanted to make this work.

He held Anna's hand all the way to London Bridge,

all the way to the station at Bank, all the way on the tube until they were back in Muswell Hill, and all the way back to her front door.

'Come in for hot chocolate?' she asked.

Not ready to leave her yet, he agreed.

Except they didn't actually get to making the hot chocolate. Although she put the milk in the microwave to heat through, Jamie spun her into his arms and kissed her. It was sweet and light and frothy at first, but then he nuzzled her lower lip and her lips parted, inviting him to deepen the kiss.

By the time he broke the kiss, his head was spinning.

'Stay with me tonight?' Anna asked, her cheeks pink and her eyes glittering.

How could he resist? 'Yes.'

This time, she kissed him, and the next thing he knew he'd scooped her up into his arms.

'I'm too heavy,' she protested.

'You're perfect as you are,' he said, meaning it. 'Though I do need directions.'

She smiled. 'Right out of the kitchen, second door on the right.

He carried her through to her bedroom, switched on the light, closed the curtains, and then set her down on her feet. 'Are you sure about this?' he asked quietly.

'Very sure,' she said. 'I know we said we weren't going to rush things, but…'

Her smile was shy, and so cute that it broke down the last of his resistance.

He liked Anna. More than liked her. He was halfway to being in love with her. And it looked as if she felt the same way about him.

So he kissed her. Undressed her. Let her undress him. Made love with her—sensibly, because she had condoms tucked in the drawer of her bedside cabinet. He'd intended maybe to slide out of bed once she was asleep and leave quietly, but he was warm and comfortable and it felt *right* having her curled in his arms. So he gave in to the yearning to stay, and fell asleep with her head on his shoulder and their arms wrapped around each other.

On Saturday morning, Anna woke first.

Oh, help.

They hadn't planned this.

She had absolutely no idea how he was going to react this morning. Would he back away, horrified at losing control? Would he be shy? Or had they both moved past everything to a new understanding?

Before she could worry herself silly about it, his eyes opened.

'Hey,' he said.

And his smile was sweet and warm and everything she could wish for.

'Hey, yourself,' she said lightly. 'I, um…' Then she stopped. What did she say?

'Yeah. I don't know what to say either,' he admitted. 'But I have no regrets about last night.'

Which made everything feel all right. 'In that case,' she said, 'how about breakfast?'

'Wonderful,' he said. 'And I'll help you make it.'

CHAPTER TEN

On Tuesday Jamie was in Theatre all day. He came out to a message from Anna.

Last Christmassy thing to convince you tonight. Meet you at the hospital entrance at five.

Her eyes were sparkling when he joined her at the hospital entrance, so tonight was clearly something she was looking forward to, he thought. But he had absolutely no idea what she'd planned, and she refused to give him a single clue.

When they got off the Tube at Covent Garden, he assumed that it was to see the Christmas decorations. But when she led him through the streets and he saw the iconic building with its glass front, the fan-shaped window and the columns, he stopped and stared. 'The Opera House.'

'Exactly,' she said, smiling. 'There's nothing more Christmassy than a performance of *The Nutcracker*—well, except maybe for a trip to the panto.'

The Nutcracker. Hestia's favourite ballet. The one he'd seen her dance in so many, many, times, as the beautiful Sugar Plum Fairy.

The last ballet she'd danced professionally.

It felt as if someone had just dropped an enormous weight on his head from a great height.

'My best friend and her husband had tickets for tonight, but he's gone down with the flu and she's feeling rubbish, too. She offered the tickets to me, so, I thought we—' She stopped abruptly. 'Jamie?'

'No. I can't do this,' he said. 'I'm sorry, Anna. I just can't.'

She stared at him. 'I don't understand.'

'Because of Hestia.' He took a deep breath. 'She was a ballet dancer. She taught ballet. This was her favourite. The last time I came here, I saw her dance in *The Nutcracker*. So I—I just can't go into the theatre now and watch it. I'm sorry.'

She looked stricken. 'Jamie, I'm so—'

'I need to be on my own,' he cut in. 'It's me, not you.' The fault was so very much his. 'I'm sorry. I just can't do this. Stay and enjoy the show. The ballet's wonderful. Just... I *can't*.' And then he turned and walked away, before he howled his pain and frustration to the sky.

Anna stared at Jamie's retreating back.

She'd had absolutely no idea that Hestia had been a ballet dancer, or she would never have brought Jamie here.

What she'd planned as a treat, as a lovely surprise that he'd enjoy as much as she would, had turned into an utter nightmare.

She'd never meant to hurt him. She'd thought they'd grown closer since Friday night, when she'd fallen asleep in his arms; they'd spent most of the weekend together, except when she'd had a shift on Sunday and he'd visited his family, and he'd stayed over at her flat again last night. She'd started to think that maybe they had a future.

How very wrong she'd been.

She'd rushed him into this. Too much, too soon.

And she wasn't sure if what they'd had could be repaired. Part of her wanted to go after him, to apologise properly and try to make things right; but he'd been very clear that he wanted to be alone. Going after him and trying to get him to talk might make things even worse. He clearly needed to process things on his own.

She just had to hope that he'd talk to her later, when he'd had a chance to come to terms with his feelings. That they could find some sort of compromise.

What now?

She could just go home.

Jamie had told her to stay and enjoy the show. How could she enjoy it, knowing that she'd hurt him so badly?

Or maybe the music and the show she loved would help her move on from this. Take her away from this misery enough to give her some perspective.

Jamie had also said she was the sort of person who made lemonade when life gave her lemons. She rather thought it would be more like bitter lemon tonight. It was way too late to call anyone else to join her; the show started in fifteen minutes.

So she walked into the foyer, took one of the tickets from her bag, showed it to the usher and found her seat.

The auditorium filled up, and Anna was painfully aware of the empty seat beside her.

Why, why, why hadn't she realised that petite,

graceful Hestia would have been some kind of dancer? Why hadn't she guessed that Hestia might've been a ballerina? Why hadn't she asked Jamie to talk more about his late wife?

She felt the sting of tears welling up in her eyes and tried to blink them away. No. She was going to take a step back, enjoy the show for what it was, let the music and the choreography and the costumes take her away from this.

Except it didn't work.

All the way through the performance, she was thinking of Jamie and how she'd virtually scrubbed the top of his scars off with wire wool tonight.

Why hadn't she asked him to go to the ballet with her first? It would still have hurt him, but not as much as this, when he was just faced with it. Why had she stupidly thought that a surprise was a good idea?

And as the sound of the celesta echoed through the auditorium to introduce the Sugar Plum Fairy, the tears slid down her face.

Hestia had been the love of Jamie's life, so it was no wonder that he couldn't recover from the pain of losing her and their baby. How stupid Anna had been to think that they could move on from their pasts together.

And how much Jamie's rejection hurt. She'd kept apart from relationships ever since her marriage to Johnny had imploded; and now, the first time she'd let herself be vulnerable, the first time she'd taken that leap of faith, it had all gone wrong. Right at that moment, she felt as if she'd fallen over the edge of a cliff and her heart had broken into tiny shards all over again.

Stupid, stupid, stupid.

They'd only known each other for a few weeks. So

why did this hurt even more than the end of a five-year marriage? Why did it feel as if all the stars had gone out?

She should never have let her barriers down. Never have tried to reach Jamie. Never have let herself believe that she might actually be enough for someone—because she quite clearly *wasn't* enough. All that closeness at the children's Christmas concert, the way Jamie had felt as if he fitted right into her family and her world—it had all been an illusion. An illusion that had shattered along with her heart.

Jamie walked away from the Royal Opera House, thinking of Hestia dancing across the stage as the Sugar Plum Fairy. He was almost oblivious to his surroundings as he headed down the Strand, just putting one foot in front of the other and concentrating on moving away from Covent Garden. Eventually he found himself at Trafalgar Square, with the massive pine Christmas tree covered in white lights, almost guarded by the Landseer Lions and the fountains.

Hestia had loved the National Gallery, too. Van Gogh's *Sunflowers* had been her favourite painting. She'd said it filled her with sunlight.

Swallowing hard, he cut down through Charing Cross to the river. Across the other side of the Thames, the London Eye was lit up, and the Christmas lights shimmered on the South Bank. He walked along the Embankment, past Cleopatra's Needle, and down to Waterloo Bridge. He could hear the Christmassy music from Somerset House; it reminded him of the night that Anna had taken him to the skating rink. The night he'd kissed her accidentally for the first time. When they'd backed off from each other and agreed to be friends.

Except he hadn't been able to resist her warmth and her sweetness.

They'd walked together along the river after the carol concert, hand in hand. He'd been full of peace and joy. The night they'd made love together for the first time.

Right now, everything felt in pieces. The loss and loneliness of losing his wife and his baby, the years of the whole world feeling empty, came back sharply.

Yet Anna had broken through his barriers. She'd filled his world with sunshine just as surely as Van Gogh had filled Hestia with sunshine. She'd taken the sting out of Christmas for him, taught him to find the joy in the lights and the love and the laughter. She'd been so careful to check with him that he was OK with each step, so sensitive and kind—until tonight, when she'd surprised him, though he'd never mentioned Hestia's dancing to her so how was she to have known?

But it wasn't just that she'd taken the sting out of Christmas for him. Being with Anna made the world feel a better place.

He liked her family, and he knew that his family would adore her. Yet here he was, on the verge of throwing it all away and going back to be mired in the misery of his past, focusing on what he'd lost and mourning what might have been.

He could see Anna's face, stricken, when he'd told her that he couldn't go to the ballet with her. She'd been so upset to think that she'd hurt him. It hadn't been her fault. There wasn't a mean or spiteful cell in her body. And he'd hurt her. He'd stamped on the joy she clearly found in *The Nutcracker*—not the same as Hestia's, because Anna enjoyed the ballet as part of the audience rather than performing it. But he'd ignored everything; he'd simply walked away and shut her out.

As he leaned on the railings of the bridge, looking out over the Thames, it started to snow. Tiny flakes, not settling, but still snowing.

Snowflakes.

The Sugar Plum Fairy.

The music he knew so well echoed in his head.

'Hestia,' he whispered. 'Right now I'm lost. I'm lonely. I miss you. I've found someone I can be happy with, and I know you'd be furious with me for being such an idiot right now and letting all that slip through my fingers.'

She didn't answer. Of course not. She couldn't. He knew that. But the music still echoed in his head, as if Hestia was pirouetting through his memories. Meeting her. Falling in love with her. Going to watch her on stage, being spellbound by her grace and the way she could bring a story to life through movement alone. Their wedding day. Learning that they were expecting Giselle. Discovering their baby was a girl. Feeling her kick inside Hestia's stomach, watching his wife bloom with their much-wanted baby.

And then the blackness. The loneliness. The way the world just didn't feel right, whatever he did. The walls climbing higher and higher around him.

And then a tall, smiling woman with sea-green eyes chipping away at the mortar and letting the light through the cracks. Tiny ones at first, growing bigger and bigger. Showing him the joy.

All he had to do was reach out for it. Say yes.

And then he heard it.

The song he always tried so hard to avoid at this time of year.

Before he realised what he was doing, he found himself walking into the square at Somerset House, watching the skaters on the rink. Holding hands, some of them nervously keeping to the edge and some of them showing off more fancy moves.

All he wanted for Christmas…

…was Anna.

The song felt as if Hestia was giving him a hard shove and telling him to move on. To listen to the music. To think about what he really wanted.

'I'll always love you, Hes,' he whispered. And hadn't Anna herself said that he'd always have room in his heart for Hestia because he'd loved her and she was part of him? Warm, generous, lovely Anna—who really didn't deserve to be treated the way he'd treated her. He'd been as selfish as her ex.

'But it's time for me to move on, Hes. You're right. I can't spend the rest of my life in limbo. I want to move on with Anna. I think we could be happy together.' If it wasn't too late. 'You'd like her, Hes. A lot. She's got the same warmth and sweetness that you had, except she isn't you and I don't expect her to be.' He took a deep breath. 'And I've really messed this up. I don't know how to even begin fixing this. I've hurt her and it wasn't fair of me to walk away without explaining.'

The song's words flitted into his head, talking about wishes coming true.

He knew what he wished. That he could move on with Anna. Be with her for Christmas and for always.

Would she let him explain? Would she give him a second chance, even though he'd been so unfair to her?

He glanced at his watch.

Would Anna have stayed to watch the show without him, or would she have gone home?

If he called her, either it would either go to voicemail— telling him that she was still at the Opera House and he had enough time to get back to Covent Garden before the show ended—or she'd be at home and answer.

He hoped.

He grabbed his phone and pressed her number. For a moment, he thought it wasn't going to connect, and then his call went to voicemail.

Please let that mean she was still in the centre of London with her phone switched off, rather than that she was at home and was ignoring his call.

But it would be very easy to miss someone coming out of the Royal Opera House in a crowd. He typed quickly.

I'm sorry. We need to talk. Please will you wait for me by the mistletoe chandelier in the middle of Covent Garden Market?

Please let him not have messed this up too much. Please let her give him a chance.

Crossing his fingers mentally, he sent the text and hurried back to Covent Garden, where he waited by the enormous mistletoe chandelier.

It would serve him right if she left him to wait there. Because he really, really hadn't been fair to Anna. He'd let his past get in the way. It was time to move on, and he wanted to move on now—with her.

He sat on the bench and waited.

And waited.

And waited, while the snow drifted down and started to settle.

Eventually people started to stream past, some clutching programmes and chattering, telling him that the ballet must have ended.

Would Anna come to meet him? Would she let him apologise and explain? Or had he pushed her away for good?

He waited.

The crowds thinned.

He waited.

There was no sign of Anna.

He glanced at his watch. Maybe she was one of the last out; maybe she'd only just switched on her phone and seen his message; or maybe she wasn't coming.

He'd give her another ten minutes.

Time seemed to have changed its speed; five seconds felt more like a minute.

Nine minutes later, he was starting to think that, yes, he was too late, so he should just give up and go home. Not that his flat was a real home; it was just somewhere to sleep and store his things.

And then Anna came and sat on the bench next to him. 'Hi.'

His heart skipped a beat. She'd come to meet him. 'Anna. I'm sorry. Thank you for coming here.'

'I nearly didn't,' she admitted.

Because she had doubts about him?

As if he'd spoken the question aloud, she said, 'I forgot to turn my phone on again after the show. But I was late out and ended up at the back of the queue for the lift in the Tube station, so I checked my phone while I was waiting. Your message came through just as I was about to walk into the lift.'

'I'm really glad you came.' He took a deep breath. 'I'm sorry. I've been so unfair to you tonight. I've let my past get in the way.'

'Uh-huh.' Her voice was neutral and her face was expressionless.

All he could do was open his heart and tell her how he felt. And hope that it would be enough to make her give him a second chance.

'I walked down by the river when I left you,' he said. 'And I was thinking about Hestia, and about you. You've made my world a different place, Anna. You've given me back something I thought I'd never have again.' He took a deep breath. 'And I won't blame you if you don't want anything to do with me now.

'I should have told you about Hestia being a ballet teacher and dancing in *The Nutcracker,* and I should've thanked you for the opportunity to see the show and gone with you instead of throwing it back in your face and storming off. I've been an idiot. But I've had time to think about it and get my head around things, and I'm so sorry I hurt you.' He took both her hands in his.

'I know we haven't known each other that long, but you make my world feel like a much better place. With you, I see the sunlight. You've taught me to move on— and I want to move on, I really do. More specifically, I want to move on with you.' He looked at her. 'I could hear the music from the ice rink. They played the song I find really difficult, and it made me think about what I wanted. For Christmas and for always. I want *you,* Anna. I love you. Will you marry me?'

* * *

Marry him?

Anna stared at Jamie, unable to process this. She thought she'd pushed him away—that he still wasn't ready to move on and she'd hurt him by pushing him too far, too fast. He'd reacted by walking out on her. Would he do that again? Because she didn't want to be in a relationship where she had to second-guess her partner's feelings all the time, be careful what she did and said and tiptoe around certain subjects instead of being completely honest and open.

This wasn't going to be an easy conversation, but she needed to know.

'How do I know,' she said, 'that you won't walk away from me the next time something reminds you of Hestia, of what you lost?'

'You don't,' he said. 'It'll be a risk. But I'm asking you to trust me that I won't make that mistake again. That instead of stomping off I'll talk to you and we'll get past whatever the problem is together.'

That was what she wanted, too: but she still wasn't sure. 'You lost your wife and your baby—and I can't give you a baby. Not without complications, and there are no guarantees that IVF will work. How do I know that I'm enough for you as I am?'

'You're enough for me as you are,' he said.

'Maybe for now,' she said, 'but what about the future? What if you change your mind and decide that you want children?'

'Honestly?' He grimaced. 'I'll warn you in advance, this is going to sound terrible and I don't mean it to be that way.'

'Honesty,' she said, 'is the best thing right now. I

need to know what's going on in your head and you need to know what's going on in mine. Pussyfooting around the subject isn't going to work for either of us.'

'OK.' He took a deep breath. 'I was looking forward to being a dad—but losing Hestia and Giselle has left me terrified at the idea of taking that risk again. And, yes, I know the statistics. But there's still a chance it could happen again.'

'So you don't want children.' And then the really nasty thought hit her. 'I can't have children, so that makes me a safe option.'

'That did occur to me at one point,' Jamie admitted, 'and I know how selfish that is. But that's only part of it. I love you, Anna Maskell, for who you are, and it's got absolutely nothing to do with your fertility. And I know you said you've come to terms with not having children, but I've seen the way you are with the kids in your family. I know how family-orientated you are. I think you'd be an amazing mum—so if you want children, then I'll do my utmost to damp down my fears and I'll do whatever it takes to make our family happen. I guess what I'm trying to say is that I love you enough to take a risk that scares me spitless.'

'IVF is a high-risk option,' she reminded him. 'And it might not even work.'

He nodded. 'But if that's what you want, we'll try.' He gave her a wry smile. 'Though if we do try that option and we're lucky enough for it to work, I'll warn you now that you're probably going to have to yell at me for wrapping you up in cotton wool throughout your entire pregnancy.'

'And if the IVF doesn't work?' Would he walk away from her, the way Johnny had?

'If it doesn't work, I'll stay right by your side, and we'll get through the sadness together,' he said. 'IVF isn't the only option. You mentioned that Jenna was a surrogate mum for her sister. We could maybe find a surrogate. Or adopt. Or foster. Or we can just enjoy being an uncle and aunt, and day to day it'll be just the two of us. We have options, Anna.'

'Can it really be that easy?' she asked.

'Yes, it can really be that easy,' he said softly. 'You told me you weren't going to let your infertility define you. It's not going to define us, either. Whether we have children or not, we can still make a family together. You and me. And George the gorgeous goldfish,' he added with a smile.

'How do you know I'm going to be enough for you?' She hadn't been enough for Johnny and, although she'd managed to put the pieces back together, she didn't think she could do that a second time if Jamie walked away from her.

'I know you're going to be enough,' he said, 'because you've brought my world back into colour. You've chipped away at the walls around me and let the light come in. You've shown me that Christmas isn't all about loss—it's about celebrating what you have. Finding the happiness. Finding the joy.'

'I dated Johnny for a year before we got married,' she said. 'I thought he was the one. We were married for five years. And it all went wrong. He walked away from me.' She shook her head. 'I've known you for just over a month, and you walked away from me tonight. How do I know this won't go wrong in the future?'

'You don't,' he said.

She flinched.

'So it means taking a risk. All I can tell you is that you make me feel different. And I hope I can do that for you—teach you that not all men see the world the same way that Johnny did.'

'We've only known each other for a few weeks,' she said again.

'It's been long enough for me to know,' he said. 'But if you need more time, I'll wait until you're ready. Because you're worth the wait. I love you, Anna. I want you to be happy. I want you to have everything you want in your life—and I hope that starts with me.'

He'd give her the time she needed. Be patient with her.

And she could see in his eyes that he meant it.

He loved her.

He wanted to be with her. He wanted her to want him.

They'd both been through dark times in the past. She'd lost most of her choices over having children and come out the other side of a fractured marriage, having to start her life all over again; and Jamie had buried his wife and baby.

This was their second chance at happiness. Together.

She could walk away from him now, just as he'd walked away from her earlier this evening.

Or she could see past the hurt, understand why he'd had a wobble, take his hand and step forward to their future.

OK, they hadn't known each other for very long. But they'd worked together, and she liked the way he treated his patients, their parents and his colleagues. They'd spent as much time together as if they'd been dating for several months. And in that short time he'd taught her that she was worth so much more than Johnny had thought. He'd given her her confidence back. They were compatible inside work and outside it, too.

The future wasn't necessarily going to be smooth. But they could support each other through the wobbles, talk things over when they hit a sticky patch. Be honest with each other.

So did she take the risk of telling him how she felt about him and agree to marry him, or should she stay on her own, the way she'd planned?

She looked at him, and the love in his eyes decided her.

'I love you, too,' she said. 'It scares me, because I'd been so determined not to take a risk on anyone ever again. But you've had a tough time, too. And if you're brave enough to take the risk with me, then I'll be brave enough to take the risk with you. So, yes, Jamie, I'll marry you.'

'Good.' He kissed her under the mistletoe. 'And we'll seal another deal, too. You've shown me the joy of Christmas. So I'll gladly wear Santa's red suit on Christmas Day and walk through the ward with a sack of presents, saying, "Ho-ho-ho."' He grinned. 'Or I could walk backwards, saying, "Oh-oh-oh…"'

She laughed, and kissed him back. 'That's a deal.'

CHAPTER ELEVEN

ON CHRISTMAS DAY Anna drew the blinds in Jamie's office and locked the door, then helped him get into the red suit and beard that Robert had left for them.

'You're sure I look the part?' he asked.

'You need a touch more padding, I think,' Anna said. She added another pillow underneath his top, then stood back and eyed him critically. 'Yup, that's it. Perfect.'

'If you'd told me a month ago that I'd be doing this, I would never have believed you,' he said.

'I asked you to do it six weeks ago, and you said no,' she reminded him. 'I'm glad you changed your mind.'

'I see things very differently now,' he said quietly. 'I have you to thank for putting the sunshine back in my life. And now we're going to put a little bit of sunshine into the children's lives. I still think you should've dressed up as an elf.'

'No, because there are children in the ward who would recognise me. And it makes sense to them that Dr Anna will have a special guest on her ward round.'

'Let's do it,' he said, lifting up the sack marked 'Presents'. 'So each bay has its own bag?'

'And every present is named. We've taken turns

sorting it over the last week,' she said. 'Teddies for
the babies, art stuff for the under-sevens, and age-
appropriate books for the over-sevens. A big high-five
to the Friends of Muswell Hill Memorial Hospital for
raising the funds and buying the presents.'

'Definitely.'

She unlocked the door and led him out.

'Good morning, everyone,' she said to the children
in her first bay. 'I have a special visitor to the ward
today.'

'Ho-ho-ho. Merry Christmas, everyone,' Jamie said,
waving from the doorway. 'Dr Anna, Nurse Sajana
and Nurse Keely have agreed to help me give everyone a present.'

'Merry Christmas, Santa!' a little girl called from
the corner.

'Merry Christmas!' Jamie called back.

Between them, Anna, Sajana and Keely made sure
the right presents went to the right children. Jamie
blew everyone kisses, then moved on to the next bay,
until every child had a present from Father Christmas.

There were gluten-free mince pies, a big tub of
chocolates, mini festive cupcakes, a big tray of cheese
straws and a dish of tortilla chips with salsa on the
nurses' station in the centre of the department, and as
they went through the bays Anna encouraged all the
visitors to help themselves.

Anna had brought in her acoustic guitar, and between them she, Keely and Sajana got all the children
to join in singing 'Rudolph the Red Nosed Reindeer'
and 'Frosty the Snowman', as well as teaching them
all the song about robins that Jamie recognised from
the school concert she'd taken him to.

Keely's voice was amazing, and Jamie remembered Anna telling him that Keely sang in the hospital's house band, Maybe Baby; she was easily good enough to be professional. Maybe, he thought, the band might sing at his and Anna's wedding next year.

The spirit of Christmas was well and truly alive in Anna Maskell. Peace and love and kindness. She was making a difference to their patients and their families, and she'd made a huge difference to his life.

Quietly, he slipped back to his office and removed the beard and red suit, then came back in his usual clothes to join in with the singing. Even the parents who'd initially looked utterly stressed at having their child so sick that they had to be away from home at Christmas seemed to have relaxed a bit, thanks to Anna.

Finally, at the end of her shift, she came into his office and took his hand. 'Thank you for being so brilliant today.'

'Given how opposed I was to the idea in the first place, I'm blown away by how much I enjoyed it,' he said. 'Seeing them smile and look a bit hopeful, and forgetting how ill they were feeling—just for a little while. If I'm here next year, and Robert wants a break, put me down for being Santa on the ward.'

'Really?'

'Really. I've agreed to cover the rest of Nalini's maternity leave, and after that if she wants to come back part time then we might be able to work out some kind of job-share.'

'That,' she said, 'is the best Christmas present of all.'

He smiled and kissed her. 'No promises. We'll see

how it goes. But, even if we don't end up working together when Nalini comes back, we can still try to co-ordinate our shifts in different hospitals.'

'Absolutely,' she agreed. 'Are you sure you're ready for a Maskell family Christmas?'

'I am,' he said. 'And it was amazing of your parents to ask my parents and my sisters to come for Christmas dinner, too.'

She grinned. 'The more the merrier. And everyone's chipping in with desserts and trimmings, so all Mum really has to do is cook the turkey. There's enough room for all the children to run around together and play.' Her grin broadened. 'Dinner and games. It doesn't get more perfect than that.'

'Indeed.' Though Anna didn't know quite *everything,* he thought. As far as she was concerned, the jeweller was still making the pretty engagement ring they'd chosen together, based on a Celtic knot and with a single tanzanite in the centre. He'd had it delivered to her parents the previous day, along with half a dozen bottles of champagne, in strictest secrecy. Because today wasn't just Christmas Day. He'd been exchanging texts with Anna's sister, too, over the last week, and between them they'd come up with the perfect song to go with the delivery of the ring. Jojo had reassured him that it was on her phone, it was on Becky's phone too as a back-up, and she'd play it as soon as he gave her the nod.

He really hoped he'd pitched this right.

When they reached her parents' house, everyone was already there, the children were playing raucous games, a mix of Christmas songs was playing, and the gorgeous scent of Christmas dinner filled the air.

Alison, Anna's mum, greeted them warmly, and Tony, Anna's dad, shoved a glass of wine into their hands.

'Everyone's in the living room,' Alison said. 'Go and say hello.'

'Do you need a hand in here first?' Jamie asked.

'No, because you've both done a full shift already. Go and have fun.' Alison shooed them out of the kitchen.

Jamie and Anna greeted everyone, and were deep in conversation when Tony called, 'Everyone, dinner is about to be served—time to come and sit at the table!'

This was what it felt like to be a part of a big, noisy family again, Jamie thought. And he absolutely loved it.

Everyone chattered during dinner, wearing the paper hats from their crackers and taking it in turn to make everyone else laugh and groan with the cracker jokes.

Jamie helped to clear the table before coffee, but had already primed Mark, Anna's oldest brother, to make her stay put and talk while he was in the kitchen.

Out of Anna's sight, Alison gave him the box to put in his pocket, and he hugged her. 'Thank you so much for helping me.'

'You make my baby happy,' she said simply, 'and that's what matters to me.'

Jojo came into the kitchen and waved her phone at him. 'Ready?'

'I think so.' Though right then he felt incredibly nervous—as nervous as he did before the trickiest operation, all his exams and his driving test, except all rolled into one.

'Hopefully you've practised it enough to know the words,' Jojo said with a grin. 'But Mum, Becky and I will have your back for the chorus.' She ruffled his hair. 'We should've made you put the T-shirt and white trousers on and do it properly, but Anna-Banana loves you anyway so you can get away with it. But you *do* have to dance. That's not optional.'

'Go get your girl, sweetheart,' Alison said, patting his shoulder.

Together, they walked into the dining room, where everyone was still chattering and laughing. Alison tapped a spoon on a glass, and the room fell silent in expectation.

Jojo hit 'Play' and the beginning of 'Wake Me Up Before You Go-Go' came on.

Jamie sang along and danced, not caring that his voice was slightly flat and he couldn't reach the high note on the chorus, because Jojo, Alison and Becky were singing along with him.

He sang the next verse; then, as he'd arranged with Jojo, she stopped the song and he dropped to one knee.

'You *have* chased my grey skies away,' he said, 'and you make the sun shine for me, Anna Maskell. I love you, and I want to wake up with you every day. Will you marry me?' He whipped the box out of his pocket, opened it and held it out to her.

'I don't believe you just did this—and to George,' she said, crying and laughing at the same time. 'Yes! Yes, I'll marry you.'

Everyone cheered, and between them Anna and Jamie's fathers poured the champagne and their mothers poured sparkling grape juice for the children.

'To Anna and Jamie,' Tony said. 'Every happiness. And happy, happy Christmas.'

'Anna and Jamie. Happy, happy Christmas,' everyone chorused.

* * * * *

TAMING HER HOLLYWOOD PLAYBOY

EMILY FORBES

MILLS & BOON

For Deb, the most amazing big sister.
I was so lucky to have you in my life.
I miss you every day.
xx
6th October 2018

PROLOGUE

'Toto...I've a feeling we're not in Kansas any more.'

The familiar phrase from *The Wizard of Oz* popped into Oliver's head as he sat in the all-terrain vehicle surrounded by nothing but red dirt. The heat in the vehicle was stifling but he knew it was worse outside. He could see the shimmering mirage of the heat as it rose off the baked land. A trickle of sweat made its way down his back, sliding between his shoulder blades as he looked out of the window and wondered what he was doing at the end of the earth.

He wasn't in Kansas, and he sure as heck wasn't in Hollywood either. Hollywood was clean and tidy, ordered and structured. A lot of the work on movie sets in today's world was done indoors, with air-conditioning and green screens, and any dirt, gore, murders, blood and disasters were manufactured. Here the dirt and dust and heat were all too real. Too authentic. It made him wonder about everything else—the murders, blood and disasters—it was too easy to imagine all kinds of skulduggery occurring in this seemingly endless land.

He shrugged his shoulders; they were sticky under his clothing as he returned his focus to the task at hand. He'd always had an active imagination but he was sure he'd be able to handle this place—it was only for six weeks. The dirt and dust would wash off at the end of the day, he was used to a certain level of discomfort in his job, and he certainly wasn't precious—although the heat was a little extreme, even for him. It had a thickness to it which made breathing difficult, as though the heat had sucked all the oxygen from the air. It felt like the type of heat you needed to have been born into, to have grown up in, to have any chance of coping with it. Of surviving.

It must have been well over one hundred degrees in the shade, if there was any shade. The place was baking. Hot, dry and not a blade of grass or a tree in sight to break the monotony of the red earth. The landscape was perfect for the movie but not so great for the cast and crew. Adding to Oliver's discomfort was the fact that he was wearing a flame-retardant suit under his costume in preparation for the upcoming scene. But it was no use complaining: he asked to do his own stunt work wherever possible and he was sure his stunt double would be more than happy to sit this one out.

The sun was low in the sky but the heat of the day was still intense. He closed his eyes as he pictured himself diving into the hotel pool and emerging, cool and fresh and wet—instead of hot and sticky and dripping in sweat—to down a cold beer. He would love to think he could have the pool to himself but he knew, in this overwhelming climate, that was wishful thinking; he'd just have to do his best to avoid sharing it with any of the single women from the cast or crew. He didn't need any more scandals attached to his name. His agent, lawyer and publicist were all working overtime as it was.

He started the engine as instructions came through his earpiece. It was time to capture the last scene for the day's shoot.

The stunt required him to drive the ATV at speed towards the mountain range in the distance. A ramp had been disguised in the dirt and rocks that would flip the vehicle onto its side for dramatic effect. The whole scene could probably be done using CGI techniques and a green screen but the film's director, George Murray, liked as much realism as possible and he had chosen this part of the world for filming because of its authenticity and other-worldliness. It was supposed to be representing another planet and Oliver could see how it could feel that way. He had grown up all around the world but even he'd never seen anywhere that looked as alien and hostile as this.

The setting sun was turning the burnt orange landscape a fiery red. The shadows cast by the distant hills were lengthening and turning violet. He knew the dust thrown up by his tyres would filter the light and lend a sinister aspect to the scene.

He waited for the call of 'action' and pressed his foot to the accelerator. The vehicle leapt forwards. He waited for the tyres to gain traction and then pushed the pedal flat to the floor. The ground was littered with tiny stones, making it difficult to maintain a straight course. He eased off the speed slightly as the vehicle skidded and slid to the left. He corrected the slide without difficulty and continued his course but, just as he thought he'd succeeded, there was a loud bang and the steering wheel shuddered in his hands.

He felt the back of the vehicle slide out to the right and he eased off the speed again as he fought to control it, but the tail had seemingly picked up speed, turning the vehicle ninety degrees to where he wanted it. To where it was supposed to be. He let the wheel spin through his fingers, waiting for the vehicle to straighten, but before he could correct the trajectory the vehicle had gone completely off course. The front tyre dropped into a trough in the dirt and Oliver felt the wheels lift off the ground.

The vehicle began to tip and he knew he had totally lost control. All four wheels were airborne and there was nothing he could do. He couldn't fight it, he couldn't correct it, and he couldn't control it.

The ATV flipped sideways and bounced once. Twice. And again.

It flipped and rolled and Oliver lost count of the cycles as the horizon tumbled before him and the sun's dying rays cast long fingers through the windshield.

Had he finally bitten off more than he could chew?

CHAPTER ONE

OLIVER MASSAGED THE lump on the side of his head. He'd taken a couple of paracetamol for the dull headache but fortunately he'd escaped serious injury yesterday. The bump on his head and some slight bruising on his shoulder were minor complaints and he had no intention of mentioning those aches and pains. The ATV had taken a battering but could be fixed. The repairs meant a change in the filming schedule but nothing that couldn't be accommodated. A serious injury to him would have been far more disruptive.

Despite his luck, however, the incident had made George, the director, wary and Oliver had agreed to hand over some of the stunts to the professionals. The movie couldn't afford for anything to happen to its star and he didn't want to get a reputation as a difficult actor. George had been good to Oliver; he'd worked with him before and he'd been happy to give him another role when other directors had been reluctant, but Oliver knew that being argumentative, disruptive or inflexible wasn't a great way to advance a career. He wasn't stupid, he knew actors were a dime a dozen. He wasn't irreplaceable. No one was. A reputation as a ladies' man was one thing; a reputation as being problematic on set was another thing entirely.

He stretched his neck from side to side as he tried to rid himself of the headache that plagued him. He knew it was from the accident yesterday. He hadn't had that cold beer and had gone to bed alone, so there were no other contributing factors. He knew exactly what had caused his pain.

The schedule change caused by his accident meant he wasn't required for filming this morning, but now he was bored. He wandered around the site, knowing that the heat was probably compounding his headache but too restless to stay indoors.

A whole community had been established temporarily in the middle of the desert just for the movie. Transportable huts were set up as the production centre, the canteen, the first-aid centre, lounge areas for the cast and crew, and Oliver, George and the lead actress all had their own motorhome to retreat to. Marquees surrounded the vehicles and more huts provided additional, and much-needed, shade. The site was twenty miles out of the remote Australian outback town of Coober Pedy, which itself was over three thousand miles from the next major town or, as the Australians said, almost five hundred kilometres. No matter which way you said it, there was no denying that Coober Pedy was a mighty long way from anywhere else.

He'd been completely unprepared for the strangeness of this remote desert town. He'd imagined a flat, barren landscape but the town had sprung up in an area that was far hillier than he'd expected. The main street was tarred and lined with single-level shops and a few taller buildings, including his hotel, with the houses spreading out from the centre of town and into the hills. Along with regular houses there were also hundreds of dwellings dug into the hillsides. He'd heard that people lived underground to escape the merciless heat but he hadn't thought about what that meant in terms of the town's appearance; in effect, it made the town look far more sparsely populated than it actually was.

He knew he should hole up in his trailer and stay out of the heat but he wanted company.

Generators chugged away in the background, providing power for the film set, providing air-conditioning, refrigeration and technology. He was used to having a shower in his trailer but because of water restrictions apparently that was a no-go out here in the Australian desert.

If he moved far enough away from the generators he knew he would hear absolute silence. It should be peaceful, quiet, restful even, and he could understand how some people would find the solitude and the silence soul-restoring, relaxing, but it made him uneasy. He needed more stimulation. He wanted crowds, he wanted noise, he didn't want a chance to be introspective. He was an extrovert, a performer, and as an extrovert he wanted company. He needed company to energise him and as a performer he needed an audience.

He wasn't required on set but he decided he'd go and watch the filming anyway. It would kill some time and give him someone to talk to.

He turned away from the transportable huts that formed the command centre for the movie set and headed towards the vehicle compound. His boots kicked up puffs of red dust as he walked. Everything was coated in dust. It got inside your mouth, your ears, your nostrils. Everything smelt and tasted like dust. It even got inside your eyes—if the flies didn't get there first. Which reminded him that he'd left his sunglasses in his trailer. He spun around; he'd retrieve them and then grab a four-by-four and head further out into the desert to where filming was taking place.

He slipped his glasses on as he stepped back into the heat. Rounding the corner of his trailer, he heard an engine and noticed a dust cloud billowing into the air. He stood in the shade at the corner of his trailer and watched as a car pulled to a stop beside the mess hut. It was an old four-by-four, its brown paintwork covered in red dust, like everything else out here. A haze rose from the bonnet of the car, bringing to mind the story about it being hot enough in Australia to fry an egg in the sun. He believed it.

The car door opened and he waited, his natural curiosity getting the better of him, to see who climbed out.

A woman.

That was unexpected.

She stood and straightened. She was tall, slender, lithe. Her hair was thick and dark and fell just past her shoulders. He watched as she scraped it off her neck and tied it into a loose ponytail, in deference to the heat, he presumed. Her neck was long and swan-like, her limbs long and tanned.

She was stunning and the complete antithesis of what he'd expected, judging from the car she was driving. She reminded him of a butterfly emerging from a cocoon.

He blinked, making sure it wasn't the after-effects

of the bump to his head causing his imagination to play tricks on him.

She was still there.

She wore a navy and white summer dress, which must have been lined to mid-thigh, but from there down, with the morning sun behind her, the white sections were completely see-through. He wondered if she knew but he didn't care—her legs were incredible. Magnificent.

Oliver was literally in the middle of nowhere with absolutely nothing of interest to look at. Until now. The middle of nowhere had just become a far more attractive proposition.

He watched as she walked towards him. Graceful. Ethereal. Sunglasses protected her eyes but her skin was flawless and her lips were full and painted with bright red lipstick. The shade was striking against her olive skin and raven hair.

He'd seen plenty of beautiful woman in his thirty-two years, he was surrounded by them on a daily basis, but he didn't think he'd ever seen a woman as naturally beautiful. The ones he worked with had all had some help—a scalpel here, an injection there—and he'd swear on his father's grave, something he hoped he would be able to do sooner rather than later, that she hadn't had any assistance.

He watched, not moving a muscle, scared that any movement might startle her, might make her shimmer and disappear, mirage-like, into the desert.

Maybe his headache was affecting his thought processes; maybe he'd been out in the sun for too long, or simply in the outback for too long. Other than the cast and crew he'd barely seen another person for days. The hot, dusty streets of Coober Pedy were, for the most part, empty. The locals hunkered down in their underground dwellings to escape the heat, venturing out only briefly and if absolutely necessary, scampering from one building to the subterranean comfort of the next. But perhaps many of the locals looked like this. Perhaps that was the attraction in this desolate, baked and barren desert town.

She had stopped walking as her gaze scanned the buildings, looking for something or someone. Looking lost. His curiosity was piqued. His attention captured.

Her gaze landed on him and she took another step forward. Belatedly he stepped out of the shadows and walked towards her; he'd been so transfixed he'd forgotten to move, forgotten his manners, but he wanted to be the first to offer her assistance.

'Hello, I'm Oliver; may I help you?'

She stopped and waited as he approached her.

'Thank you,' she said. 'I'm looking for George Murray.' Her voice was deep and slightly breathless, without the broad Australian accent that he'd heard so many of the crew speak with. She glanced down at her watch and his eyes followed. Her watch had a large face, with the numbers clearly marked and an obvious hand counting off the seconds. Her fingers were delicate by comparison, long and slender, with short nails lacquered with clear varnish. He was trained to be observant, to watch people's mannerisms, to listen to their voices, but even so he was aware that he was soaking up everything about this woman. From the colour of her lips and the shine of her hair, to the smooth lustre of her skin and the inflection of her speech. He wanted to be able to picture her perfectly later. She lifted her head. 'I have an interview with him at eleven.'

'A job interview?'

She nodded. 'Of sorts.'

'Are you going to be working on the film? Are you an extra?'

'No.'

'Catering? Publicity?'

'No and no.' Her mouth turned up at one corner and he got a glimpse of perfect, even white teeth bordered by those red lips.

He grinned. 'You're not going to tell me?'

Her smile widened and he knew she was enjoying the repartee. 'No, I don't think I am.'

Two could play at that game. 'All right, then,' he shrugged, feigning disinterest, 'George is out on set but he shouldn't be long. Filming started early today to try to beat the heat, so they'll be breaking for lunch soon. Let me show you to his trailer.' He'd take her to where she needed to go but he wouldn't leave her.

He bounced lightly up the two steps that led to George's office and pushed open the heavy metal door. He flicked on the lights and held the door for her. She brushed past him and her breasts lightly grazed his arm but she showed no sign that she'd noticed the contact. She stopped just inside the door and removed her sunglasses, and he caught a trace of her scent—fresh, light and fruity.

He watched as she surveyed the interior. An enormous television screen dominated the wall opposite the desk, which was covered in papers. A laptop sat open amongst the mess. A large fridge with a glass door was tucked into a corner to the left, and a couch was pressed against the opposite wall with two armchairs at right angles to it and a small coffee table in between.

He wondered if this was what she'd expected to see.

'Have a seat,' he invited as he waved an arm towards the chairs. She sat but avoided the couch.

'Can I get you something to drink?'

She nodded and the light bounced off her hair, making it look like silk. 'A water would be lovely, thank you.'

He grabbed a glass and two bottles of mineral water from the fridge. He twisted the tops off and passed her the glass and a bottle.

'I'll be fine waiting here,' she said as she took the drink from him. 'You must have something you need to do?'

He shook his head as he sat on the couch. He leant back and rested one foot on his other knee, relaxed, comfortable, approachable, conveying candidness. 'I'm not busy. The scene they're filming doesn't involve me.'

'You're an actor?'

He looked carefully at her to gauge if she was joking but her expression was serious. Her mouth looked serious, her red lips full but not moving. But was there a hint of humour in her dark eyes? He couldn't read her yet. Perhaps she was an anomaly, someone who didn't immediately recognise him, or maybe he just wasn't famous out here in the middle of nowhere.

Should he tell her who he was?

No. That could wait. She still hadn't told him what she was doing here. She'd said she wasn't publicity but she could be a journalist. He didn't need more reporters telling stories about him. But if that was the case, surely she would recognise him.

Unless she was a better actor than he was, he was certain she wasn't a reporter.

He settled for vague. 'I am,' he said as the door opened again and George entered the trailer.

'Kat! Welcome.' He was beaming. Oliver was surprised; George never looked this pleased to see anyone. George was a little rotund, always in a hurry, and seemed to have a permanent scowl creasing his forehead. Seeing him so delighted to see another person was somewhat disconcerting.

He crossed the room as the woman stood. Kat or Kate, Oliver thought George had said, but he wasn't quite sure. Oliver stood too; manners that had been instilled in him, growing up as the son of a strict military man, remained automatic.

George greeted her with a kiss and Oliver was more intrigued. There was obviously some history here that he wasn't privy to. Who was she?

'I see you've met our star, Oliver Harding.'

'Not formally.' She turned to him and extended her hand. 'I'm Katarina Angelis, but call me Kat.' Her handshake was firm but it was the softness of her skin and the laughter in her eyes that caught Oliver off guard. 'It's a pleasure to meet you.'

He realised she'd known exactly who he was. Which put him at a disadvantage. He still knew nothing about her. But he did know her name seemed to suit her perfectly. He was sure Katarina meant 'pure', and Angelis had to mean 'heavenly'.

'The pleasure is all mine,' he said.

George cleared his throat and Oliver realised he hadn't let go of Kat's hand. He also realised he didn't want to. Beautiful women were everywhere in his world, but there was something more to Kat. Something intriguing. Something different.

Her skin was soft and cool. Flawless. She looked like a desert rose, a surprising beauty in the harshness of the outback, and he found himself transfixed by her scarlet mouth. Her lips brought to mind ripe summer cherries, dark red and juicy. He wondered how they'd taste.

'If I might give you some advice, my dear,' George said to Kat as Oliver finally let her hand drop, 'you should stay away from Oliver.'

'Hey!' he protested.

'You don't have to worry about me, George,' Kat replied. 'I can handle myself.'

George shook his head. 'You've never met anyone like Oliver.'

Kat was looking at him now. Studying him, as if sizing him up and comparing him to George's assessment. Oliver smiled and shrugged and spread his hands wide, proclaiming his innocence. He had to take it on the chin; he couldn't remonstrate with George in front of Kat—it would be better to laugh it off. He couldn't afford to show how she'd affected him. It was safer to return to his usual persona of charm and confidence, of not taking himself or anyone too seriously. She had floored him and he needed to gather his wits and work out what to do about it. About her. But, for now, he'd play along. 'George is right, Kat, I'm the man your father warned you about.'

She laughed. 'Don't go thinking that makes you special. My father is always warning me about men.'

He cocked his head and quirked one eyebrow. This

was even better. He had never been one to back away from a challenge.

'Don't make me regret hiring you.' George eyeballed them both. 'Either of you.'

Oliver laughed; he was used to being told off, but he was surprised to see that Kat was blushing. She looked even more delightful now.

'I mean it, Oliver—don't mess with Kat.' George looked him straight in the eye. 'There aren't too many places left for you to run to and if you hurt her you'll want to start running, believe me.'

So now they were both going to put a challenge to him. Of course, that only served to entice him even more. George could warn him all he liked but Oliver had never been one to steer clear of a challenge. But he knew he had to tread carefully. He couldn't afford any more scandals.

'Go and find something to do,' George told him. 'I need to talk to Kat.'

Oliver left but he knew it wouldn't be the last he saw of Kat Angelis. He was glad now that she hadn't admitted that she recognised him, that she hadn't said his reputation preceded him. Perhaps she'd have no preconceived ideas about him and he could try to impress her without any rumours or innuendo getting in the way.

He was still none the wiser as to her actual reason for being on set but, if George was hiring her, he'd make sure their paths crossed again. If he was going to be stuck in this town for the next few weeks he might as well have some fun. He knew it was his choice, almost, to be here—George had made him an offer that his publicist thought was too good to refuse—and timing was everything. But that didn't mean he couldn't enjoy himself. He wouldn't misbehave, but even if he did he doubted anyone would ever hear about what went on out here. Coober Pedy and the Australian outback seemed to exist in its own little time capsule. It really was a whole other world.

Kat watched on as George shooed Oliver out of his office. Of course she'd recognised him—Oliver Harding was a star of multiple Hollywood blockbusters. He had been the lead actor in several recent box office hits and he played action heroes just as well as he carried romantic leads. He was in the news regularly, if not for his movies then for his off-screen exploits with his leading ladies or other Hollywood 'It' girls. Kat may be a small-town girl, living out in the desert in the middle of nowhere, but she had television, magazines, the internet and the local drive-in movie theatre, which showed new movies every Saturday night. Oliver Harding was famous and she would have to be living under a rock not to know who he was. The thought made her smile. She did actually live underground, like so many of the local residents, but that didn't mean she didn't know what went on in the rest of the world. Oliver Harding appeared in a new movie every six months, and with a new woman far more frequently. Having met him now, she could understand why. He was handsome on the silver screen but incredibly gorgeous in real life. He had charm, charisma and a twinkle in his bright blue eyes that had made her lose her train of thought on more than one occasion already.

'I'm serious, Kat,' George cautioned her again. Had he mistaken her smile to mean she wasn't paying attention to his warning? 'I've seen that look in his eye before. You really don't want him to set his sights on you. Stronger women than you have fallen for his charms. He loves the thrill of the chase and he hates to let a pretty girl go unappreciated, but he has a tendency to leave a trail of broken hearts behind him.'

He had a cheeky appeal and amazing eyes and his smile made her stomach tumble, but Kat wasn't about to succumb to his charm. She'd met charming men before and didn't intend to be another notch on his bedpost. And she hadn't been kidding when she'd said she knew how to handle herself. There was no denying Oliver Harding was gorgeous and charming but she was *not* the type to fall for charming and handsome. Well, that wasn't technically true but she wasn't the type to have flings with famous men who were just visiting. That was something irresponsible people did. Spontaneous people. And she'd learnt not to be either of those.

'Don't worry about me, George. I really can handle myself.'

'He has a reputation for seducing women, but, in his defence, don't believe everything you read or hear. He's a nice guy but still a flirt and definitely incorrigible.'

'I'm here to work, not fool around with the staff,' Kat stated, reminding herself of her obligations as much as she was reminding George. 'So, what exactly did you want to see me about?'

George sighed. 'Oliver has it written into his contract that he gets to do a proportion of his own stunt work. A large proportion. But yesterday things didn't go quite to plan. He was involved in an accident. The vehicle he was driving was supposed to crash but instead of going into a controlled sideways tip it flipped at speed and ended up on its roof. He seems to be fine.'

Kat thought back—she hadn't noticed a limp or any bruising or protective postures, but she hadn't been looking for signs of injury. She'd been too focused on his mesmerising blue eyes and on trying not to act like a star-struck fan.

'But,' George continued, 'since the incident our first-aid officer is refusing to be responsible for Oliver's safety and I must say she has a point. We have a stunt coordinator who is also Oliver's double but… sometimes things go wrong. I think it would be prudent to have someone on set who has more experience than just a first-aid qualification. Not full-time, just when we're doing the stunts. Do you think, if I gave you the filming schedule, you might be able to work with us? Would you be interested?'

'I think so.' George had outlined his thoughts on the phone to her last night but she needed more details. 'Can you give me a basic idea of what would be required, mainly how much time?'

She listened as George ran through the filming schedule with her.

'I'd still need to be available for ambulance shifts—even with the volunteers we don't have enough staff to allow me to give those up,' Kat said. Getting qualified paramedics to work in rural and remote areas was always tough and Kat knew she would have to make sure she didn't put her colleagues under any additional pressure by requesting time off in order to do something that was purely to satisfy her own desires. As tempting and exciting as it was to think of working on a movie set, not to mention with Oliver Harding, her commitment to her career had to be her priority.

'We could work around your schedule to a certain

degree. As long as you could be on set when we're doing the stunt work. Would that be possible? I don't want to wear you out.'

From what George had described to her last night, the movie wasn't really her cup of tea—she preferred drama and thrillers to science fiction—but she had to admit it would be exciting to work on a film set, and getting to work with Oliver would be an added bonus.

'I reckon I can work something out. I'll see if I can swap some of my day shifts for nights. We're on call overnight. With a resident population of just over two thousand people there's not usually a lot to keep us busy. It's tourists that swell our numbers and keep us occupied.'

'That's great. I'll get a contract drawn up; you'll be fairly paid for your time.'

'I don't need—'

'Don't argue,' George interrupted. 'I need it to be all above board and your wages will be a drop in the ocean that is our budget. Think of it as spending money—put it aside and treat yourself to something.'

Kat couldn't remember the last time she'd treated herself to something. She couldn't even begin to imagine what she would do, but it was easier to agree.

'There is one other thing,' George added. 'A favour. I need some extra locations. The cave where I wanted to shoot is apparently sacred Aboriginal land and I can't get permission to film there. You don't happen to know of anything else around here?'

'I do know something that might do,' Kat replied. 'It's on my godfather's land about ten minutes out of town. I can take you out to see it later today if you like. Shall I meet you at the hotel?'

Kat picked up the copy of the film schedule that George had given her, kissed him goodbye and made arrangements to meet at five. She stepped out of the trailer and found Oliver waiting for her.

'Now are you going to tell me what you're doing here?' he asked as he fell into step beside her. His voice was deep and pleasant, his accent neutral. She'd expected more of an American flavour. Had he been taught to tone it down?

'I live here.'

'Really? Here?'

She could hear the unspoken question, the one every visitor asked until they got to know Coober Pedy. *Why?*

She never knew where to start. How did one begin to explain the beauty, the peace, the wildness, the attraction? She loved it here. That didn't mean she never entertained the idea of travelling the world and seeing other places, but this was home. This was where her family lived. And family was everything.

She had no idea how to explain all of that, so she simply said, 'Yes, really.'

'But you know George?' He was walking closely beside her and his arm brushed against hers every few steps, interrupting her concentration.

She nodded.

'Are you going to tell me how?'

'It's not my story to tell.'

'At least tell me why you have the filming schedule, then.'

She stopped walking and turned to look at him. She had to look up. She wasn't short—she was five feet nine inches tall—but still he was several inches taller. 'Are you always this nosy?'

'Yes.' He was smiling. 'Although I prefer to think of myself as having an enquiring mind. It sounds more masculine. I'm happy to be in touch with my feminine side, but only in private.'

'I'm going to be working on the film,' she said, hoping to surprise him.

'Doing what?'

'Keeping *you* out of trouble,' she said as she continued towards her car.

'Trouble is my middle name,' he laughed.

She didn't doubt that. She'd only known him for a few minutes and regardless of George's warning she already had the sense that he was trouble. But she couldn't help smiling as she said, 'So I hear.'

Kat reached her car and stretched her hand out to open the door, which she hadn't bothered locking, but Oliver was faster than she was. He rested his hand on the door frame, preventing her from opening it.

'And just how exactly do you plan to keep me out of trouble?' His voice was deep and sexy, perfect for a leading man.

She turned to face him. He was standing close. Her eyes were level with his chest. He was solid—muscular without being beefy, gym-toned. He didn't look as if he'd done a hard day's work in his life, and he probably hadn't, but that didn't stop him from being handsome. With his chiselled good looks, he could have come straight from the pages of a men's fashion magazine.

He smelt good. He looked even better.

His blue eyes were piercing, his square jaw clean-shaven. His thick brown hair was cut in a short back and sides, slightly longer on top, like a military-style haircut that had been on holiday for a couple of weeks.

She wondered if it was to fit the movie script or if it was how he chose to cut his hair. It suited him. It emphasised his bone structure.

'I'm your insurance policy,' she said.

He frowned and raised one eyebrow. She wondered if that came naturally or if he'd cultivated that move. Was it possible to learn how to do that?

'I'm a paramedic,' she continued. 'I'm going to be on set for the stunt work. Just in case.'

She'd expected him to object but he took it in his stride.

'Good,' he said simply before he grinned widely. 'I'll be seeing plenty of you, then.'

He was so confident, so comfortable. She wondered if he'd ever been told he couldn't do something. She imagined that if he had he would have chosen to ignore the instruction.

His arm was still outstretched, passing beside her head as he leant against her car. 'So, Kat, tell me your story.'

'Why do you want to know?'

She was caught between his chest and the car. She could step out, away from the boundaries he'd imposed, but she didn't want to. She didn't feel threatened. He was smiling at her. He looked genuine, friendly, but she needed to remember he was an actor. He was probably trained to smile in a hundred different ways. She remembered George's warning but she chose to ignore it. Just for a moment. She wanted to see what would happen next. She felt as if she was in a movie moment of her own.

His smile widened, showcasing teeth that were white, even and perfect. His blue eyes sparkled. 'Because I want to make sure I'm not overstepping any lines when I ask you out.'

He looked like a man who was used to getting his own way and she didn't doubt that; with women, at least, he probably did. But she did doubt that she was the type of woman he was used to meeting. 'And what makes you think I'd go out with you?'

'I didn't say you would, I'm just letting you know I will ask you to. The choice is completely yours.'

'What did you have in mind?' She shouldn't ask but she wanted to know. She should heed George's warning and get in her car and drive away but it had been a long time since she'd been asked on a date and she was interested to hear his thoughts. She was interested full stop.

He smiled. 'I don't know yet but I'll think of something.'

There weren't a lot of options in Coober Pedy and Oliver, not being a local, would know even fewer.

Kat couldn't remember the last time someone had flirted with her or the last time she'd met anyone she wanted to flirt with. She couldn't deny she was flattered by the attention. She'd need to be careful. She'd been hurt before; a monumental break-up had left her questioning her own judgement and she'd avoided getting romantically involved ever since. She wanted her own happily-ever-after but she'd been scared to go out to find it. She'd focused instead on her career and her family and it had been a while since she'd even thought about going on a date. George's warning repeated in her head again but she had no idea if she was going to be able to heed it.

The touch of Oliver's hand had set her pulse racing

and the look in his eye had made her wish, just momentarily, that she was the sort of girl who would take a risk, take a chance.

But that wasn't her. She'd learnt that taking risks was asking for trouble, and Oliver Harding had trouble written all over him.

CHAPTER TWO

KAT PULLED INTO the courtyard in front of the Cave Hotel. She found a spot to park under a gum tree in the shadow of the hill, seeking shade out of habit rather than necessity at this time of the evening. The air was still warm but the searing heat of the day was beginning to dissipate.

The sun was setting behind the hotel, turning the sky orange. The hotel was the town's only five-star accommodation. Kat doubted it could be compared to five-star indulgence in Paris, London or New York but it was luxurious by Coober Pedy standards and all that Kat knew. She'd never travelled outside Australia and had never stayed in anything rated above three and a half stars.

'Do you have a little more time up your sleeve?' George asked as Kat switched off her car. 'As a thank-you for showing me those caves I'll buy you a cold drink and introduce you to the cast. I imagine they'll gather in the bar before dinner and it would be a good chance to meet them before you start work.'

'Sure,' she replied. 'I'll just make a call and then I'll meet you inside.'

Like a lot of the dwellings in town, the hotel had

been built into the side of a hill. It had newer wings that extended out from the hill but Kat always recommended that people book an underground room as a preference, for the atmosphere and experience plus the fact that the rooms were bigger and cooler. The original, subterranean floorplan had been designed to enable the rooms to maintain a constant temperature year-round, a bonus in the scorching heat of summer and during cold winter nights, but it meant that cell phone reception could be erratic inside.

The hotel had air-conditioning, an excellent restaurant and shops, and the courtyard parking area had been covered in bitumen, which, in contrast to the dusty streets, was perhaps all that was needed. More importantly it had an outdoor pool, secluded behind an adobe wall and surrounded by palm trees. Kat had always thought the palms a bit incongruous, considering the environment, but they seemed to thrive.

She stepped under the covered walkway that ran from the pool to the hotel foyer, seeking the shade. She called her father, letting him know she'd be late and checking that he was happy to wait for dinner. As she finished her phone call she heard the pool gate slam shut behind her. She turned her head and saw Oliver walking her way.

He had a beach towel slung over his right shoulder but he was still wet. He was bare-chested, his skin smooth and slick and golden brown. Damp swimming trunks hugged his thighs.

Kat's mouth went dry as she tried not to ogle him, but it was a difficult task. Eventually she lifted her eyes and saw him smiling at her. His smile was incredible. It started slowly; one corner of his mouth lifted first and then his smile stretched across his lips before they parted to reveal perfect white teeth and a wide, engaging smile.

'This is a pleasant surprise. I didn't expect to see you. What are you up to?'

He stopped at her side, took the towel from his shoulder and started to dry his chest. There was a purple bruise on his right shoulder and Kat was going to ask about it, but that was before she got distracted. Oliver's arm muscles flexed as he rubbed the towel over his body, diverting her attention. He ran the towel over his abdomen and she couldn't help but follow his movements. His stomach muscles rippled as he twisted to reach his hand behind his back and Kat's heart skipped a beat as she forced herself to concentrate. She was yearning to reach out and run her hand over his shoulder and down his arm. To feel his biceps tense and flex under her fingers. If she thought he was attractive fully clothed then he was something else altogether when he was partially naked.

She swallowed as she tried to rein in her imagination. 'I've just brought George back—we went to scout some locations.'

'You've already got the lingo, I see,' he said as he slung the towel back over his shoulder. 'What are you doing now?'

'I'm having a drink at the bar. George is going to introduce me to a few people.'

'Great, I'll see you inside.' He started walking towards the hotel and Kat focused on walking beside him, on putting one foot in front of the other.

He held the lobby door open for her but stopped at the entrance to the bar. 'I'm not dressed appropriately—

I'll get changed and come back. Are you OK to go in by yourself?'

Kat wasn't used to people checking on her; everyone in town knew her and the locals expected people to look after themselves. On the whole women weren't treated any differently to men but she stopped herself from giving a short reply of 'of course', as she realised he was just being polite. He was just treating her with courtesy, showing some respect. It was something her father would have done for her mother.

Her father would have been horrified if her mother had gone into a hotel unaccompanied. When they had been courting there would have been separate bars for the men and women, and women would never have been permitted in the 'public' bar, but times had changed and no one now would bat an eyelid at a woman going into a bar alone. Kat knew she would feel uncomfortable in a different setting, in a different town, but everyone knew her here; she still appreciated Oliver's manners though. She nodded. 'Yes, I'm fine, thank you.'

The bar was cool and softly lit. It was in the original part of the hotel, dug into the hill. Its walls and ceilings were the colour of ochre, the same colour as the land, but the walls had been coated with a clear lacquer to stop the dust that would otherwise coat everything in its path. It was a large room and felt spacious even though there were no windows. Indoor plants helped to delineate the space, creating smaller areas and a sense of privacy while helping to disguise the fact that they were several feet under the surface.

George was waiting for her and introduced her to several of the cast and crew as she nursed the drink he had purchased for her. She tried to focus on who everyone was but she was constantly scanning the room, waiting for Oliver to return. She hated knowing that she was waiting for him, looking forward to seeing him, but she couldn't help the feeling.

She did a slight double-take when a tall man walked in—his build and even his gait were so similar to Oliver's that it wasn't until he removed his cap that she registered that not only was he not Oliver, but he also had a shaved head and was not nearly as good-looking. But his movements had been similar enough that she'd had to look twice, so it was no surprise when George introduced him as Chris, the man who was Oliver's stunt double. Kat shook his hand, noticing his brown eyes even as she noted that the touch of his hand didn't set her heart racing. He was pleasant enough, fit and young, but very definitely not Oliver.

'When you see Oliver,' Chris said to George after shaking Kat's hand, 'let him know I'll meet him in the gym for his training session.' He turned to Kat. 'Good to meet you, Kat; I'll see you on set.'

When Oliver finally entered the bar, Kat wondered how she could have mistaken Chris for him. There was an aura about Oliver, something drew her to him and she found it almost impossible to turn away.

'Hello, Kat.' He was looking at her intensely. Did he look at everyone like that? she wondered.

She felt as though he could see inside her, see all her secrets. Not that she had any. Something about him made her wish she was a little mysterious, wish she wasn't so ordinary. She wished there was something about her that could intrigue him.

'Chris is waiting in the gym for you.' George was

speaking to Oliver and his voice brought her back to the present.

'That's OK, I promised Kat a drink first. Chris will wait.'

Kat opened her mouth to object—Oliver hadn't promised her any such thing—but before she could speak he winked at her and grinned and she kept quiet.

George's assistant, Erica, came to the table and spoke softly in George's ear.

'If you'll excuse me, I need to speak to Julia. It appears she is having a crisis.' George stood before adding, 'Behave yourself, Oliver.'

Oliver just grinned in reply, apparently brushing George's warning aside without a thought as George left the table, leaving them alone and leaving Kat a little nervous. To fill in the pause in conversation she asked, 'Will she be OK?'

'Have you met our leading lady yet?' Oliver replied.

Kat shook her head.

'Julia is always in the middle of a crisis,' Oliver told her. 'I attract scandals, she attracts crises. We probably shouldn't be allowed to work together. There's always a danger of too much drama.' He laughed and Kat found herself relaxing. 'Now, tell me, what are you drinking?' he said.

'Are you sure you shouldn't be meeting Chris?'

Oliver shrugged and shook his head. 'Not yet.'

'Won't you be in trouble?'

'I'm used to it. Trust me, you are far better company than Chris, not to mention better-looking, and I might not get this opportunity again.' He smiled his slow, drawn-out smile and Kat's stomach flipped and fluttered in response. It was almost as though his smile

kept time with his thoughts but she felt at a distinct disadvantage because, while she could hazard a guess, she
actually had no idea what his thoughts were.

'Besides, I told you trouble is my middle name.'

Kat smiled back. There was no denying his charm.
'Maybe trouble should have been your first name.'

Oliver laughed as he stood up and even his laugh
was perfect. Deep and rich, he sounded like someone
who laughed often. 'Chris will make me sweat for making him wait. I might as well enjoy a beer if he's going
to take his revenge in dead lifts and push-ups anyway.'

'OK, thank you; a beer sounds good,' Kat said, accepting his invitation.

'Explain to me how the stunt double thing works,'
she said when Oliver returned from the bar. 'I get that
Chris has a similar physique to you and even moves
a bit the same, but he doesn't look like you. Is that a
problem? Is that why you're doing some of your own
stunts?'

'No. Chris has been my body double on several
movies and he wears a wig if needed, but in this movie
he's often wearing a helmet, so his hair, or lack of it,
is irrelevant.'

'What about his eyes?' Oliver's were such a distinctive, vibrant blue, Kat couldn't see how they could
work around that.

'He's not in any close-up shots, so we don't need
to see his eyes, but he could probably wear coloured
contact lenses if necessary. The make-up girls are
good and nowadays there's always CGI.'

Oliver was distracted by something over Kat's right
shoulder. She wondered if Chris had come to force him

into the gym and so was surprised when she heard her name.

'Kat?'

She turned to find her cousin, Dean, and his wife, Saskia, standing behind her. While she knew almost everyone in town, she hadn't been expecting to see any familiar faces in this particular bar. The Cave Hotel was expensive and usually frequented exclusively by tourists.

Kat stood up and greeted them both with a kiss. 'Hi. What are you doing here?'

'Dean is taking me to dinner at Mona's. It's our wedding anniversary.'

The hotel restaurant, Mona's, was the best in town and was the one drawcard for the locals, who often chose to dine there to celebrate special occasions.

'Of course it is,' Kat replied. 'Happy anniversary.' But Saskia had turned her attention to Oliver by now and was looking at him with interest.

'Hello. I'm Saskia and this is my husband, Dean.'

Oliver was already on his feet. 'Oliver Harding,' he said as he shook Saskia's hand and then Dean's.

'What are you two up to?' Dean asked.

Kat could see the look of approval on Saskia's face but, whereas her expression was one of appreciation, Dean looked wary. That wasn't unexpected—Kat, Dean and his brother, Roger, were more like siblings than cousins and the boys had always been protective of Kat, particularly when it came to who she dated, but she didn't need Dean trying to rescue her from this situation. There wasn't a situation at all. This was just a work meeting.

To his credit Oliver didn't seem fazed by Dean's

abrupt question but Kat jumped in before Oliver could
say anything that could be misconstrued. She didn't
need any rumours getting back to her father. 'Oliver
is an actor in the movie that's being shot in town. I'm
going to be working with him.'

'As what?' Dean asked. His piercing gaze would
have pinned a lesser man to the spot but Oliver seemed
completely unperturbed by the attention.

'The emergency response officer,' Kat replied.

'That sounds appealing,' Saskia said with a slight
smirk. Kat glared at her but Saskia just smiled, while
Dean continued to size Oliver up.

Kat watched them both. Oliver was squaring up to
Dean and she wondered if she'd need to step in between them. As fit as Oliver was, she wasn't sure he'd
be a match for her cousin in a physical confrontation.

The men were much the same height, both a couple
of inches over six feet, but Dean was probably twenty
kilograms heavier with a hardness about him that Kat
knew came from growing up in this environment. Oliver's muscles came from gym work, which was different from the muscles gained from working outdoors
in the heat and dust of the Australian outback. Dean
was neat and tidy but he had a toughness about him,
except when he was with his wife and kids.

Oliver was groomed, not tough, still all male but a
more polished version. He was gorgeous but, as far as
Kat knew, he was used to Hollywood. In comparison,
Dean was used to the outback, which was tough and
rugged and, Kat imagined, just about as far from Hollywood as it was possible to get. Dean's life couldn't be
more different from Oliver's.

'And what exactly does that entail?' Dean asked.

'It's exciting. I'll tell you about it over dinner,' Saskia said as she tucked her arm into Dean's elbow and prepared to lead him through the bar and into the restaurant.

Kat had told Saskia about the job offer. Saskia and Dean had been together since high school and Saskia was like a sister to Kat. As an only child, she appreciated the relationship she had with her cousin's wife. She was slightly envious of her cousins' marriages; they had what she wished for. They had found their 'one'.

Once upon a time, Kat had had that too. She had thought she was going to get her own happily-ever-after, but things hadn't turned out how she'd expected and now she was starting to wonder if she was ever going to find her soulmate. She was pretty sure she wasn't going to find him in Coober Pedy—the town was dwindling; people were leaving. Would she have to leave too?

'I would jump at the chance to take on that job if I didn't have you and the kids and work to worry about,' Saskia said, bringing Kat back to the present, 'if I was single and free, like Kat,' she added, directing her less than subtle remark to Oliver.

Kat needed to move them on before Saskia said something that would embarrass her. She hugged them both and said, 'Enjoy your dinner,' as she put some gentle pressure against the small of Saskia's back, encouraging her to leave and take Dean with her.

But Saskia wasn't done yet. 'Will we see you on Sunday or are you working?'

'I'll be there.'

'What's happening on Sunday?' Oliver asked when they were alone again.

'Family dinner.' It was a weekly occurrence and there was an expectation that everyone would attend, but Kat didn't mind. She adored her family. Kat had moved back in with her father after her mother passed away, and her extended family—her aunt Rosa, Dean and Saskia, Roger and his wife, Maya, and their children—had dinner together every Sunday.

'Family?'

Kat nodded. 'Dean is my cousin.'

'Your cousin! Do you have other family here?'

'Yes, of course. My whole family is here. This is where I grew up.'

'Here?'

'Yes. I told you that.'

'No. You never said you grew up here. You told me you lived here. Those are two different things.'

'I know what you're thinking,' Kat said.

'How can you know what I'm thinking?'

'Because it's what everyone who's not from here thinks. You assumed I moved here for work because why would someone *choose* to live here?'

'I guess I did think it was for your job,' Oliver agreed. 'But that's partly because everyone I know moves where their job takes them.'

'I've lived here my entire life, just about.' Give or take a few years in Adelaide, but she tried not to think too much about those years. 'I choose to live here because my family is here. And because I miss it when I'm not here.'

'What do you miss?'

'The community. The people. The beauty.' She could see from his expression that he didn't believe her. 'I'll show you. There's more to the outback than dust and flies.'

'It's a date,' Oliver said, smiling again, and Kat realised, just a fraction too late, that he'd played her and got just what he wanted.

'It's not a date,' she protested.

'You can call it whatever you like,' he said with a smile, 'but I'm going to call it a date.'

He reached towards her and Kat thought he was going to pick up her empty glass, but his fingers reached for her hand. His thumb stroked the side of her wrist before he turned her hand over and ran his thumb over the sensitive skin on the underside. Kat's insides turned liquid, she felt as though her bones were melting, and it took all her energy not to close her eyes and give in to the heat that flooded through her.

She needed to leave. To get out from under the spell he was casting over her. She was feeling vulnerable and she knew she was in danger of falling for his charm. He created an energy around him, around her.

'I should go,' she said as she pulled her hand away, breaking the spell before she made a complete fool of herself.

'I guess I'd better get to the gym,' he said as he stood, 'but I'll walk you to your car first.'

He kept a slight distance between them as they walked outside but even so she was aware of a field of attraction and desire surrounding them. Or at least surrounding her.

She turned towards him as they stopped at her car.

'I'll see you at work,' he said as he opened the door that she'd once again left unlocked. 'And I'm looking forward to our date,' he added, 'but until then...' he said as he bent his head and leant towards her.

Kat didn't intend to but she lifted her face, angling it up to him.

Was he going to kiss her?

Her eyelids drifted down, half-closed.

She could feel his breath on her cheek and then his lips pressed against her cheek, just in front of her ear, briefly touching her. Too briefly.

She opened her eyes.

He'd kissed her but not how she'd expected him to. Not how she wanted him to.

He was watching her and she knew he could read her mind. She'd wanted him to kiss her properly. She knew it and he knew it.

She needed to get a grip, she thought as she slid into her car. She was sure he had the same effect on dozens, hundreds, of women. Just because she felt something didn't mean he did. He probably didn't notice it. It was probably something he did out of habit. George had warned her but she couldn't ignore or deny the feelings he evoked in her. She shouldn't be so fascinated but she hadn't met anyone like him. Ever. It was as if he was from a different world.

He scared her. Not in a frightening sense but in a sense that he would have seen far more than she ever had; she had no doubt he would have had his share of beautiful women around the world and she wasn't worldly enough to compete. She didn't *want* to compete. Not unless she knew she could win. And she suspected there would only be one winner if she let Oliver Harding get his way.

She was certain he was not the man for her. Just as

she knew she wasn't the woman for him. She wasn't going to be anyone's conquest. But she couldn't deny he was attractive. Charming. And sexy.

She knew it would be almost impossible to deny her desire if he kept up his charm offensive, so she suspected the question wasn't *could* she resist him, but rather how long could she resist him for?

'Good morning! How was your date?'

Kat jumped, spilling her coffee over the kitchen bench as Saskia's voice interrupted her morning routine. 'Jesus, Sas, you scared the life out of me.'

'Daydreaming about a cute actor, were you?'

'No,' Kat fibbed. 'And it wasn't a date.'

'Looked like one to me.'

'I was just there to meet some of the cast and crew,' she said as she mopped up the spilt coffee. But she couldn't help the blush she could feel creeping across her cheeks as Saskia's comment reminded her that she had promised Oliver a date. At least, in his words she had.

Saskia raised one eyebrow but didn't comment. She leant on the kitchen bench and sipped from her own mug that she'd brought in with her. Kat knew it would still be hot; Saskia hadn't come far. She and Dean lived next door.

Saskia and Dean, Roger and Maya, plus Kat's aunt and uncle all lived in the same street, with their underground houses dug into the same hill. As their family had expanded they had simply dug more rooms and added new entrances so they all had their own front door. Kat's own parents had dug a house in the same hill and she had moved back in with her father when she returned to Coober Pedy from Adelaide. She didn't mind living close to her family—she enjoyed the feeling of belonging—but sometimes the proximity could be disconcerting.

If the houses were viewed from outside, all that was obvious were the front doors and some windows. Gardens, or what passed for gardens in the arid country, were at the front, complete with barbecues or pizza ovens and outdoor seating areas used on the warm nights. The houses themselves extended back into the hill. Internally her father's house had white, lime-washed walls, which gave a welcome break from the perpetual sight of red earth. A few skylights and air vents protruded from the surface, but there was no way of telling how large the houses were from outside, and some were very large.

'When do you start work on the movie?' Saskia asked as she sat down at the kitchen table.

'I'm going out to the set this morning, but only to get a feel for filming. There are no stunts today.'

Saskia looked Kat up and down. 'Is that what you're wearing?'

Kat was wearing black three-quarter-length trousers and a loose camisole top. The clothes were comfortable and cool, perfect for the late autumn heatwave they were experiencing, but she could tell by Saskia's tone that she didn't approve. 'What's wrong with this?'

'Nothing, if you don't mind Oliver seeing you dressed like a homeless person.'

'I'm not dressing for him,' she said, even as she began to rethink her outfit.

'You're right. It probably doesn't matter. He probably

doesn't care what you're wearing—he's only interested in getting you out of your clothes.'

'Saskia!'

'How about you?' Saskia continued, ignoring Kat's exclamation. 'Are you interested? You'd have to be co-matose not to be.'

'He's not my type.'

'What? Drop-dead gorgeous isn't your type?'

Kat smiled but shook her head at the same time. 'He could have his pick of women—what would he want with a country girl like me? Even if he did set his sights on me, I'm not going to fall for him just because his pickings are limited out here.' How did she explain to Saskia that he made her nervous and that it was a mix-ture of excitement and uncertainty? She suspected he was far too experienced for her, and she didn't want Saskia to laugh at her by telling her so.

'I'm pretty sure he's already set his sights on you, and it wouldn't matter where you were, Kat, you'd get noticed. But if you think you can't handle him…' Saskia paused, waiting for a response, but when noth-ing was forthcoming she continued '…then you might as well go dressed as you are, or I could find you some-thing else to wear?'

Kat checked her make-up in her rear vision mirror. She wasn't wearing much as it was too hot and most of it would just slide off her face, but she touched up her signature red lipstick, telling herself she didn't want to look like a country cousin in comparison to the actors on set but not admitting that she was really driven by a desire to look good for Oliver. She felt a little silly that she'd let Saskia talk her into changing her outfit but she had to admit she did look more presentable, and that boosted her confidence. The white fitted top clung to her and showed just a few centimetres of tanned, toned midriff, and the black and white vertical-striped loose trousers hugged her hips before flaring out over the pair of low wedge sandals she'd added. She was only on set as an observer today—it was a chance to get a feel for how things worked before her attendance was officially required and, because there were no stunts scheduled for today, she didn't need to be in clothes that would have to withstand an emergency.

She was met by George's assistant, Erica, who escorted her to the make-up trailer.

Oliver winked at her as she stepped inside and Kat's nervousness about being on set was replaced by the nervous excitement that she felt every time she saw him. It had been a long time since anyone had paid her some attention and she couldn't deny she found it extremely flattering.

In Coober Pedy all the locals knew her and she didn't really interact with the tourists, except when they needed her medical expertise. She preferred to be at home when she wasn't at work, but that habit wasn't conducive to meeting people. She couldn't remember the last time someone had asked her out.

'All done.' The make-up artist removed the disposable collar that protected Oliver's costume and he stood up. He was wearing a space suit, dirty and torn, and his make-up made him look as though he'd been through an ordeal, lost on an alien planet. He hadn't shaved, and Kat assumed he was supposed to look dishevelled, thirsty, and possibly in pain, but, to her eyes, he looked unbelievably good. The fake dirt and dust made his eyes even more noticeable, a more vivid blue.

'What are you filming today?'

'Do you know the plot?'

'Not really. George gave me a little overview but not a script. I know it's a science fiction movie but I have to admit that's not really my thing. I like romantic comedies.'

'I'll have to remember that. OK, the plot in a nutshell: Earth has set up a space station, an air force base in the sky, the first line of defence against alien attack. One space station has been badly damaged and we are supposed to be evacuating and returning to Earth, but my "ship" is hit and crash-lands on another, previously undiscovered, planet. I have a dozen crew on board. Mechanics, scientists, astronauts, physicists, defence. I'm the commander, the most senior defence person on the ship. The planet has an atmosphere but it's thin. Low oxygen—a bit like high altitude. There are no trees, nothing green, it's a barren place, but gas readings indicate moisture and we think there could be water somewhere. I've gone off to scout.

'I crash my vehicle and damage the windshield, so I'm affected by exposure to the heat and by altitude sickness. I lose consciousness and when I wake up I find myself in a cave. We're going to use the caves you showed George—it's been added to the schedule. I don't remember crawling into the cave but I see drag marks in the dirt. It looks like someone dragged me in, and then I notice cave drawings—signs of alien life. The cave goes deeper into the earth and I go as far as I can without any light, and I'm sure I can smell water.

'The scene we're filming this morning is a few days

later; I'm feeling better and I've managed to fix the all-terrain vehicle. I still haven't seen any other life forms but in the film the audience knows I'm being watched by something, although they haven't seen anything yet either. I return to the spaceship, where I'm greeted very warmly by the leading lady, who thought I must have died.'

Oliver was smiling and Kat could imagine how that reunion scene was going to play out.

'That's Julia?'

'Yep,' he said as they reached the set. 'Grab a seat here,' he told her, indicating a chair next to George and handing her a pair of headphones so she could listen to the dialogue.

Filming began with Oliver arriving back at the spaceship. Julia's character saw the ATV approaching and came out of the spaceship to investigate.

The scene moved inside and Kat repositioned herself so that she could continue to watch on a screen.

Julia was playing a space soldier, Oliver's second-in-command. She had some medical training and had to attend to his injuries. She insisted that Oliver be quarantined and undergo a medical check-up. They were alone in the scene and Kat could feel herself blushing as Oliver's character stripped down to his underwear.

There were several screens in front of Kat, each showing a different angle. There was a wide shot and then close-ups of Julia and Oliver. Kat focused on the screen showing Oliver. She couldn't keep her eyes off him. He drew her in…the incredible colour of his eyes, the intense look on his face. She felt as if he was looking directly at her, even though she knew he wasn't.

She could see why he was such a star. He was gorgeous, charismatic.

The scene intensified. Julia's character leant towards Oliver and then they were kissing. Kat felt hot and flustered, unsure where to look. It felt voyeuristic but she couldn't look away. She wondered what it would be like to be Julia.

The scene had taken most of the morning to film and in between takes Oliver chatted to the cast and crew. Kat could see why women fell for him: he was nice to everyone. Finally, they broke for lunch and Oliver came and sat beside her. He had stripped off his costume and was wearing a pair of shorts and a T-shirt now, his character's persona discarded with his clothes.

'Are you OK? You're not bored?' he asked.

'Not at all. I'm used to sitting around, waiting. As a paramedic it's part of my job description; we're happy when things are quiet. And this is a far more interesting way to pass the time.' It was exciting. The whole experience was a novelty. She wasn't bored, far from it, although she was a little bit jealous. 'Julia seems to have recovered from her crisis of the other night,' she said.

'For now. Let's hope things have calmed down on that front, although I doubt it.'

'What happened?'

'Her husband had an affair. Julia didn't want to work on this movie, she didn't want to leave him alone, but she was contractually obligated, so she's not happy that she has to be here, so far away from home. I think George has promised to fly her husband out here but it remains to be seen if he'll turn up. This movie could save my reputation and end her marriage, so I understand why she's upset, but the less drama we have, the quicker filming is wrapped here and the sooner she can get home to the States.'

'She didn't look like she was missing her husband during those scenes.'

Oliver laughed. 'That's the idea. She's a good actress.'

'Are you sure that's all it is?'

'Are you jealous?'

'No,' she lied.

'Believe me, it's all acting. I may have a reputation of romancing my leading ladies but not the married ones, and I'm really trying to clean up my image. I don't need any rumours circulating. If she wants revenge I'm not the one who's going to oblige. I don't want to get into any arguments with irate husbands. I do have empathy for her, though; I've been cheated on before and it's not a good position to be in. It's bad enough going through something like that in private, but when your disastrous love-life gets splashed across the tabloids it makes you wary. I feel for her but I can't afford to make her problems mine—I've got enough of my own.'

Oliver picked up their plates and took them back to the serving counter, leaving Kat to wonder who cheated on him and why. Had it made him more careful about his affairs?

It didn't seem so if the tabloids were to be believed, but there were always two sides to a story. Maybe his romances were just casual, or for publicity. That would be one way to protect yourself from heartache. She wondered what it would be like not knowing who you could trust.

'Are you staying a bit longer?' he asked when he

returned. 'Do you want to watch more filming? The next scene involves some of the other characters, while I'm missing, presumed dead.'

'Do you always film out of sequence?' Kat asked; she hadn't imagined it happening like that.

'More often than not, I guess we do, but it depends on a lot of things.'

'Like what?'

'Weather and location mostly. Or sometimes if an actor has to lose or gain weight or change their hairstyle through the movie…that will affect the order. It also might depend on who is required for the scene, if we need a lot of extras, things like that; they might be brought in for a few days to do all their scenes. Then, of course, there are always retakes, which can be difficult to manage, particularly if we've got other filming commitments for other projects. Would you like to watch? Otherwise we could hang out in my trailer?'

'I thought you didn't want any rumours.'

'Rumours with you I don't have an issue with—you're single and over the age of eighteen,' he said with a smile.

'With protective relations who spend their days blowing things up for fun. Are you sure you want to take them on?'

'They blow things up for fun?'

'Yes, but it's legitimate. They're opal miners.'

'And they mine using explosives?'

'Sometimes.'

'OK, forewarned is forearmed, I guess. If you like I can show you the reels from the other day; you can see what the stunts look like and why the first-aid officer quit. No ulterior motive, I promise. I'll even leave the door open if it makes you feel more comfortable.'

'I can't believe you walked away without a scratch,' she said when she'd finished watching the footage. She had forced herself to concentrate but it had been difficult. They were sitting side by side on the couch, as it had the best view of the screen, but, while Oliver appeared relaxed, Kat was a bundle of nerves. She was super-aware of him beside her. She could feel him breathing, and every time he moved she braced herself in case he touched her. Each time he did her heart raced, her mouth went dry and her skin tingled.

'I had a few bruises and a headache but I'm fine.'

'Why on earth would you do your own stunts?'

'Because it's fun.'

'Don't you worry about getting hurt?'

'I've always loved testing my limits. My brother and I grew up in a house with very strict rules, thanks to our father, and I always enjoyed breaking them. I guess I thought of them more as recommendations.'

'What happened when you got caught?'

'We were punished, so I learnt the hard way to balance risk and reward. If I thought the risk wasn't worth the punishment I learnt to rein in my wild side. Stunts are calculated risks, mostly. The buzz I get from doing them outweighs the risk that something might go wrong. It's Chris's job, and yours, to keep me safe.'

'If Chris does his job right then you shouldn't need me,' she retorted. 'There's only so much I can do.'

Kat liked to follow the rules. She'd seen too many times the things that could go wrong when rules were broken.

There was a knock on the door and Oliver was summoned back to Make-Up and Wardrobe.

'We're filming a love scene this afternoon, so the set is closed,' he told her, 'but if you're free later, why don't you come back for dinner? I'm helping out on the grill.'

'I have an ambulance shift tonight.' She could have left it at that—he didn't know how things worked around here—but she found herself elaborating. 'But I can be on call. I'll let Dave know where I am and he can call me in if he needs me.'

'Are you sure? I don't want to be held responsible if you're needed.'

'Positive. As long as I'm contactable it's fine.'

She had intended to heed George's warning and resist Oliver's charms, but it was harder than she'd anticipated. It was one thing to tell herself that she could resist him when she was home alone, but quite another when he greeted her with a big smile and laughter in his blue eyes. He was charming and irresistible and she suspected it was only a matter of time before he would win her over.

CHAPTER THREE

KAT PUSHED OPEN the door to the police station and squeezed herself inside. It looked as if the whole town had come running when the cry for help had gone out, and the small station was bursting at the seams. She'd been getting ready to go back to the film set for dinner when she'd received a call telling her that a missing person report had come in. She had called Oliver with her apologies and headed for the station. Unfortunately, a missing backpacker trumped her other plans. She searched the crowd for her cousins, knowing they would be in the thick of the action, as she wondered if she'd get another dinner date. No, not a date, she reminded herself, an invitation.

She'd just spotted her cousins when she heard someone calling her name. She turned around to find Oliver coming through the door behind her.

'Oliver! What are you doing here?'

'Well, I thought your excuse was either the best rejection I'd ever received, or if it was true we figured you could use some help.'

'We?'

Kat looked at the men filing in behind him and saw

that Oliver had brought Chris and some of the crew with him.

'Someone has gone missing?' he asked.

'Pietro Riccardo, an Italian backpacker, has been reported missing by his girlfriend. He went noodling—fossicking for opal,' Kat clarified when she saw several confused expressions, 'on his own. The girlfriend didn't go with him because she had a headache, and Pietro hasn't come back. There's a public noodling area in the centre of town but he's not there. The police have called the hotels, bars, pubs and clubs, thinking he might have just stopped for a drink, but he's not at any of those either. We have to start spreading the search.'

'Is there something we can do? Can we help?'

'If you'd like to, thank you. I'll see if I can get you assigned to my search party.'

'You're searching? You're not taking the ambulance?'

Kat shook her head. 'The crew who were already on shift will stay at the station. We don't know which way Pietro's gone, so there's no point sending the ambulance off in one direction, only for them to have to turn around and head a different way. We'll split up into search parties, and the search will be coordinated by the Coober Pedy mine rescue team.'

'You're telling me this happens often enough that you have an official search and rescue unit?'

'Yes. There are enough accidents on the mines with both miners and locals that we are needed fairly often.' Kat and her cousins were all members of the team. 'We're assuming the missing backpacker is injured, which is why he hasn't returned of his own accord, but there's also a high possibility that he's fallen down a disused mine shaft.'

'Are there really exposed mine shafts around here?'

'Of course. There are thousands of them. You've seen the warning signs, haven't you?'

'The signs that say "Don't Run", "Deep Shafts", "Don't Walk Backwards"?'

'Yes.'

'Those signs are serious? They're not just for the tourists to take selfies with?'

'They're definitely serious. We're not on a movie set; this is real.'

Oliver frowned. 'And just how often do people fall down mine shafts?'

'More often than you'd think and far more often than we'd like. You were told to watch where you walk around town, weren't you?'

'Yes. But I didn't really think about why.'

'Luckily for you most of the shafts in town have been covered over. It's just once you get out of town you need to be careful. People have gone missing and never been found. It's presumed they're down a hole somewhere. It's a perfect way to get away with murder.'

'You're kidding.'

'I'm not actually, but don't worry, that doesn't happen as much now. It's not the wild west it once was out here. People are a little more law-abiding.'

'OK, let me get this straight. We're going to be wandering around, in the dark, looking down old mine shafts.'

'He could be anywhere, and he might not be down a mine shaft, but if you're worried, no one will mind if you back out.'

'I'm not backing out. I offered to help and unless I'm going to be in the way I'm happy to be another pair of eyes.'

'The more people we have searching the better. Pietro didn't take his car, which is good and bad. Bad because we can't search for the car, which would be easier to find, good because it means he needs to be within walking distance of town, but bad again because we don't know in which direction he's gone and his mobile phone either isn't on, is flat or is out of service range.' She broke off as she was approached. 'Hey, Dave. Oliver, this is Dave Reed, another paramedic. Dave, this is Oliver Harding; he and some of the cast and crew from the movie have offered to help search.'

'Good to meet you; appreciate the help.' Dave was his normal, relaxed self; good in a crisis, he was one of Kat's favourite colleagues. They had been rostered on together for the night shift until the missing-person report changed their plans. Dave and Oliver shook hands as the crowd was silenced so instructions could be given.

They were spilt into search parties to head out of town in all directions. Kat took Oliver with her and they joined Dean and Roger. She was glad to be in the same search party as her cousins, not only because of their search and rescue skills but also because they were experienced miners who were fit and strong, but she was a little concerned about whether they would see Oliver as a valuable asset or as a liability. She'd been aware of them watching her as she'd spoken with Oliver and she hoped they didn't make him uncomfortable. As far as she was concerned, he was welcome to join them, and she didn't need her cousins to run interference on her behalf.

They collected their torches and Dave also handed Kat a backpack full of supplies that he had collected from the ambulance station on his way.

'What about tracker dogs?' Oliver asked after he'd offered to carry Kat's backpack and hoisted it onto his shoulders.

'The police force doesn't have tracker dogs, and the Aboriginal trackers we do have said the ground is too dry and there are too many prints in town to follow. If they knew which direction Pietro went in then maybe they'd have a chance, but,' she shrugged, 'we'll just have to walk and hope.'

Their group headed south, walking in a long line, side by side. They were supposed to spread out, swinging their lights in an arc several metres to either side of them, but Oliver kept bunching up, walking nearer to Kat, staying close to her. She wasn't sure if it was deliberate or if he wasn't aware that he was doing it, but she was very aware. He was quiet, there were no jokes, no banter, so he appeared to be taking this seriously, but she was still super-conscious of him.

The desert night was quiet and still, the air clear and cold. The sun had long since set, taking the heat of the day with it. The search party continued their slow and steady pace, taking it in turns to call Pietro's name.

'Are you sure his girlfriend was at the hostel?' Oliver asked after several minutes of silence. 'They didn't have an argument and she saw an opportunity to get rid of him?'

Kat laughed. 'I don't think she's a suspect and I think you've got an overactive imagination!'

'Maybe I've read too many movie scripts, but there's always a twist in the tale.'

They were into the second hour of the search, when Pietro was finally located, injured but alive, at the bottom of a disused mine shaft.

Oliver sat on a rock in a desert in the middle of South Australia and listened to the experienced rescuers plan Pietro's extraction from the mine shaft. There were literally thousands of mine shafts, as Kat had told him, and he'd thought it was an impossible task to find someone who could have fallen into one, so had been amazed when Pietro had actually been tracked down. The whole situation was surreal.

He listened to Pietro's apologies echoing up from the shaft. Oliver felt for the guy. He sounded embarrassed. It turned out he was a doctor, in Australia on a three-month holiday before he was due to return to Italy to start his surgical residency. He was mortified that he had sustained an injury and needed rescuing, but Oliver thought he should be grateful that he'd been found, that the people of Coober Pedy knew what to do.

But even Oliver couldn't believe what he heard next. What those same people were planning on doing. Or, more to the point, who was going to be doing it. He stood up and approached Kat, forgetting in his consternation that he probably should stay out of the way and that this retrieval had nothing to do with him.

'What are you doing?' he asked. 'You're not going down there?' The shaft was pitch black, the opening narrow, maybe only three feet wide, but the drop to the bottom was deep. When they had shone their torches down hundreds of these while looking for Pietro, Oliver had got the impression that this was what the mines looked like until Kat had explained that a lot of these narrow shafts were from exploratory drilling. If opal traces, or anything that had potential, was found the miners would excavate further. They might go down the hole for a look but most of the mines were now open cut using big machines. But it seemed as though Kat was about to descend into this darkness.

'Of course I am,' Kat replied. 'Someone has to. That shaft is over thirty feet deep. He says he's broken his ankle but he could have sustained more serious injuries. He needs to be assessed and then he needs to be brought up to the surface, which means he needs a harness. Someone has to attach that to him. There's not much room, and I'm the only one with the right experience who will fit.'

'Is it safe? It won't collapse?'

'It's sandstone. The same rock we build our houses with. It's safe enough. You don't need to worry—I've done this before. It's no more dangerous than when you do your own stunt work. Probably safer. You're not worried because I'm a woman, are you?'

'No, of course not. I work with stunt women all the time, and I know they're as capable as men.' But he was worried because it was Kat.

'I'm trained for this. I'll be fine,' she told him as she stepped into a harness.

Oliver watched, his heart in his mouth, as Kat's cousin Roger checked the harness. He had to trust that Kat knew what she was doing but that didn't mean he had to like it. He didn't want anything to happen to her before he got a chance to know her better. He had never met anyone like her and the more time they spent together the more fascinating he found her. She looked like a supermodel but seemed completely unaware of how stunning she was. She was smart and sexy but with an unusual air of innocence. He knew he had to be careful. She didn't seem as wise in the ways of the world as the women he normally mixed with, and he'd seen how her cousins kept one eye on her at all times—which meant they had one eye on him too tonight, which, he had to admit, made him a little uncomfortable, but he was respectful, and despite what the tabloids said about him that had always been his way.

A winch on the front of the four-by-four police vehicle lowered Kat into the hole. Oliver didn't think he breathed once until, after what seemed like a lifetime, she finally emerged again. With Pietro strapped to her.

Oliver wanted to rush over to her to make sure she was OK but this was not about the two of them and this time he forced himself to wait in the background as Kat, Dave and the other paramedics, who had arrived with the ambulance, attended to their patient. He felt like a teenage schoolboy longing to be noticed, but he was prepared to wait.

Eventually, as Pietro was being loaded into the ambulance, Kat came over to him. 'I'm sorry, I have to go. Pietro's English is good but his Italian is better. I speak Italian,' she said with a shrug, 'so I've offered to go with him to the hospital.'

'Of course.' Oliver didn't have any expectations that they'd get time together tonight; he realised that her job came first. Much like his. He couldn't object to that.

'Thank you for your help. I'm sorry I couldn't make it to dinner.'

'That's OK. I've got tomorrow off. If you're free we could reschedule till then.'

She hesitated and he prepared himself for the brush-off, but she surprised him when she said, 'I'd like that. But, assuming the rest of my shift is quiet, why don't I pick you up in the morning? I have a place I'd like you to see. Can you be ready early? Say, eight o'clock?'

Saskia was ready and waiting when the ambulance pulled up at the hospital.

'This is Pietro Riccardo...'

Kat pushed the stretcher through the emergency doors as she listened to Dave's summary of Pietro's suspected injuries, most of which Saskia knew from the phone call they'd made en route, and then the summary of treatment so far.

'Put him in the first cubicle. Damien is already here; we'll get him sorted,' Saskia told them, before turning her attention to the patient. 'Hello, Pietro, my name is Saskia.'

'Italian is his first language,' Kat told her before translating for Pietro. 'Saskia is a nurse and this is our doctor, Damien,' Kat continued the introductions as they wheeled Pietro into a treatment bay. 'They're going to do a more thorough assessment and I'll stay to translate if you need me to, OK?'

'*Grazie.*'

'Are you in pain?'

Pietro was still clutching the little green Penthrax whistle but he shook his head.

Despite the pain relief he seemed quite capable of following the proceedings and understanding what Damien and Saskia were saying—perhaps due to his medical training the English words didn't sound too unfamiliar—but Kat stayed with him until he was taken for X-rays.

He was lucky. He had a fracture dislocation of his left ankle which needed surgery and a suspected ligament tear in his right shoulder, but he'd escaped more serious injury.

'I want him to have some detailed scans of his lower back, head and right shoulder, but I think he's been relatively fortunate,' Damien said as he reviewed the plain X-rays, which was all they were equipped to take at the Coober Pedy hospital. 'We'll need to call the flying doctor and get him transferred to Adelaide. Is he travelling with someone?'

'His girlfriend,' Kat said. 'She should be here—someone was going to collect her from the backpackers' hostel.'

Kat explained what was happening to Pietro while Saskia got him comfortable, and then she and Kat left him dozing while they waited for the retrieval team.

'So, I hear Oliver helped with the search,' Saskia said as she made them coffee.

'How did—?' Kat began to ask before realising she already knew the answer. 'Dean told you.'

Saskia just grinned in reply.

'What else did he say?'

'Nothing much.'

Kat knew that wouldn't be true. 'C'mon, Sas, Dean always has an opinion about any man in my life.'

She knew she'd made a mistake as soon as she'd finished the sentence and if she'd hoped Saskia had missed it she was out of luck.

Saskia almost spat out her coffee. 'I knew it! You

like him. Not that anyone could blame you—there's a reason Oliver Harding has been voted the world's sexiest man. Twice.'

'I said *any* man.'

'You say tomato…' Saskia was still grinning. 'Dean said that Oliver couldn't keep his eyes off you.'

'He said that?' Kat felt a warm glow.

'Mmm-hmm.' Saskia considered her. 'So, you like him.' It wasn't a question.

'I do. But—'

'No buts—'

'But you know how people talk in this town.'

'You worry too much about what people think. Besides, you're twenty-seven, you're a grown woman, you're your own boss.'

'That's not exactly true. You know what it's like when you've grown up here—everyone has an opinion on how you live your life.'

'Well, all I'm saying is that he seems keen and it would be a shame to let this opportunity go to waste. If it's not you spending time with him, it will be someone else. Is that what you want?'

No. She didn't want that.

'You don't have to marry the guy,' Saskia continued. 'Don't overthink things, just have some fun. Oliver looks like he knows how to have fun. How long is he here for?'

'Only a few weeks.'

'If you're worried about what people think I'm sure you could manage to be discreet for that long. Treat it like a holiday romance.'

'I'm not looking for a holiday romance. I'm looking for the person I'm going to spend the rest of my life with. What's the point of starting something that can go nowhere?'

'Are you kidding? The point is there's a man in town who has literally been voted the sexiest man alive and who seems to have taken a fancy to you. You've been bemoaning the lack of men here for months. Are you seriously telling me you'd pass up this opportunity? With a man who looks like he does? You must be crazy.'

She wasn't crazy but she was scared. Scared she wouldn't be able to control things. He had awakened her senses, he was making her feel things she hadn't felt in a long time. He made her laugh. He made her nervous. Excited. Happy. She liked him, really liked him, but she was worried things would get complicated. Coober Pedy was a small town. How could she expect to have fun without everyone else knowing her business? Could she keep him separate from her everyday life? She didn't need to be the centre of town gossip or to have any interference from her family.

Had she made a mistake by asking him to spend the day with her tomorrow?

Maybe she had, but she didn't want to change her mind. She had planned to take him away from town; she wanted to show him the wildness and beauty of her world. She could still do that. She had the perfect spot in mind. A place where she doubted they would see another soul.

Oliver was waiting in front of the hotel when Kat turned off the main street and climbed out of her dusty four-by-four. She was wearing a T-shirt and a pair of very short denim cut-offs. She looked amazing, but that wasn't enough to keep his attention. He was completely distracted by the canoe that was strapped to the roof of her car.

'Now I think I've seen everything,' he said as he kissed her cheek. She smelt of soap and sunshine. 'What on earth have you got planned for us? I thought we only had a few hours.'

'We do.'

'So the canoe is just for show?'

'You'll have to wait and see. Did you get my message?' she said as she looked him over. 'Did you bring something to swim in?'

'I did. But you have me intrigued. A canoe and a bathing suit. I flew into Coober Pedy and I don't remember seeing any water for about four hundred miles.'

'You weren't looking in the right places,' she said as they got into the car and slammed the doors. 'The name Coober Pedy means boys' waterhole.'

'Does it? I was told it meant white man in a hole.'

'That's sort of true. In the local Aboriginal culture a boy is a male who hasn't been through an initiation ceremony. There was a waterhole for those boys near here. The Pitjantjatjara word for white man is the same as for boy, as neither of them have been initiated, so some people translated it as "white man's waterhole" as opposed to "boy's water hole", and somewhere along the line it became "white man in a hole".'

They headed east out of town, past the never-ending mullock heaps that dotted the landscape—piles of dirt that had been dug out of the earth in the quest for opal—past numerous damaged, abandoned cars and dead animals that were decaying on the side of the road.

'The two often go hand in hand,' Kat said when Oliver commented on the roadside carnage. 'People don't drive according to the conditions. You shouldn't really drive at night out here if it can be avoided. Cattle, emus, kangaroos, even wombats can do a lot of damage to your car if you hit one of them, particularly at speed. We have a high number of fatal accidents.'

'But why don't the cars get towed?'

'Most do eventually,' she said as they drove past a utility vehicle that was crumpled, bonnet compacted, windscreen smashed. Black skid marks could be seen across the road. 'That one was recent. Just a couple of weeks ago. The teenage driver swerved to avoid a cow, lost control and rolled the car.'

'Were you here?'

She nodded. 'Dave and I were on shift.'

'Was everyone all right?' he asked as he kept his eyes on the wreck.

'No. There was a fatality. A boy had been riding in the tray of the ute—he was thrown out and died at the scene. Another was in a critical condition and was evacuated by the flying doctor, and two more were taken to the local hospital.'

'I can't imagine doing your job. It must be tough. How do you cope with it?'

'It's a rewarding job. I like feeling as though I'm making a difference. Even with that accident, the fatality was dreadful, a terrible waste of a young life, but Dave and I managed to keep the other boy alive until the flying doctor got here. I've seen so many accidents like this, so you take the good with the bad, but it's why I like to follow the rules, not break them. Life isn't something that should be taken for granted.'

He remembered her comment about him doing his own stunts and wondered if she would accuse him of taking life for granted. He didn't take it for granted but he did think that life was for living and he wasn't going to sit around and watch other people living their lives. He wanted to be a participant.

Kat slowed her car and turned off the road onto a smaller dirt track. The faded signpost read *Lake Cadibarrawirracanna*.

'There's a lake out here?'

Kat nodded. 'A salt lake.'

'Does the name have a meaning?'

'It does. It means *stars dancing on the water.*'

'It sounds beautiful,' he said, although he didn't think it actually would be. He couldn't picture a lake in this barren landscape. Not even his active imagination could envision that.

'It is. I wanted you to see the beauty in the desert. You just need fresh eyes.'

'Wow.' They crested a small rise and Oliver was stunned at the sight of a vast lake, shimmering silver in the sun, before them. It stretched for miles across the flat landscape, a few trees clinging to its edges. A flock of birds rose off the water and took to the sky, startled by the sound of the engine, but other than that there was nothing else but land, water and sky. Now that the birds had flown he couldn't see another living thing except for him and Kat.

Kat parked in the shade of a stand of trees and he helped her lift the two-man canoe from the roof of the car.

'Do you want to take the canoe out on the lake?' she asked as she passed him a blanket and some cushions from the back of the car.

Oliver spread the blanket on the sand. He didn't want to paddle just now. He wanted to just sit and take in the view. And Kat.

'Later, I think. I can't remember the last time I sat and did nothing. I'm usually doing a movie, learning lines for a movie, doing publicity, interviews, going to red carpet events.'

'Or going to parties.'

Something in her tone put him on alert. 'Have you been reading about me?'

'A little,' she admitted.

'Don't believe everything you read.'

'George told me the same thing. That's why I thought I'd ask you; you can tell me what was and wasn't true.'

'Such as?' he asked, although he was pretty sure he knew what she would have read and what subject she would be interested in.

'Did a girl overdose and die at a party at your house? Is that true?'

'Yes.' He wasn't surprised by her question, that story was currently the first thing that popped up if someone did an internet search on his name.

'What happened?'

'I'm not one hundred per cent sure. I was away; I was in New Orleans working on a film and had friends staying in my house. They held a party. From what the police told me the girl who overdosed allegedly brought the drugs with her, something went wrong and she died.'

'You weren't there?'

'No, but it was my house, so I was linked by association. My publicist and agent thought it would be a good idea to keep me out of Hollywood for a bit longer while it was investigated so they sent me here. I thought it was probably a good idea too but this time I haven't left any friends staying there. I used to host a lot of parties, but I'm rethinking that scene now. I'm going to make some changes to my lifestyle when I get home. This trip down under will give me a chance to reset.' He stood up; he didn't want to talk about his old life any longer, and he was telling the truth when he said he was thinking about making changes. It was time to start behaving more responsibly. He was thirty-two years old; he couldn't continue his partying ways for ever. 'How about that paddle now?'

They worked up an appetite taking the canoe out on the lake, but Kat had anticipated that and had packed a picnic.

'Where did you get all of this on a Sunday morning?' Oliver asked as she unpacked cold meats and fruit from an ice box.

'I raided the pantry. My family is Italian. Someone is always in the kitchen making something or preserving something. I have my father's salami, my aunt Rosa's sun-dried tomatoes, my cousin's wife's bread,' she said as she handed him a loaf of bread.

'This bread smells fresh—surely that wasn't in the pantry?'

'No, Maya, that's Roger's wife, made it this morning. She lives next door.'

'Next door?'

'Yes. My whole family lives in the same street. In the same hill.'

'That sounds a bit close for comfort.'

Kat shrugged. 'It's how it's always been.'

'I'd love to see inside an underground house.'

She was tempted to invite him to hers but there was bound to be someone around. If not her father, it would be her aunt or cousins. 'It's not so different to your hotel. We have front doors, front windows, electricity, running water. It's just on a smaller scale than the hotel.'

'What happens if you're claustrophobic?'

'I don't know. It doesn't bother me. The rooms are light and ventilated. We have skylights and air vents. You must have noticed all the metal shafts poking up out of the hills in town. Those are ventilation shafts. They're wrapped with wire to stop the snakes entering through them.'

'And it's safe? The houses don't collapse?'

'The rock around here is sandstone, and it's very stable—we can excavate large spaces without needing structural support. We've got some enormous underground spaces in town. The Serbian church and a couple of the museums are massive. If you want to see a house, Faye's is open to tourists.'

'You're not going to invite me over?'

'It's not my house. It's my father's.'

'You still live with your parents?'

She felt the familiar pang at the mention of parents. 'I live with my father,' she clarified. 'My mother died a few years ago.'

'I'm sorry, Kat. How old were you?'

'Twenty-two. She was killed in a car accident.'

'Out here?'

She nodded. The memories were still painful. Her feelings of guilt still high. 'A bus had been sitting behind a truck, trying to overtake, the driver got impatient and pulled out over double white lines to have a look, and my mother was driving in the opposite direction. He smashed into my mother's car. It was his fault, he didn't obey the road rules, but he survived, while my mother died at the scene.

'I came back here after she died to be with my dad. And I'm still here. I am the single daughter of an Italian father. We don't move out until we get married.' Her family owned a lot of land and the only thing that would change when she married was that her father and uncle and cousins would dig her a house next to the rest of them, but Oliver had sounded so shocked she didn't think he needed to hear that too.

'How old were you when you left home?' she asked. Oliver was watching her closely and she wondered if he was going to let her change the subject. She hoped so; she didn't want to talk about her mother, she didn't want to be sad. She breathed a sigh of relief as Oliver followed her lead.

'I went to college in California when I was seventeen. My parents were in Japan.'

'You went to college? To study acting?'

'Actually, no. I went to law school. Acting wasn't considered a career and one of my father's sons was always expected to go into the defence force. My brother refused, so that left me. I had no intention of joining the force either so I enrolled in law school under the pretence that I could join the armed forces that way. But once I got to college, I realised I had visions of myself as a lawyer standing in front of a court room arguing cases. Performing, I suppose. Much like what you see in the movies. *That's* what I wanted to do. So I joined the drama clubs and I found I had a talent for it, so then I started auditioning for movie roles and when I got my first one I dropped out of law school. My father has barely spoken to me since.'

'Because you didn't join the army?'

'Because I am a disappointment and he disapproves of my career choice. Because I chose acting over fighting.'

'And what about your mother? What did she think?'

'My mother is the daughter of an army general and now a wife of an army general. She followed orders.'

'What?'

'Orders *might* be the wrong word,' Oliver said, but to Kat's ears it sounded as if it was exactly what he meant, 'but she certainly never questioned Dad's decisions. Never argued. I can't say that I blame her. Isaac and I learnt that lesson early on too. The moment we were old enough we left home. It was the only way we could do what we wanted. Our mother didn't have that option.'

'How often do you see your parents?'

'I don't visit. I speak to my mother when my father's not around. She believes her loyalty is to her husband, but I think she's happy if I'm happy.'

'And are you happy?' Kat couldn't imagine being happy without her family.

'Yes. I get to experience all kinds of things; I travel the world pretending to be other people and giving people an escape from their everyday lives, from the world. I'm having fun.'

'So, what's next for you, after this movie?'

'I would love to have a role in a musical. I've done comedy, action, romantic leads, but I'd love an opportunity to try something new. I'd be the next Hugh Jackman if I could. You know, he started on the stage in musicals.'

'Can you sing?'

'Not well.'

'Dance?'

'Not as well as I sing,' he laughed. 'But dancing I can learn. Growing up, I wasn't allowed to have dancing lessons. It wasn't something boys did. Of course the more I was told I couldn't do something the more I wanted to. Would you like to come dancing with me?'

'In Coober Pedy? There aren't a lot of places to dance around here.'

'All you need is some music and a willing partner. Actually, music is optional. We could dance right now if you wanted to.'

Kat had learnt by now that Oliver didn't take anything seriously. His life was all about fun. In comparison, she took *everything* seriously.

He was making her nervous. Not in a bad way, but she was worried that he was going to convince her to dance and she didn't think she'd be able to handle that. She knew being in his arms would be her undoing.

She stood up.

'Are we going to dance?' he asked.

She shook her head and reached for the ice box. 'No, we need to get going. I've got to get back—I'm going to my cousin's for dinner.' She tidied up the remains of their picnic, picked up their glasses and packed them away.

'The one who lives next door?'

'Yes.'

'You're having dinner together again?'

'It's kind of a weekly ritual.'

'Really? Wouldn't you rather stay here with me?' He was standing now too. He lifted her hair and tucked it over her shoulder. His fingers skimmed her flesh, making it hum where he touched her. He was standing close and his eyes were mesmerising. He was engaging, funny, charming and incredibly good-looking, and Kat was tempted but she didn't give in.

'I'm expected there.'

'And do you always do what's expected?'

'Pretty much.' Following the rules and doing what was expected was part of her personality, but circumstances had also influenced her behaviour. She'd seen death and disaster first hand, and growing up in such a harsh environment had tainted her perceptions of what she could get away with.

'That's a pity. We could have fun.'

She'd forgotten what it was like to have fun. To have dreams.

'You're blushing,' he said. 'Do you think I'm flirting with you?

Kat didn't reply. She couldn't. Oliver was standing so close, with his hand on her arm, and his proximity stripped her of the capability of speech.

'You should,' he added. 'I am.' He grinned, his slow smile stretching from one corner of his gorgeous mouth to the other.

'Why on earth would you want to flirt with me?'

'Because you are incredibly beautiful.'

She laughed. She wanted to believe him but she

couldn't. 'You must have met hundreds of women who are more beautiful than me.'

'I can honestly say I haven't met one as beautiful as you who hasn't had any help. So either you have an amazing surgeon and I am a blind fool or you are naturally stunning.'

'I am ordinary.'

'I disagree. You are beautiful and interesting. A little mysterious. It's like finding a pearl or a diamond out of place. A thing of beauty in a hostile environment.'

'I think I'm more like an opal. Tough and at home in the outback.'

'Perhaps, but that definitely makes you unique, which makes you more interesting. At least to me. My father moved us around the world when I was growing up and for the past twelve years I've continued to travel in the world of showbiz, but I don't get to meet many people like you. You fascinate me. Your background, the career you've chosen, the fact that you look so unexpected out here and yet you seem so comfortable. Content. Everyone I meet is competing for something—the next part, the next girl, the next dollar. You're refreshing.'

'And you are a flatterer.'

'Is it working?'

Yes, she thought, but that's not what she said. 'Not yet. You'll have to try a bit harder. I'm not that sort of girl.'

She suspected that, where Oliver was concerned, she might be exactly that type of girl, but she would make him work just a little bit harder. It wouldn't do him any harm.

He bent his head, brushing his lips over her ear, and

she almost gave in then and there. Could he feel it? she wondered. Could he feel her self-control slipping?

'Well, I'm not going to give up and, to be fair, I have warned you, the more I'm told I can't have something, the more I want it.'

He was teasing her, testing her, and she knew she would eventually give in. She didn't have a hope in hell of resisting him for ever.

CHAPTER FOUR

KAT WAS ON set early for her first official day of duty. The sun was still rising in the east and the morning light streaked the sky with pink and gold and turned the earth a muted red. The landscape looked as though it had been touched up by an artist's brush using all the colours of an Aboriginal painting—ochre, gold, crimson, scarlet and the pink of a galah's feathers. The view was incredible and Kat hoped the colours would be captured on screen.

She sat on a chair behind George. She could see Oliver on two different screens over the director's shoulder but, looking across the flat planes of the earth, she could also see him standing on top of the hill, waiting for his cue.

Her mind drifted as she waited for filming to begin. Once again, she found her thoughts returning to the day they'd spent together at the lake. She had been pleasantly surprised about what a good time she'd had. They had flirted and laughed but, more importantly, they had talked and talked. She had shared things with him that she hadn't talked about in a long time, things she had never talked to anyone except Saskia about. And Oliver had listened.

Kat was beginning to think that maybe they could have a relationship that had some substance to it. There was definitely an attraction between them and they shared a sense of humour, but was that enough to overcome the differences she also knew they had? He was worldly, charming, independent and liked to push the boundaries. She was sheltered, sensible, a nurturer and a rule-follower. He might think she was refreshing but she suspected he might soon be bored. She suspected that, in reality, she was too vanilla for him.

'Action.'

The command came through the headset she was wearing and jolted her back to the present.

She saw Oliver start walking. The land was dry, the earth hard-packed, but Oliver's feet were sinking into sand. She knew George wanted the effect of soft ground making it arduous going for Oliver's character, and the prop crew had added a deep layer of fine red sand to the hill, reminding Kat that, in Oliver's world, nothing was really as it seemed.

The camera zoomed in and Kat switched her attention to the screen. She couldn't look away as the camera focused in on Oliver's face. His blue eyes were electric against the rose gold of the sky.

He continued to trudge across the ground and she could see him scanning the horizon and then, suddenly, he disappeared from the screen.

Kat heard her sharp intake of breath and flicked her gaze back to the hill. Oliver was tumbling down, head first.

She knew this was a stunt but it looked so real. She saw Oliver bouncing off the ground and wondered if, or hoped, he was wearing protective padding. It looked dangerous. And painful. She didn't want to watch but she couldn't look away.

Her whole body was tense. Her hands were clenched into tight fists and she couldn't breathe. The whole stunt probably lasted twenty seconds but it felt like a lifetime before Oliver finally hit the bottom of the hill, landing with a thud. Kat imagined she could feel the air being forced out of his lungs.

She waited, still holding her breath, for him to get up. For him to move.

The set was quiet.

No one moved. No one spoke.

What were they waiting for?

Kat didn't know but one thing she did know was that Oliver still hadn't moved. Surely he should be up by now?

He must be hurt.

Winded. Injured. Unconscious.

He could be any of those things.

Her instincts kicked in. She leapt off her chair and dropped the headset onto the seat. She grabbed her backpack, which was at her feet, and took off across the red sand, sprinting as fast as she could over the stony ground, hoping someone would think to grab her heavier, second bag of equipment.

'Cut!'

She was halfway across the site when she heard George's direction. Were they still filming? Had she just ruined the scene? Was this all part of the action?

She didn't break stride. It was too bad if she'd ruined it. She didn't care. It would be much worse if their star was injured and she left him lying on the ground.

She was going to do her job and she wasn't going to let anyone stop her.

She reached Oliver's side.

He still hadn't moved.

His eyes were closed but she could see his chest rising and falling. As she dropped her backpack in the dust and knelt beside him, he opened his eyes.

She looked into his piercing blue eyes. Was one pupil slightly more dilated than the other?

She placed one hand on his chest. 'Don't move.'

Kat's face swam into focus.

The first thing he noticed were her red lips. The rest of her was a little fuzzy around the edges. Maybe he was hurt worse than he thought.

'Are they still filming?' he asked.

'What?'

'Are they still filming? I'm supposed to get up and keep moving.' At least, that was what he thought he was supposed to do. His mind was a little hazy.

'They're not filming but you're not getting up until I've checked you out. You've just fallen down a hill and got the wind knocked out of you.'

'I was supposed to fall down the hill. It's called acting.'

He could see George and some of the crew approaching. He felt bruised and sore but there was no way he was going to lie meekly on the ground. It was time to get up. Kat's hand was on his chest, keeping him on the ground. He could stand if he wanted to—she wasn't putting any pressure on him, just a warning hold.

He lifted his head and felt the earth spin a little. There was a sharp, stabbing pain in his left side as he sat up and he struggled not to wince, hoping Kat didn't notice.

'Oliver! You're obviously hurt—lie down and let me check you out. What am I doing here if you're not going to listen to me?' It seemed she hadn't missed the grimace.

She insisted that he stay down while she examined him. She was obviously annoyed with him; he thought she was poking and prodding him a bit harder than was necessary. She made him breathe deeply, move his limbs and head this way and that. He managed to do everything she asked, albeit with some discomfort, but he was sure he wasn't badly injured.

Kat seemed to have a different opinion. 'I think you might have cracked a rib. You should go to the hospital for precautionary X-rays.'

'Is that really necessary, Kat?' George asked. 'Isn't there something you could do for him here? We're behind on filming already.'

'He's not in any condition to film any stunts until he gets checked,' Kat argued.

'What if I shuffle scenes so there is no more stunt work today? You can stay and supervise. If you think we're putting his health at risk I'll let you take him off for X-rays. But if he's managing he can have X-rays at the end of the day.'

'There's no crepitus, just tenderness and pain on inhalation.'

'I have no idea what that means.'

'I'm thinking out loud,' Kat said. 'It means that with strapping, some pain relief and anti-inflammatory medication he might be OK. Give me twenty minutes now—that's enough time for oral pain relief to kick in—and then we'll reassess.'

Oliver was able to strip his costume off with some assistance. His ribs were painful but he was determined not to give Kat any reason to cart him off to hospital. Once again he was semi-naked and being attended to, but this time it was Kat, not Julia, assessing his injuries. Unfortunately they were in a tent in the middle of the desert, surrounded by dozens of crew, and his injuries were real, which put a bit of a dampener on things.

Kat strapped his ribs and he managed to work through the rest of the day. He was stiff and sore as the day wore on but he didn't quit. Kat had watched him like a hawk and the moment they wrapped for the day she bundled him off to the hospital.

'Hello again, Oliver. This is a pleasant surprise.'

He recognised Saskia as he and Kat stepped through the doors into Emergency. 'I didn't realise you were a nurse,' he said, his hopes that he could talk his way out of an examination evaporating. He knew he wouldn't be able to convince both Kat and Saskia that he was fine.

He suffered through more tests with the doctor before he was sent for X-rays.

'You have a mild concussion,' he was informed. That made two this week, Oliver thought, but he kept that information to himself. 'But there's no apparent fracture,' Damien said when the X-rays were developed. 'That doesn't mean you can't have a small crack somewhere that's just not showing up, but there's no major skeletal damage. Just soft tissue—a sprain, some swelling and bruising. Ice packs, some pain relief and some anti-inflammatory meds should do the trick. Rest tonight and then movement as comfortable.'

'I can go back to work?'

Damien nodded.

'What about monitoring the concussion? He's staying at the Cave Hotel,' Saskia asked before looking knowingly at Kat and adding, 'Alone. Shouldn't he have some supervision?'

'You haven't got any nausea? Haven't vomited?' Damien asked.

'No,' Oliver replied. He wasn't going to consent to supervision or to being admitted to hospital. He had a dull headache but he wasn't going to jeopardise the movie or his career by appearing incapacitated. Besides, his vision had cleared.

'I'm not sure we can justify a bed,' Damien said, 'But if you feel unwell either come back in or call 000. That's the emergency number.'

'000 will just call Kat,' Saskia told him as Damien left them.

'That doesn't sound like a bad compromise.'

'No, it won't get me,' Kat said. 'I'm not working tonight.'

'Even better,' Saskia replied. 'Why don't you take Oliver with you now, Kat? You don't have anything else to do, do you? And that way you can keep an eye on him. Make sure he's OK.'

That sounded good to Oliver. 'I'll buy you dinner,' he offered.

'This isn't a date.'

'OK, but one day we'll have a proper date.'

He figured she could call it whatever she liked but he would treat it like a date.

It had been a long time since he'd asked a woman on a date because he'd wanted to get to know her. He'd been burnt once and had since shied away from dating except when he needed to do it for publicity. It kept things simple. There were no expectations if it was purely a business arrangement. There was no chance of disappointment on either side if the 'date' was mutually beneficial, and if the night ended with the two of them between the sheets it had always been mutually agreed upon with no suggestion that it made the evening into anything more than what it had been.

But he was well aware that he needed to curtail his brief encounters, he needed to clean up his reputation and make an effort to redeem himself from a party-going playboy to a serious, eligible, respectable man. He needed to commit some time to getting to know someone on a deeper level, to having a conversation that was about more than what cocktail he could buy them or what they'd like for breakfast, and he could do much worse than spend that time with Kat. He had no problem with getting to know her better. And, at some point in the near future, he would get her to agree to go on a proper date with him, but for now he'd be happy with whatever time she would give him.

In the end Kat agreed to dinner. Her only other option was to take Oliver home with her to feed him, and she was *not* going to introduce him to her father. Introducing someone she was dating was difficult enough, let alone someone for whom she had no label.

She knew she was being silly. If he was just a friend she wouldn't hesitate. But how would she explain Oliver? A work colleague? A movie star? Someone from out of town? Any of those descriptions would do but they wouldn't hide the fact that she was attracted to him and she hated to think what her dad would do or say if he noticed. He always seemed to be of the opinion that no one was good enough for his daughter and it would be humiliating if he gave Oliver the third degree. Oliver had made his intentions clear; he was pursuing her, but he had no more serious intentions than that. If he got her into bed she was certain that would be the end of it. She definitely didn't need to introduce him to her father.

She'd dropped Oliver at his hotel to shower and change before she raced home to do the same, cursing Saskia and her meddling ways all the while. Although she couldn't be too cross. There was a lot to be said about spending an evening with Oliver Harding. Even the anticipation was exciting.

She'd thrown a few supplies into the back of her four-by-four before picking him up again and driving him a few hundred metres to the petrol station.

'Do you want me to fill up the tank for you?' he offered as she turned off the road.

'No, thank you. I'm good,' she replied as she parked the car in a space out the front. 'This is where we're having dinner.'

'A roadhouse?' He sounded offended. 'I offered to buy you dinner. I can afford something fancier than a roadhouse diner.'

'Trust me, it's good. It's owned by Dean's best friend and there's a private room out the back.'

'Do you have a connection to everyone in this town?'

'Pretty much.'

Oliver held the door for her as they entered the roadhouse. They were warmly welcomed and ushered out the back, where they had the space to themselves. He pulled her chair out for her as she sat. She liked the attention. They ordered pizzas and talked about the places Oliver had lived in and travelled to. Kat had been to Adelaide to study and she'd been to Sydney once. Her life experiences were totally different to his but he didn't make her feel inexperienced. He was an entertaining storyteller, even for an audience of one, and Kat enjoyed listening to his tales. He questioned her about her childhood, what it was like growing up in Coober Pedy, and got her to divulge her most interesting work stories. She felt as if they could talk all night.

He picked up the bill when it was delivered to their table but it seemed he wasn't ready to say goodnight just yet. 'It's only early. Don't you think you need to keep an eye on me a little longer? Shall we have coffee? Dessert?'

'We can have dessert at the next stop.' Kat was pleased that he didn't seem keen for the night to end. She had other plans for them.

'There's more than one thing to do in town on a Saturday night?'

She bristled. 'There's plenty. I'm just not sure how much you'll appreciate.'

'Relax. I'm kidding.'

She unlocked her car and climbed in as Oliver held the door for her. She reached into the back seat and handed him a baseball cap.

'What's this for?'

'Protection.'

He raised an eyebrow and smiled. 'For you or me?'

'You.'

'You sure do things differently out here,' he said as Kat pulled onto the main street and drove back through town, turning right at the far end and onto a dirt road. She drove past a chain link fence. On the other side was a large screen.

'We're going to the movies?' Oliver asked.

Kat nodded. 'Outback style.'

She handed over cash at the gate before driving in to the outdoor theatre and reversing into a spot.

To their left was a small building housing the projection unit which also doubled as the kiosk. A couple of long benches were bolted into the ground in front of the kiosk for any patrons who hadn't driven, but these had been ignored in favour of a few, more comfortable, deckchairs. The whole set-up was very basic. Money had recently been spent on a new screen but funds were desperately needed to upgrade the rest of the facilities.

Kat tuned the radio and opened her door.

'Are you sweet or savoury?' she asked.

'Sorry?'

'The dessert I promised you. I'll get us something from the shop.'

'My buy.'

'No—' she started to argue, but he cut her off.

'I was buying dinner. If this is dessert then technically it's still part of dinner.'

She looked at him. Even with the baseball cap he was recognisable. His clothes were too city. He was too neat and tidy, too well-groomed.

'Thanks, but let's call it movie snacks, not dessert, and let me go.'

'Why?'

'Because I think it's better if you stay out of sight.' He frowned and she could see she'd confused him. She couldn't blame him. He had no idea what movie they'd come to see. 'I don't want you to be hassled.'

'No one has bothered me since I got to Coober Pedy. I don't think anyone could care less that I'm in town.'

Kat believed him. The locals were, by and large, unfazed by anything that happened outside of their world. Coober Pedy was a popular filming location for everything from documentaries to local horror flicks to Hollywood blockbusters and the locals couldn't care less. The ones who made a living from the tourists might be the exception but, while they liked the additional revenue that a film crew and any associated publicity might bring, even they wouldn't make a nuisance of themselves by hassling the stars. The locals were focused on making money, making a living, surviving. Movies being made in town was a good drawcard for tourists, which made the town money. That was all the locals worried about, so she wasn't surprised that they were leaving the movie contingent alone, but the tourists in town might be a different story.

'Most of the town, probably not. But the people who are here tonight might. The first movie is one of yours.'

'One of mine? Which one?'

'This Is War.' She waited to see if he was going to object. 'Do you mind watching one of your own? We're a bit limited for choice out here. There's a different double feature every Saturday night and tonight it's one of yours, but we could come back later for the second movie if it's a problem.'

Oliver glanced over his shoulder at the mound of

pillows in the back of the car. 'If we stay, do I get to lie in the back with you and fool around?'

'Yes, to the first—'

'I know how this movie ends,' he interrupted with one of his slow smiles; 'you can afford to miss it—I can catch you up later.'

Kat laughed. 'My point *was*, that I will get the snacks because you're bound to be recognised here and I don't think it will make for a relaxing experience.'

'Relaxing in the back of your car with you was exactly the experience I had in mind.'

Kat raised her eyebrow and gave an exaggerated sigh. 'Sweet or savoury?'

'Surprise me.'

'Make yourself comfortable,' she said as she hopped out.

She returned with an armload of sweets and some cans of soft drink, passing everything to Oliver before climbing into the back. 'Take your pick. I have popcorn or FruChocs.'

'Fruit chocs?'

'FruChocs—chocolate-covered apricot balls. You have to try one. I've got beer too,' Kat said as she popped open a can, 'but you should probably steer clear of that if you've got a headache.'

'My headache seems to have gone,' he grinned. 'I'm feeling much better.'

The opening credits started to roll and Kat settled back. She was looking forward to the movie; it was a romantic comedy, which was much more her style than science fiction, but she knew she'd be happy to see anything that Oliver was in and was more than happy to be curled up in the dark with him. He had rearranged

the pillows, making more of a semi-circle, encouraging
the two of them into the middle of the car, like a little
nest. She had to sit close, their shoulders and thighs
touching. She didn't mind that at all.

She enjoyed the movie. At some point she felt Oliver's arm wrap around her shoulder. She was tucked
against his side in the dark. Despite the fact they were
surrounded by other cars, it had felt secluded and private and the nervous tension she usually felt when she
was around him had dissipated. Maybe it was because
she couldn't see him, but she was still aware of him.
The nervous tension had been replaced by a heightened
awareness. She had felt every movement he'd made,
every breath he'd taken.

She'd felt his fingers twirling the ends of her hair
and making tiny patterns on her bare shoulders. Her
skin had come alive under his touch and she felt as if
she could have stayed there for ever, cocooned with
him in a world of their own.

'What did you think?' he asked as the final credits
started to roll.

The film had made her cry. And laugh. And, not
that she'd admit it, she'd got a little turned on in the
sex scenes. 'I thought you were great,' she said, grateful for the darkness as it hid the fact she was blushing.

'You don't have to be nice. It's OK if you thought
it was terrible.' He was looking at her, his blue-eyed
gaze bright even in the dim light. He was smiling. She
wondered if he was always happy.

'No, really, it was fun, but do you find it weird
watching yourself on screen?' She had wondered if
he'd enjoy it or find it uncomfortable.

'A bit. I tend to focus on everyone else's characters. Especially in the sex scenes.'

'About those. Were you sleeping with the lead actress in real life?' Her imagination had run away with her during those scenes. Lying in Oliver's embrace, it was all too easy to imagine that she was watching him make love to her.

'She was engaged.'

'That doesn't change my question.'

'You don't think much of my acting.'

'On the contrary. Those kisses looked pretty authentic. I just wondered if you really are *that* good.'

'At kissing or acting?'

She noticed he still hadn't answered her original question but she was prepared to let it go for now. She had other things on her mind. She wanted to know how it would feel to be kissed the way he'd kissed the heroine. She wanted to know what it would be like to be kissed by Oliver.

'Kissing,' she replied.

'Those kisses were nothing. It's just part of acting.'

'Is it true there are acting classes to teach people how to kiss?'

'Yes. But I'm not going to admit to having to learn how to kiss a girl properly.'

'So, you've never done one of those classes.'

'No. I've never needed to.'

She would bet he hadn't. She was sure he knew exactly what to do in the bedroom, exactly how to get a girl into bed with him and what to do with her when she got there. He would have had plenty of experience. All he'd have to do was look into her eyes and then smile. Say a few charming words. Kat knew that if she spent enough time with him and he kept up his charm offensive it would only be a matter of time before she succumbed. She was horny just watching him on screen, let alone having his arm around her, his thigh resting against hers. She could still feel his breath on her cheek, his fingers in her hair. Her heart was pounding and she wondered if he could hear it. Her hands were sweaty, her underwear damp.

'Don't confuse real life with acting. In a movie you have to think about everything except the act itself. That's scripted. In a movie you have to get the angles right. You don't want hands in the wrong places, noses getting in the way, too much tongue, too much saliva. It's *usually* all make-believe. And there are lots of different kisses.'

'What do you mean?'

'Think about the way you kiss your dad or your cousins and then think about the way you kissed your first boyfriend.'

She cringed at the thought. 'I'd rather not think about that.'

'Why not?'

'I was fifteen and it was a disaster.'

'Your second boyfriend, then.'

'That was a bit better.'

'How many boyfriends have you had?'

'A few. The choices are a bit limited out here, and you said it yourself—everyone is connected somehow. We all went to school together or are related.'

'I've learned that's not completely true. Plenty of people seem to have moved here from somewhere else. Surely there's an opportunity there. And what about when you were in Adelaide?'

'Yes, there were definitely more options then.' With the added bonus that they didn't have to be introduced to any of her over-protective family. But the only serious relationship she'd ever had had ended when she came back to Coober Pedy. She'd hoped he might follow her, but what was there here for him? She couldn't blame her ex for not wanting to live here. She had never intended to still be here at the age of twenty-seven. She had wanted to see the world but she felt duty bound to stay in Coober Pedy. She was waging a constant battle between her own desires and her beliefs as a daughter. 'What about you?'

'No boyfriends,' he smiled.

'Girlfriends?'

'Not as many as you might think. Now, where were we?' He reached towards her and ran his hand from her shoulder down her arm as he redirected the subject. Kat's skin tingled and her body sprang to life. He flipped her hand over and his thumb made slow circles over the sensitive skin of her wrist. She could scarcely remember her own name, let alone what they'd been talking about. 'We were talking about kisses, I think.'

Kat took a deep breath, closed her eyes briefly and then forced herself to refocus as she opened them. 'What's next after the first kiss?'

'Technically, the second. But in reality, there are always more first kisses.'

'How do you figure that?'

'Every new person is a new kiss. Another first kiss.'

'Until you find *the* person,' she argued. 'The one you want to spend the rest of your life with.'

'Let's forget about numbering the kisses and just think about the way you want to kiss me.'

'I never said I wanted to kiss you.'

'Are you sure?' he teased and she nearly gave in. But she wanted him to make the first move. 'Anyway,' he said when she stayed silent, 'there are plenty more types of kisses.'

'Like what?'

'The kiss between two friends.'

He leant in close and kissed her on the cheek. His hands were on her elbows. The kiss was chaste.

The light from the movie screen played across his face, illuminating his eyes. He was looking at her closely and she was spell bound. He lifted his hand and ran his thumb across her cheek, stopping just in front of her ear. His fingers slid under her hair, gently caressing her neck.

Her eyes were locked with his. Her lips parted.

He brought his face close to hers and said, 'And then there's this one.'

CHAPTER FIVE

HE PRESSED HIS lips close to her ear. She felt them on her earlobe as he ran his fingers down the back of her arm. The hairs on her arms were tingling. She'd never known the back of her arm could be an erogenous zone. Her whole body was tingling, desperate for his touch.

His other hand was behind her neck, his fingers splayed along the bones of her spine. His head dipped towards hers as her eyes drifted closed.

His lips pressed softly against hers.

She sighed and parted her lips on a breath.

Oliver's touch grew firmer and Kat opened her mouth further. His tongue was inside her, touching her, tasting her. He tasted like chocolate.

She melted into his embrace as the kiss deepened.

Their first kiss.

'I've wanted to do that since I first saw you,' he said when they finally came up for air.

'Was it worth waiting for?'

'You tell me.'

She nodded. It had been everything she'd hoped for. And more.

'Now do you believe me? My acting kisses are very different. That was me. All me. There's a big difference to kissing someone when you're surrounded by cameras, and when you're alone under the stars.'

'We're hardly alone.'

'You've been on set. You've seen how crowded it gets. This is as much privacy as I need when I'm kissing someone.'

'Can I have that one again?'

He shook his head. She was disappointed; it had been a pretty amazing kiss.

'We only get one first kiss,' he said. 'That's why it had to be perfect.'

'What comes next?'

'This one.'

He rolled her over, resting her back on the pile of pillows, trapping her under his weight. He pressed his lips to the side of her face, in front of her ear, before moving lower, dropping kisses along her jaw. His mouth moved lower still as he dropped feather-light kisses down her neck and along her collarbone.

He flicked the strap of her sundress off her shoulder and his fingers grazed her breast. Her nipple peaked as his lips pressed against the swell of her breast.

She put her index finger under his chin and lifted his head, bringing his lips back to hers. She slid her arms around his neck as she pressed herself against him.

His tongue explored her mouth. Tasting. Teasing, deeper and harder this time. There was an urgency to their movements now.

His mouth moved back to her jaw line, her neck. He pushed the fabric of her dress aside and cupped her breast with his hand as his thumb deliberately stroked across her nipple. He pushed the lace of her bra to one side, exposing her breast to the caress of his lips. He ran his tongue over her nipple and Kat dissolved.

She felt his hand trace over the curve of her hip, the thin cotton of her dress no protection against the heat of his hand. His mouth was still at her breast, his fingers were on her bare knee. Now his fingers were on the inside of her thigh.

Her skin was on fire. A waterfall of heat and desire started in her belly, overflowed and ran through her like a river.

His fingers moved higher until they came to rest just below the junction of her thighs. It took all her willpower not to spread her legs for him and beg him not to stop. She needed to remember where they were. Who she was. But it was almost impossible. He was sending her crazy.

He seemed to sense just when enough was enough. His movements stilled, pausing right at the last moment, the moment before they wouldn't be able to rein in their desires.

Kat was panting. Dizzy. 'What was that one called?'

'That was called "Your place or mine?".' His lips were on her neck again. She could feel her pulse under the gentle caress of his mouth. He lifted his head and looked into her eyes. 'Would you like to come and spend the night with me?'

She wasn't surprised to find herself giving his suggestion serious consideration. She wasn't ready to say goodnight.

'I think my concussion still needs monitoring,' he added.

'You told me your headache had gone.'

He grinned. 'It has. I seem to have made a remarkable recovery.'

'Did you even have a headache?'

Oliver lifted his hands in surrender. 'I swear I did. But it *has* gone, and it's fun to wind you up.'

'And you're all about fun, aren't you?'

'Yes. I am. That's not a crime. Fun can be very satisfying. You've had fun tonight, haven't you?'

She nodded.

'And the fun doesn't need to stop now. I've seen this movie.' Kat hadn't even noticed that the second feature had started. 'What do you say, shall we blow this joint?'

Kat didn't hesitate. She didn't think about her answer, she just went with her feelings. She knew her night wasn't over yet. She nodded again. Decision made.

'Are you sure?' Oliver checked. 'You promised George you'd stay away from me.'

She grinned. 'We both knew that was never going to happen.'

Her capitulation had not so much been a matter of time as a matter of timing. Of opportunity. And she knew this was her opportunity. She couldn't spend the whole night with him but they had a few more hours.

There was nothing that made her think this was a bad idea. Which wasn't to say it was a good idea. It probably wasn't one of her best, but there had been so many experiences she had missed out on in life because she worried about what other people might think.

She knew that never bothered Oliver. He had publicists and agents to worry for him.

There was no one here to see what she was up to.

There were so many reasons why this wasn't a great

idea. They were complete opposites. She was all about family and helping people. He was about himself. He wasn't staying and she wasn't planning on leaving. But that was exactly why it could work. It could only ever be a fling. She was under no illusions that they could have a proper relationship and she assumed he was of the same opinion.

There were so many reasons why this wasn't a great idea but she didn't care. They were both consenting adults. No one was going to get hurt, she thought as she started the car and left the drive-in.

'Wow.' Kat collapsed onto the bed. Despite the fact that she was in Oliver's underground hotel room, where the temperature was a constant twenty-five degrees, a thin veil of sweat coated her body, testament to their energetic lovemaking.

'You can thank Lotte,' Oliver said.

'Lotte?'

'A German girl who took my virginity when I was fifteen and introduced me to the wonderful delights of women.'

'If I ever meet Lotte I will remember to thank her,' Kat smiled.

'You're not shocked that I was fifteen?'

Kat laughed. 'I might have only been having my first proper kiss, if you could call it that, at fifteen, but most of my friends skipped that bit. They went straight to getting married and having babies, sometimes not in that order. How old was Lotte?'

'Nineteen.'

'Now, *that's* a bit shocking. Is that even legal?'

'I have no idea. Possibly not. But I didn't care.' He

shrugged and grinned. 'Show me a randy fifteen-year-
old boy who is going to say no to a gorgeous, experienced older woman.'

'Where does a fifteen-year-old go to meet a
nineteen-year-old Mata Hari?'

'My father was stationed in Germany at the time. I
had one of my brother's IDs. We looked enough alike
that the bars and clubs didn't really care. Isaac had just
left home—Dad kicked him out when he announced
he was gay. That really started my rebellious years. I
was sick of following the rules. What did it get us? I
realised it was always going to be my father's way or
the highway, so I started exploring the highway. Sneak-
ing off, lying. I couldn't wait to get out of home. I was
miserable and I missed Isaac.'

'Where did he go?'

'He got a scholarship to university. He's an architect
now. Living in Spain.'

'Do you see him very often?'

'Not often. Our lives are very different. He's married now, to his long-term partner.'

'Do you like his partner?'

'I do. But we don't have a lot in common any more.
Our careers are different, our lifestyles too. I don't
mean because he's gay, but he's very settled, nine-to-
five work days, four weeks' holiday, vacations in Eu-
rope and Africa. He's happy.'

'And what about you? Are you happy?'

'I am now. Leaving home was the best thing I ever
did. Our father was constantly disappointed in us.
Nothing we did was ever good enough. I stopped trying to please him. Leaving home was the only way I

was going to be able to find out who I was. And what about you? When are you going to leave home?'

'I went to Adelaide to study when I was eighteen but I came back when my mum died.'

'That was a while ago now; you said your friends are married with kids, but not you? You've escaped all that? Or do you have an ex-husband hiding in a mine, waiting for the chance to hunt me down?'

'You've been in too many movies. I don't have an ex-husband. I want to find someone who will give me what my parents had. My parents were married for thirty-two years and they adored each other. I am looking for my soulmate.' She rolled onto her side and tucked her leg over Oliver's, craning her head to kiss him firmly on his mouth. 'And now I need to go.'

'You're not staying?'

She shook her head. 'My father will expect me home. He always leaves a light on and he'll look for my car in the morning. If he doesn't see it, he'll worry.'

'Why don't you call him?'

'And tell him what? That I'm staying out all night to have wild sex with a gorgeous man?'

'I'm flattered. But perhaps your father doesn't need to hear all the details.'

'You do remember what he does for a living?'

'So, it's not an ex-husband but a father I have to worry about.'

'Remember, he warned me against men like you.'

Oliver burst out laughing. 'Men like me? What does that even mean?'

'Charmers. Heartbreakers. Men who are only after one thing.'

'I told you, don't believe everything you read. I've

dated a lot of women—it keeps me in the headlines and is good for my career—but I certainly haven't slept with them all. I will admit, though, that I am after you.'

'And now that you've had me, is that it?'

'No. Stay here and I'll prove it to you.' His fingers found her naked breast and he brushed lightly over her nipple, sending waves of desire through her.

She placed her hand over his and lifted it from her body before she capitulated. 'I can't, I have to go. I need to get some sleep.'

'You can sleep here in a minute,' he said as he lowered his head and took her nipple in his mouth.

Kat arched her back as his tongue circled her breast. She almost gave in. 'I have to go to work early tomorrow.' He sucked on her nipple as his hand slid from her waist over her hip. 'But why don't you come over for dinner tomorrow night?'

She hadn't intended to invite him but the invitation was out there now and she couldn't take it back. She would blame her hormones. She couldn't think clearly while his mouth and hands worked their magic.

She wriggled out from underneath him and sat up. She needed to go before she said anything else she didn't really mean. Her mouth was working independently of her brain, or maybe her brain just wasn't working at all; maybe it was too overloaded by her other senses.

'I can't. We're filming tomorrow.'

'At night?'

Oliver wouldn't meet her eyes and she knew he wasn't telling her everything. She should just let it go. She should be relieved that he said no but she knew he was lying to her about something and she couldn't leave it alone.

'No,' he admitted.

'So, you have got what you wanted and now you'll walk away?'

'I'm not walking away but I don't do family.'

What the hell did that mean? She was desperate to know but she let it slide. She knew from his tone he wasn't going to discuss it further and she didn't need to know.

She bit her tongue as she got dressed. She didn't want to end the night on a fight. She didn't need to push the point. She shouldn't have invited him in the first place.

Oliver had been tempted to accept Kat's dinner invitation for this evening before common sense prevailed. Going on a few dates and fixing his reputation was one thing. Meeting her family was another thing altogether. It wasn't something he needed to do. It wasn't something he was prepared to do.

He was only in town for a few weeks, long enough to have some fun but not long enough for anything serious, and that suited him fine. Besides, he didn't have a great track record with families, his own included. And even if hers were wonderful, what would be the point of meeting them? He liked Kat but he wasn't going to get involved in her life. He knew he couldn't give her the things she wanted.

She'd told him she wanted to find her soulmate, and that wasn't him. He didn't believe in soulmates. His brother was the one exception. He though Isaac and his partner were a perfect match.

Oliver had never let himself fall in love. He'd had one relationship that he'd thought had the potential to become something serious but it had ended badly. His girlfriend had cheated on him, blamed him for not paying her enough attention. He knew he'd failed, he'd been focused on establishing his career, and he'd disappointed her.

He didn't want to be in a position again where he could disappoint someone, so he chose to keep his distance from people. He didn't date seriously and he didn't see his family. It was better not to get involved. That way people didn't develop expectations and he wouldn't disappoint.

His family was fractured.

He was a disappointment.

He avoided families for those very reasons.

But he couldn't get Kat out of his mind. He spent the afternoon filming a scene with Julia but it was Kat's face he was picturing. Her dark eyes, her smooth, lithe body. Her full red lips that did, amazingly, taste like summer cherries.

Jesus, he was hard again even now.

And, even though he knew he wouldn't go to dinner, it didn't stop him from thinking about Kat, from imagining what she was doing right at that moment, from thinking about what he was missing.

He knew that Kat's family had shaped her into the person she was. Into the compassionate, generous and open-hearted woman he was enjoying getting to know. He knew they were close and assumed they weren't as broken or as complicated as his own, but that still didn't mean he needed to meet them. He didn't want to risk disappointing Kat. Or her family. He knew he wasn't the man she was looking for. There was no need for him to meet her family.

It wasn't family he was missing. Kat's or his own. He was simply missing Kat.

Kat was glad she was rostered on to work; it gave her something to keep her mind occupied for the day. She might as well be at work, seeing as Oliver had blown her off. Being busy would stop her from thinking about him. Well, that had been her reasoning. She'd thought it would keep her busy but the shift had been quiet. Usually she was happy about that but today she needed the distraction. Just a minor vehicle accident or a suspected heart attack that turned out to be indigestion would have been enough. But she'd had far too much time on her hands and she spent it vacillating between reliving last night and wondering why Oliver wouldn't come to dinner. Was it really that he just didn't like being around other people's families, or did it mean he'd got what he wanted and she wouldn't see him again?

She'd been kidding herself to think they could have something meaningful. Family was everything to her and she couldn't imagine being with someone who didn't understand that.

She'd checked the filming schedule—Sunday was supposed to be a rest day—and she'd seen that nothing was listed. She hated that she was checking up on him but she couldn't stop herself. He'd said it was a closed set. Was it a love scene? Was he lying? Her thoughts went backwards and forwards…there were a thousand possibilities and she knew she could go crazy trying to work out what it all meant. Maybe it meant nothing.

She was relieved when the phone finally rang.

'Ambulance. What's your emergency?'

'I've got a fifty-eight-year-old man with severe stomach pains.'

'Oliver? Is that you?' she asked before her initial excitement at hearing his voice gave way to the realisation that he'd called 000, not her specifically.

'Kat? Yes, it's me. I'm with George. He's in a lot of pain and I don't know what to do.'

'Where is his pain?'

'Right side. Under his ribs. Could he be having a heart attack?'

'Tell me what other symptoms he has,' she said, trying to keep him calm. 'Any shortness of breath?' She could hear Oliver relaying her questions to George.

'No,' came the reply.

'Oliver, can you put the phone on speaker? George can hear my questions—he'll only have to nod yes or no and you can then pass the information on to me.' She paused briefly and then continued, 'Chest pain?'

'Yes,' came Oliver's reply.

'Back pain?'

'No.'

'Arm pain?'

'No.'

'Has he vomited?'

'Yes.'

'But he's not having difficulty breathing?'

'No.'

Kat scribbled a note to Dave while she spoke to Oliver.

Chest pain?
Abdominal pain?

Dave began a quick check of their supplies before lifting the keys for the ambulance off their hook.

'I don't think I can get him in the car to take him to the hospital,' Oliver told her.

'It's all right. We'll come to you. Where are you?'

'Still on set. We're in George's trailer.'

Kat was mollified. Oliver hadn't been lying to her about having to work. 'We're on the way.'

Kat and Dave arrived on set to find a restless George; he was unable to find a comfortable position.

The air-conditioning was working overtime but he still felt hot to the touch. Kat took his temperature and observed his colour. He had a tinge of yellow about him.

Kat removed the thermometer from his ear and re-layed the elevated reading to Dave. She lifted George's shirt to palpate his stomach.

'Where is the pain?'

George indicated his right side.

'When did the pain start?'

'After lunch, maybe a couple of hours ago,' he said.

There was a small, faded scar in the right lower quadrant. 'Have you had your appendix removed?' Kat asked.

George nodded as Kat continued to feel his abdomen.

Dave was busy attaching ECG leads to George's chest. Kat clipped an oximeter onto his finger and listened to his respiration rate. His oxygen saturation was slightly low, heart rate was elevated, respiration rate rapid, temperature high, but the ECG trace was normal.

'Take a deep breath for me, George,' Kat instructed as she pushed her fingers into the upper right quadrant of his abdomen. George gasped with pain, holding his breath until Kat released the pressure on his gallbladder.

'OK, George, good news—it's not a heart attack and it's not appendicitis.'

'What's the bad news?' Oliver asked.

'I think it's probably a blocked bile duct.'

'What causes that?'

'Gallstones. I'm not surprised you're feeling terrible, George—it is a very painful condition, but easily remedied. You'll need further testing though.'

'Here?' Oliver asked.

Dave drew up a dose of analgesia to start controlling George's pain.

'No,' Kat replied. 'We'll take him to the hospital for pain relief but he'll need to go to Port Augusta or Adelaide for further tests.'

'And then what?'

'If it's gallstones he'll probably need surgery.' Kat was almost certain that her diagnosis was correct and with acute cholecystitis surgery was almost always required. 'It's not emergency surgery but it should be done some time in the next three days. The flying doctor will transfer him if necessary.'

CHAPTER SIX

KAT EMERGED FROM the water and Oliver's brain froze. Droplets of water clung to her body and her skin glistened. She wore a black bikini; he'd seen a thousand different women wearing black bikinis before he had a house on Malibu Beach and gorgeous women were everywhere—but none of them had affected him the way Kat did.

He couldn't believe she'd accepted his invitation to come to Adelaide with him.

George had been transferred to Adelaide for surgery, so filming had been put on hold, giving Oliver, and the rest of the cast and crew, a few days off. Oliver had offered to fly down to Adelaide as well. George didn't need him—he had his assistant, Erica—but Oliver used it as an excuse to invite Kat to go too. And here she was.

They would have at least three days in the city. Three days that had the potential to be so much better than any date he had imagined. He'd booked them into the only five-star hotel at Glenelg Beach and as he watched the sway of her hips as she came towards him he wondered about his chances of getting her back to their suite and ravishing her before dinner.

No, he'd show her that there was more to him than the persona that the tabloids loved to write about. His womanising ways were, as he'd told her, mostly fabricated for publicity and he wasn't searching for publicity today. He had a corporate credit card and he'd used his alias when he'd booked the hotel room. The next couple of days were about him and Kat. He hadn't asked what she'd told her father—he didn't care; it wasn't any of his business.

Her olive skin was tanned and golden and Oliver feasted his eyes on her as she came out of the ocean. Her dark hair was slick and wet and he watched as she lifted her arms and gathered her hair in one handful and squeezed the salt water from it. Her breasts rose with the movement, two perfect golden orbs, and Oliver struggled to keep his eyes up.

Jesus, she made him feel like a horny teenager. He was in a constant state of arousal when she was near him, and her being almost naked was not helping. He couldn't remember the last time a woman had driven him to distraction the way Kat did and it made it difficult to remember that he was trying to be on his best behaviour. But try he would.

He couldn't, however, resist just one kiss.

He stepped towards her and met her in the shallows. He slid his arm around her waist. Her skin was damp and cool and smooth. He bent his head and kissed her.

He needed to keep it brief; he was only wearing a pair of swim shorts—there wasn't much to keep him decent.

'Are you worried someone will see you?' she asked as his lips left hers.

He noticed she didn't say 'us' and he knew she was

thinking of him being stalked by the paparazzi, but he really didn't care. Not today. Not now.

'No one knows we're here,' he told her, including her with him. 'No one is expecting to see me.' He was wearing a baseball cap, more out of habit than for a disguise, but it had the added advantage that it shaded his eyes. He knew they were his most identifying feature. He had booked into the hotel under an alias and as far as he knew no one had been tipped off. He supposed the airline staff could have said something if they'd recognised him, but their plane tickets had been booked using the same corporate card and the plane had been tiny—twenty seats at most—and no one knew where they were headed once it had landed in Adelaide. He was confident they could go undetected. He had to admit, while he courted the paparazzi in LA, as it was important to keep them on side, it was refreshing to be incognito. It was a novelty to be able to pretend he had a normal life even if he suspected he'd grow tired and bored of normal after a while. But, for the moment, if it meant he could hold Kat in his arms on a public beach and be left alone he was all for that.

He kissed her again for good measure before taking her hand. He picked up one of their towels from the warm sand and wrapped it around her shoulders, hugging her close as he dried her back. The sun was low over the horizon now, turning the sky pink and gold, and he had plans to sip champagne on their balcony as they watched it set.

He took her hand and walked along the beach, leaving footprints in the soft sand by the water's edge. The tide was on its way out, the moats around the sandcastles were emptying and the beach was starting to empty too as families thought about getting home to feed their kids. There was still a group of teenagers jumping off the jetty into the sea. They stopped temporarily if the lifeguards or police turned up before they were at it again. Oliver thought it looked like fun and it was exactly the sort of thing he would have done in his youth too, but he didn't tell Kat that. He knew she liked to abide by the rules.

They walked into the shade underneath the jetty and as they emerged from the other side he heard a woman screaming. Her English was heavily accented and her distress was making her hard to understand, but when he looked in the direction she was pointing, into the distance, into the waves, out past a rocky outcrop, he thought he could see a head bobbing in the water and being taken out to sea with the outgoing tide.

The lifeguard station was empty, unmanned at this time of day, although the surf lifesaving club was still open. But, even so, he and Kat were the closest people.

Oliver didn't hesitate. He knocked his baseball cap from his head, let go of Kat's hand and ran into the shallows, ignoring Kat's cry of, 'What are you doing?'

He splashed through the water until it was knee-deep and running became difficult. He dived into the sea and struck out around the rocks. He was a strong swimmer. He was used to the Pacific Ocean and, in comparison, the calm waters of the gulf didn't look too difficult, although he knew it was one thing to swim in calm waters and another to try to rescue a frightened, drowning man. Maybe he should have waited for the lifeguards but that extra minute or two could be the difference between a good outcome and a bad; between life and death.

He was getting closer. He saw the man's head disappear under the water. Oliver put his head down and kicked harder, willing himself to reach the man before it was too late.

The man was sinking.

Oliver dived down, searching underwater for the man.

He found him. He was fully clothed and wearing shoes. His eyes were closed.

Oliver came up behind him and got an arm around his chest. He was a dead weight as Oliver kicked to the surface. He hoped the man was only unconscious—surely he couldn't have drowned that quickly?

He knew he had to keep the man on his back, facing away from him, in order to keep control of the situation. If he regained consciousness and panicked, he'd most likely drag them both under.

It seemed to take for ever to reach the surface, and Oliver was breathing heavily as he broke through the waves. It was hard work. He fitted his fingers around the man's chin, keeping his head above water as he kicked in a side-stroke action and headed for the shore, recalling the lessons learned a lifetime ago in his summer swimming lessons as a schoolboy.

Two lifeguards appeared beside him on a board. One took the unconscious man from Oliver and dragged him onto his belly across the board.

'He's not breathing,' Oliver panted.

'Do you need a hand?' The second lifeguard held out a hand to Oliver as the first began paddling back to the beach. They were only fifty metres from the sand. Oliver was tired but now that he wasn't towing a ninety-kilogram dead weight he knew he'd make it.

'I'm OK, thanks,' he said. His pride wouldn't let him be rescued. 'I can swim in.'

His feet hit the sand and he stood, aware that his legs were shaky with fatigue and adrenalin, but he knew he'd be fine as long as he kept moving.

Kat was waiting on the shore. He wrapped one arm around her shoulders, careful not to lean on her, even though it was tempting.

The lifeguards had started performing CPR on the rescued man and he could tell Kat was itching to help, but it wasn't her beat.

As they reached the lifeguards the man's chest started to move. The lifeguards quickly rolled him into the recovery position as he retched, sea water gushing from his mouth.

Bystanders had gathered, hovering around as the lifeguards called for an ambulance. Oliver was always amazed by people's curious fascination with disaster. He understood being curious—as an actor he'd made a habit of people-watching—but sticky-beaking at a potential tragedy was a whole different level in his opinion.

The lifeguards came over and thanked him for his assistance, even though he was sure some of them would have liked to berate him for diving in without thinking.

'You look like that actor,' said one.

'Oliver Harding,' said another.

'I get that a lot,' Oliver replied, not giving anything away. 'Name's Frank.' He stuck out his hand and shook theirs.

'Well, we appreciate your help, mate.'

'No worries,' he replied in his best Australian accent.

He could feel Kat looking sideways at him. She handed him his baseball cap and said, 'We need to get going, *Frank*.'

She waited until they were out of earshot from all the bystanders before she stopped walking and turned to Oliver.

'What was that all about?'

To his credit he didn't pretend not to know what she was asking. 'Frank is one of my aliases.'

'One of?' She raised an eyebrow. 'Is Oliver your real name?'

'Yes. Oliver James Harding, at your service,' he said with a mock bow.

'And when did you start speaking in an Aussie accent?'

'That's my job. Most of the movie crew are Aussies, and I've been paying attention on set. It's the best way to make people believe I am just a doppelgänger.'

'Why do you need a fake name?'

'I usually use it for checking into hotels, restaurants, that sort of thing. I don't expect special treatment, so I don't need to broadcast my movements. There's no need to give everyone a heads up about where I'm going to be and when. The paparazzi pay people to divulge that sort of information. If I want them to know my whereabouts there are ways of getting that information out to them, but if I want some privacy I need some measures to protect it. Mostly I'm happy to sign autographs or pose for photos, but I didn't think the lifeguards needed to deal with that palaver as well. I'm not saying that all of those bystanders would have wanted selfies or whatever, but in my experience at least some of them would and that can become a bit of a circus. It wasn't necessary and, besides, for the next couple of days I want it to just be us.'

She was more than happy for it to be just the two of them as well. She found it liberating being able to walk down the street and hold Oliver's hand and not worry about what people might say or think. If she found it liberating, she could just imagine how Oliver must feel. He was used to his every move being scrutinised and potentially splashed across the cover of a magazine, so she could understand the appeal of hiding his true identity.

They reached the hotel and Kat stepped inside as the doorman held the door. She felt as though she should apologise as they left sandy footprints on the spotless tiled floor. She smiled to herself as she wondered what the staff in this five-star hotel thought. She wondered if they could tell that she wasn't used to this level of luxury and attention. That she had never before stayed in a five-star, or even a four-star, hotel, had never been picked up from the airport by a chauffeur, had never slept with a Hollywood star.

'What name did you use to book the hotel?' She wondered if the hotel staff knew who he was.

'The same alias—Frank Foster.'

'How do you come up with the names? Is there a list somewhere of the top ten aliases?'

Oliver laughed. 'No. It was the name of one of my characters, one of my favourite parts.'

'That was the character in the movie we saw at the drive-in!'

'It was,' he said as he swiped the room card and held

the door for her as she entered the penthouse suite. 'Would you like first shower before dinner?'

She smiled and reached one hand behind her back. She was looking forward to the next few days, and nights, in Adelaide. She was looking forward to spending time with Oliver, just the two of them without interruptions, with no work, no family. She hadn't hesitated when he'd asked her to come with him; she had three rostered days off and she was eager to spend more time exploring their attraction. One night in Coober Pedy hadn't been enough and she was prepared to forget that he 'didn't do family'. If he was keen to spend time with her alone she was happy with that.

Her fingers found the tie for her bikini top. 'I thought we could share,' she said as she tugged at the string. His mouth fell open as her top fell to the floor. She walked away from him but he caught up to her before she reached the bathroom. She stretched one hand out and turned the tap for the shower. He stretched one arm out and put his hand on her waist. He slid it up her belly until he was cupping her breast.

She turned towards him and pulled him under the water.

'What do you fancy for dinner?' Kat asked.

She was wrapped in the thick towelling robe from the hotel and he knew she was naked underneath. They'd only just stepped out of the shower but he debated about ordering Room Service and staying in. But he'd promised himself he would take her out and show her some fun. They'd be back in their room soon enough.

'Your choice,' he said. He couldn't care less what they ate. He wasn't thinking about food.

'I usually choose seafood when I come to the city. Fresh seafood isn't something we get a lot of in Coober Pedy.' She slipped the robe off as she walked into the walk-in wardrobe and Oliver wondered if it was too soon to take her to bed again.

No. He could wait. Sometimes letting the anticipation build was worth it. 'Can you guarantee me that no one will choke on a fish bone?'

'What do you mean?' She emerged from the wardrobe carrying a pair of high heels and dressed in a simple black halter-neck dress that highlighted her shoulders.

'We keep running into people who need saving. I need a rest from all that. No more blocked bile ducts, drowning men or pulling men out of mine shafts. In fact, we should just steer clear of all men for the next two days.'

Kat laughed as she sat on the edge of the bed and slipped her sandals on. She lifted one foot and rested it on her opposite knee, sliding her sandal on and fastening the strap around her slender ankle. Her dress rode up to reveal the inside of her thigh. Her legs were long and smooth and tanned. He never knew watching a woman get dressed could be as sexy as watching one undress.

'We need to visit George tomorrow.'

Oliver swallowed and tried to focus on what she was saying as he reminded himself to behave. He didn't want her to think that sex was all he had on his mind and that he wasn't interested in spending time with her if she had her clothes on. 'OK, apart from George. No more emergencies, just us.'

'OK.'

Kat stood and leant towards the mirror that hung over the dressing table beside the bed. Her dress clung to her hips as she bent forwards. Oliver's gaze travelled up, over the curve of her buttocks. He watched as she applied her red lipstick and it took all of his self-control to let her finish, take her hand and lead her out of their suite.

He held her hand as they walked along Jetty Road. A signboard outside a hotel caught his eye. 'What about here? They have karaoke.'

'Karaoke? I thought we were looking for somewhere to eat?'

'We can do both.'

'I don't think karaoke places are renowned for their food,' Kat said.

Oliver pointed to an announcement painted on the pub window. 'It says they won "Best Pub Restaurant" last year.'

'You really want to go to a karaoke restaurant? I thought you said you couldn't sing.'

'I said I wished I was a better singer. And I never said I intended to sing tonight.'

'Well, I certainly won't be singing,' Kat laughed.

'Let's have a look at the menu and then decide. It'll be fun.'

She knew he was all about fun and, looking at his expression, she didn't think she could refuse him. 'OK,' she said as he held the door for her and they stepped inside.

'Have a seat,' he said as he pulled a chair out for her, 'and I'll get some menus.'

He returned with menus, a glass of wine for her and a beer for him. 'Is wine OK? I can get you something else if you prefer?'

'This is fine, thanks.'

'What do you think?' Oliver asked as she perused the menu.

The pub looked newly refurbished, the crowd was well-dressed and the menu looked good. Kat watched as a waitress delivered plates of food to an adjacent table. 'The food looks good,' she admitted, 'I think I can maybe overlook the fact that I'll have to listen to some karaoke.'

Oliver smiled. She could overlook anything at all if she got to sit opposite him for the evening, she decided.

'Where did you learn to swim?' she asked after they had ordered. He had been amazing today, jumping in without hesitation to rescue that man.

'I live on the beach in LA. At Malibu. The swell today was nothing compared to the Pacific Ocean. I've always lived near water. I was born in Italy, lived in Turkey, Hawaii and Germany. All the army bases had swimming pools and we spent summer holidays around the Mediterranean. I spent a lot of my spare time in the water. What about you?'

'I can swim but there's no way I'd be confident enough to jump in like you did. You've seen where I grew up. The town has a pool, and you've seen the lake, but I'm not used to waves. I didn't go out of my depth in the sea today.'

'Can I ask you something? The lifeguards revived the man, so why did he have to go off to hospital?'

'There is a latent risk after people take water into their lungs,' Kat explained. 'There's something called post-immersion syndrome, where your throat can spasm due to irritation of the vocal cords, which makes breathing difficult—that's more common in children—and there's also secondary drowning. If water gets into the lungs it can irritate them and cause pulmonary oedema, which is a build-up of fluid in the tiny air sacs that makes breathing difficult. He needs to be monitored, especially given his lack of English. The hospital will organise an interpreter to explain the risks and he may be discharged if they think he and his girlfriend understand what to watch for.'

'Will he be OK?'

'I would think so. He survived the drowning, and deaths from secondary drownings are extremely rare. At worst he might be unwell.' Kat reached across the table and held Oliver's hand. 'You saved his life.'

'A good day, then.'

'A very good day,' she said with a smile.

The karaoke began as they were finishing their meal, making conversation more difficult. Some of the singers were good, some were woeful, but because there was a prize at the end of the night there were plenty of participants. The winner would be decided by an audience vote.

'Some of these people should definitely save their singing for the shower,' Kat commented.

'You sure you don't want to have a go?'

'I'm positive,' she laughed.

'Can you excuse me?' Oliver said. 'I need to use the bathroom. Will you be all right on your own for a minute?'

'Of course, I'll be fine.' She loved the attention he paid her.

There was a scattered round of applause as another singer finished their song.

'And now, one final karaoke contestant. Give it up for…Frank!'

Kat looked at the stage. Was the MC introducing Oliver? He hadn't returned to their table yet but the stage was empty.

Then she heard a voice through the speakers. A male voice. Unaccompanied.

There was still no one on stage but he obviously had a microphone and, whoever it was, he could sing.

Kat looked around the bar.

Oliver was walking towards her. His blue eyes pinned her to the seat and the spotlight followed him as he sang.

A second spotlight fell on Kat and she hurriedly hid her face behind her hands as Oliver continued to sing about how he couldn't keep his eyes off her. She could feel herself blushing, and part of her wanted to slide under the table, but another part of her couldn't look away. She peeked through her fingers in time to see Oliver stop just before he reached her and step up onto the stage. He was poised and confident.

The music started up in accompaniment, just loud enough to be heard but still letting Oliver's voice shine. Kat was mesmerised. Oliver was born to be on stage.

The second spotlight dimmed, putting her back into the shadows.

The focus was all on Oliver. He didn't seem to mind. Kat knew he loved an audience but she also knew he was singing to her.

The crowd had fallen silent as soon as he'd started singing. They were expecting something special, nothing had been anywhere near as good as what they were hearing now.

He reached the chorus and invited everyone in the restaurant to sing with him. They didn't need to be asked twice. They didn't need to know the words; it was a simple repeat.

Oliver jumped down from the stage and offered his hand to Kat as the audience sang and clapped.

She knew he wanted to get her out of her seat but she hesitated for a fraction of a second, reluctant to dance in front of strangers. She was so used to worrying about what people would think, but then she realised that no one here knew her and no one would care about what she did—they were all too focused on Oliver.

He had the room eating out of his hand as he performed, so she could probably do naked cartwheels across the stage and still no one would give her a second glance.

She let him pull her to her feet.

He twirled her around, spinning her out and away from him as the crowd accompanied them vocally before pulling her in close, her back tucked into his side as he sang the next verse. She swayed with him as they moved in time to the music, oblivious now to the audience.

Thunderous applause surrounded them as he kissed her at the end of the song and returned her to her seat. He took a bow before he was unanimously declared the winner.

He graciously accepted his prize before quickly settling their tab so they could sneak away.

'Well, I don't know about you but that Frank Foster sure can sing,' Kat laughed as Oliver took her hand as they walked back to the hotel.

'Did you have fun?'

'I did.' It was the most fun she'd had in a long time; perhaps she should care less about what people might think and just let her hair down more often.

Kat felt as if she were floating. She was relaxed, sexually satisfied. Happy.

She and Oliver had gone for an early-morning swim, followed by a room service breakfast, followed by more lovemaking, and then they'd wandered through the shops. She was carrying several shopping bags, filled with clothes that would probably never see the light of day in Coober Pedy but which Oliver had insisted on buying for her as well as some gifts for her family.

'I could use a drink after that retail therapy,' Oliver said as he offloaded their purchases to the concierge. 'Would you like to grab a drink in the bar or...?' He paused, his train of thought interrupted, his attention caught by something else.

Kat turned and saw a woman walking towards them. She was short, blonde, extremely thin and expertly put together. Her hair, make-up and clothing were all immaculate. She looked just the type of person who would be in the lobby of a five-star hotel, and Kat's curiosity was piqued.

'Philippa! What are you doing here?' Oliver greeted her.

The woman looked over at Kat, not trying to hide her curiosity. 'Who is this?' she asked as she looked Kat up and down.

Kat frowned. She was wondering the same thing.

'This is Kat Angelis; she's an emergency paramedic, and she's overseeing my stunt work.'

'You're not working right now, though. George is in hospital,' the woman stated, clearly implying that she thought Kat shouldn't be there.

'Kat, this is Philippa Corcoran, my publicist.' Oliver introduced her, choosing to ignore the woman's implication.

Philippa nodded in Kat's direction before turning back to Oliver. 'I need to speak to you, Oliver. In private.'

Kat waited for Oliver to tell her that this wasn't a good time, but Philippa hadn't finished.

'We have a problem,' she added before Oliver could speak.

CHAPTER SEVEN

PHILIPPA WAS BEING rude and Oliver thought about arguing, but something in Philippa's demeanour stopped him from dismissing his publicist.

'How did you find me?'

'You checked in with your credit card. I see the statements.'

She had tracked him down and then flown halfway across the world to see him. Her news must be bad. Too bad for her to deliver over the phone, and he didn't want her to tell him what it was in front of Kat. Who knew what Philippa had to say? He didn't want Kat to hear anything sordid about him. Not without his knowing first what was going on.

'I'm really sorry, Kat, but could you give us a minute?'

'I'll get a coffee in the lounge,' she said.

He could tell from her expression that she wasn't happy, but she didn't argue. He'd make it up to her later.

Kat headed for the lounge and Oliver swiped his card and called the lift for the penthouse suite.

The penthouse door had scarcely closed behind them before Philippa pulled a folder out of her designer bag and handed it to Oliver.

He took it reluctantly. 'What is this?'

'You're being sued.'

'Sued? By whom?'

'The parents of Natalie Hanson, the girl who over-dosed at your house.'

'What? That's ridiculous. I wasn't even there.'

'Unfortunately that doesn't matter. She died on your property.'

'And that gives them grounds to sue me?' Oliver stood in the middle of the living room and rifled through the folder. There was a legal document, he assumed the lawsuit, and photos of a young girl. He knew it was Natalie. She was beautiful, happy, smiling, looking as if she didn't have a care in the world. He felt for her parents, they didn't deserve this, but that didn't make it his fault.

Philippa took a seat on the sofa. 'They're saying you had a duty of care. They're saying their daughter didn't have a drug problem. That she must have got the drugs at your house.'

'The police thought she brought the drugs with her,' he said as he dropped the folder onto the coffee table.

'They haven't been able to prove that. There's a copy of the police report in that file.'

'Well, I definitely didn't supply them!' This could ruin his reputation. He'd been working hard to clean up his image, but stories about the number of celebrities he'd dated would seem trivial in comparison to an alleged drug problem. 'In all the thousands of stories I've had printed about me there's never been anything to suggest I'm into illegal drugs.'

'I know that,' Philippa said calmly. 'I know most of what they print about you isn't true, but you know the saying—throw enough mud and some of it will stick. We've worked hard to get you back in the good books, to keep you employed. The movie studios are jumpy. They don't want bad publicity. We need to manage this.'

Oliver sank into a chair. He didn't care what people thought about him but he did care about his career. 'How bad is it?' he asked.

'They're not suing you as a dealer. They're suing you as the landlord. Their argument is that you are liable because it's your property. We need to make sure your name is cleared.'

He had been sent to Australia to make a film in the middle of nowhere as a way of supposedly keeping him out of trouble, but that plan obviously hadn't worked and he knew this lawsuit could be a big problem.

How was he going to explain this to Kat? He really didn't want her to think trouble followed him. Thank God she'd agreed to give him and Philippa some privacy. He hated to think of her hearing this.

Philippa was talking and he forced his mind off Kat and back to what she was saying.

'This is serious. I've spoken to your lawyers already but we need to do some damage control and we also need some positive publicity to counteract any negative stories that come your way.'

'What do you suggest?' He couldn't think straight. All he could think about was Kat's reaction. She was so black and white; she thrived on following the rules. What would she make of this latest scandal? What would she think of him?

'I think you should get engaged.'

'What?'

'You need to show that you've reformed your partying, playboy ways. I know you don't have a drug-taking history, but drugs and partying are a marriage made in heaven for the media, and it only takes a few tabloids to make some suggestions and you have an even bigger PR problem.'

'But that playboy persona was just an image. You know that's not really me. You helped create it!'

'Again, *I* know that, but it's an image you've—we've—spent years selling. Now it's about how we manage it. An engagement is a perfect solution. You need a fiancée, someone who will stand by you and support you while you sort out these allegations. It will give you some positive publicity.'

'And who will agree to be a fake fiancée? Where do you suggest I find someone to play that role?'

Philippa didn't miss a beat.

'Someone trustworthy,' she said. 'An actress. We need someone who is wholesome, which will give you credibility. Someone the public can trust. A fan favourite. Someone they will believe is with you for all the right reasons and therefore you couldn't possibly have done the things you've been accused of because otherwise how would you have got her to fall in love with you?' She reached into her bag and pulled a stack of glossy A4 pages from it. Each page had a photo on it and Oliver could see they were actor bios. She handed him the sheaf of photos. 'I have a short list of actresses who I think would be perfect. I'm pleased you're out of America. That will work in our favour. We'll get you back to Coober Pedy asap, where the paparazzi and the media can't find you. You choose someone from those bios and I will organise a media announcement. I will control it all.'

'Is that why you're here, in person?'

Knowing that he, once again, needed someone to clean up his image was upsetting. Particularly as he was in this situation through no fault of his own.

Philippa was nodding. 'I needed to find you and speak to you before the paparazzi did. I needed you to see that my idea makes sense.'

'No.' Oliver threw the pile of photos onto the table. 'None of this makes sense. It's ridiculous. I had nothing to do with that girl's death and I will fight the lawsuit. Why do I have to create fake news about myself? I thought we were trying to clean up my reputation; I thought part of that was to stay out of the media spotlight. Isn't that one of the reasons I'm down under?'

'Yes. But the story is already out. Natalie's parents have gone to the media. We have to do something. We really do need to counter-attack with something positive. We can't have the media linking your name to a lawsuit and a lawsuit only. We need to give them something else, something good. I think it's our, *your*, best option.'

'I'm not interested.'

'I think you should consider it. Maybe read the stories that have been printed so far. You might agree you don't really have much choice.'

Philippa passed him a third stack of paper, this time printed copies of tabloid magazine articles. He took a cursory glance—he didn't need more than that to see they were all saying the same thing—this actress had died in his house. His name was being linked by association and her parents were suing him. It didn't matter that the tabloids weren't actually mentioning that he hadn't been in the house, that he'd been on location, filming. Fans would put two and two together and get whatever the hell number they pleased; he knew how this business worked. A few photos, a few quotes taken out of context, a few interviews with 'close friends' and there was a story. Suddenly he was into illegal drugs and a girl had died because of it. It was all that was needed to sell the magazines.

'Think of it as a job,' Philippa said. 'A role. You can play the part of the law-abiding, conscientious, clean-living, loved-up fiancé.'

He sat quietly while he thought. He knew he would have to do something. He was at a disadvantage, on the other side of the world, away from the publicity juggernaut that was Hollywood. He'd have to go on the attack. His father, the military general, would be pleased, he thought wryly.

'All right, I'll go along with this but I have one condition.'

Philippa nodded.

'I get to choose my fiancée...'

'Of course.' Philippa started to gather up the sheaf of actress biographies that Oliver had discarded but he shook his head.

'... But not from those.' He knew what he wanted. Whom he wanted. 'I want it to be Kat.'

'The girl downstairs?'

'Yes. It will be far more believable to think I've fallen in love with someone in Australia rather than with a Hollywood actress who I've absolutely no history with.'

'Give me some credit,' Philippa argued. 'If you have

a look through those bios you'll see several women in there with whom you have been romantically linked in the past.' She shrugged. 'I'll say you rekindled an old flame.'

'No,' Oliver insisted. 'It will be better if she's not a celebrity. There's no dirt to dig up.'

'Are you sure?'

He wasn't sure at all. Not about Philippa's plan and not about getting Kat to agree—but admitting that would get him nowhere. 'Yes. Trust me. I can do this.'

'Yes, I don't doubt that. But can she?'

Would she? was actually the question. 'There's only one way to find out,' he said as he stood up. 'I'll go and get her.'

Oliver closed his eyes and rested his head on the wall of the lift as it descended to the lobby. How did he tell Kat about this? What if she believed that he was to blame for Natalie's death? What if she believed he had a history of drug use? He knew she wouldn't abide that. He knew she'd be disappointed in him and that was the last thing he wanted.

She was sitting at a table by the window, flicking through a magazine. He sat opposite her and reached for her hands, an apology ready. 'Kat, I'm sorry about that.'

'Is everything OK?'

'Not really. Can you come upstairs? I'll explain then.'

Kat followed without question and Oliver let himself breathe again. Maybe it would be OK.

He opened the door to their suite and held it for her.

'Philippa is still here,' he warned, 'and there's something I need to ask you.'

Kat looked wary. 'What's going on?' She was looking from him to Philippa and back to him again.

'Oliver needs a fake fiancée for a fake engagement—'

'Philippa! Please.' Oliver held up a hand. 'I'll handle this.'

Kat's wary expression changed to one of confusion. 'Handle what exactly?'

Oliver still had hold of her hand. He led her to the sofa in the sitting room. He sat on the edge of the coffee table, his knees touching hers. 'Apparently I'm in the headlines again. You remember we spoke about the girl who died of a drug overdose at my house?'

Kat nodded.

'Her parents are suing me. They're saying their daughter didn't have a drug problem and that as the owner of the property I am partly responsible for her death.'

'Are you?'

'No. I told you I wasn't there.'

'Where did the drugs come from?'

'I have no idea. Not from me. I have never touched illegal drugs.'

He saw her glance down at the coffee table. The photo of Natalie's smiling face was poking out from under the pile of papers, touching his thigh.

She picked up the photo. 'Is this her?'

Oliver nodded.

'Do you think they have a case against you?'

'I don't know.'

'Oliver's lawyer will have something to say,' Philippa said.

Kat looked at Oliver enquiringly.

'I have to argue this. I can't stay silent. I am innocent.'

Kat was quiet. Oliver waited anxiously, his heart lodged in his throat, to see if she was going to believe him.

'What if they win? What happens then? It doesn't bring their daughter back,' she said.

'They want money,' Philippa replied. 'If they won there would be a financial settlement, but that's not really the problem. If they win it could ruin Oliver's career.'

'What are you going to do?' Kat looked at Oliver.

'We're in damage control,' Philippa interjected. 'Oliver will refute the charges but he also needs something to boost his image, to maintain his appeal. Something to counteract any negative publicity. He needs something to make him look like a saint, not a sinner.'

'And what does this have to do with me?' Kat looked at Oliver.

'I want you to marry me.'

'*Marry you?*'

He hadn't just said that, had he? That wasn't what he'd meant to say. He was *sure* that wasn't what he'd meant to say.

'You don't have to actually get married,' Philippa responded. 'Just agree to be engaged.'

'And that would entail what exactly?' Kat's tone was frosty.

'Pose for some photos together. Maybe give a couple of joint interviews.'

'Why me?'

'It makes sense,' Oliver told her. 'We can have a whirlwind romance.' It wouldn't be difficult at all to pretend to be in love with Kat. She was gorgeous, kind, smart, and he liked who he was when he was around her. She made him a much better version of himself. He wanted her to think highly of him, he wanted her to respect him.

He didn't want this lawsuit to paint him in a bad light, not to his fans but especially not to Kat. She was becoming important to him. Asking her to be his fake fiancée did make sense, but that wasn't his primary motivator. He couldn't imagine asking anyone else. But he was hesitant to tell her his real reasons. He wasn't sure if he could handle hearing her thoughts. What if she thought he was a disappointment?

'That's a good idea,' Philippa finally agreed. 'You can say you fell head over heels, madly in love the moment you met. It was love at first sight. The fans will lap that up. At least the ones who didn't dream of marrying you themselves. They'll be hoping it all falls through.'

Oliver looked at Kat. She didn't look impressed. 'I don't think you're helping, Philippa,' he said before doing his best to get Kat on board. He really didn't want to pretend to be engaged to anyone but her. 'Kat, it'll be fine. When we get back to Coober Pedy we'll be tucked away in the middle of the desert, so you don't have to worry about crazy fans—I don't think even my craziest fans would find us there.'

'You actually have fans who stalk you?'

'On occasion. But I'll look after you. And this is only temporary. Please?'

'That's right,' Philippa spoke up again, 'it's only temporary. Just continue with the story until this gets sorted. I'll organise everything for your public engagements, your wardrobe, hair, make-up et cetera for any interviews and photo shoots, and you'll be financially compensated for your time and inconvenience.'

'You're going to pay me?'

'Of course. Think of your assistance as being a service for hire, if you will.'

Kat wished Philippa would stop talking. The more she spoke, the more incensed Kat became. She couldn't believe Oliver's publicist thought this was a good idea.

She turned to Oliver to give him a piece of her mind, but he looked devastated. With the exception of when he was acting, she'd only ever seen him in a good mood. Seeing him so despondent gave her pause for thought. 'Is this the best idea you could come up with?'

'Yes,' Philippa answered, even though Kat's question had been directed at Oliver.

She kept her gaze focused on him.

'I'm not sure. It would work,' he paused, 'but whether it's the only option or the best one, I don't know.'

'Why would you choose me?'

'Because I think it's the most believable scenario. I wasn't in a serious relationship when I left the States, so for me to suddenly become engaged it needs to be to someone I've met in Australia. I know you better than anyone else here. But you need to be comfortable with the idea.'

'Can I have some time to think about it?'

Oliver looked at Philippa, reminding Kat again that the whole exercise was staged. Like Oliver's life, everything was manipulated for publicity, for the media, for the fans. Her life was so simple and straightforward by comparison. Would she be able to pull this off? Did she want to?

'We have a little bit of time,' Philippa said. 'It's the middle of the night back home. Your lawyer will make a start on getting character statements about you and he'll look into Natalie's past as well. Can I leave it with you to discuss and let me know tomorrow? I've booked into this hotel too.'

Oliver nodded and showed Philippa out of the suite.

Kat remained on the couch. Stunned. She wasn't sure what to think and even less certain about what to do.

'Are you OK?'

'I'm not sure I understand what just happened.'

'I need your help.'

'That bit I understand, but I need some time to get my head around it.'

Oliver's phone pinged with a text message, distracting them both. She was relieved; she didn't want to talk about the situation right now.

Oliver took his phone from his pocket and looked at the screen. 'It's George; he's out of Recovery and ready for visitors. Did you still want to come or would you rather stay here?'

She didn't want to stay behind. Going to the hospital would give her something to do, something else to think about. 'I'll come with you.'

'I don't want to mention this lawsuit to George. Not yet. He's got enough to worry about.'

Kat nodded. That suited her. She didn't know how they would explain the situation they were in.

* * *

She was pleased to find George in good spirits after his laparoscopic surgery to remove his gall bladder. He was alert and his pain seemed to be under control.

'What's the story, George?' Oliver asked. 'How long before we're back filming?'

'Apparently I can be discharged once my pain is under control and I can move about comfortably. I think I should be back on deck at the end of the week.'

'Did you tell the doctor you'll be going back to Coober Pedy?' Kat asked.

'I said "on location". And that I need to fly. The airline will need a letter from her giving me permission to fly and I need to have someone accompany me.'

'We can do that, can't we, Kat?' Oliver asked. 'We've got to fly back at some point.'

Kat wasn't sure they should rush it. She turned to George. 'It's one thing being comfortable in hospital in the city, George, but it's another thing being in the desert, five hundred kilometres from town.'

'Days off are costing the studio money,' he replied. 'I promise I'll follow medical advice. I'll sit in a chair and direct. You can keep an eye on me.'

'I can't be there twenty-four-seven,' Kat said as she refilled George's glass from the water jug on his bedside table.

George gestured at the jug as Kat emptied it. 'Oliver, could you please find a nurse and see if I can have my water jug refilled?' He waited until Oliver had left the room before turning back to Kat. 'What did he mean, "We've got to fly back at some point"? What's this "we" business? Why are you here? I meant it when I told you to stay away from him, Kat. I don't want you getting hurt.'

'It's OK, George. I can handle it. I'm not going to get my heart broken.'

Thank God they hadn't mentioned the latest development and Oliver's proposal. She hated to think what George would have to say about that. Agreeing to Oliver's request would be the antithesis of staying away from him. A holiday fling was one thing; pretending to be his fiancée was another. The more she thought about it, the more she thought she couldn't do it. She'd have to tell Oliver.

'Oliver and I have decided we've had enough drama,' she continued as Oliver came back into the room; she didn't want him to think they'd been discussing him behind his back, 'so if you promise you will take it easy and can stay out of hospital, I'll agree to be responsible for your health.'

'I know you think I have a chequered medical history but I am normally, fit and healthy.'

'So it's just when I'm around, then?'

'Seems to be.'

'You never did tell me how you two met,' Oliver said as he looked from one of them to the other.

'I was scouting some bush locations in the Adelaide Hills years ago. I twisted my knee and tore some ligaments and had to be carried out. Poor Kat was one of the paramedics at the scene. We got talking about where I'd filmed, what I was looking for. Kat told me about several films that had been shot in Coober Pedy. I'd heard of it, of course, but had never been. I was keen to film there, so when this movie got off the ground I got in touch with Kat to see what connections she had.'

'I told him I'd moved back to town.'

'And the rest is history.'

Their third day in Adelaide began just as perfectly as the others. Oliver hadn't pressed her for her answer yet. He'd planned a day's outing for them and was keen to get on the road. Kat didn't argue. She didn't want to tell him her decision, not yet; she didn't want to disappoint him and potentially taint their last day in the city.

Oliver had organised a car and a driver through the hotel and Kat was enjoying being chauffeured around the Fleurieu Peninsula. Oliver had wanted to get out into the country and see something green, so they had visited a couple of wineries in McLaren Vale, played tourist at the weird and wonderful d'Arenberg Cube, before stopping for lunch at a clifftop restaurant recommended by the hotel concierge that overlooked the beach at Port Willunga.

They were seated on the veranda of the restaurant looking over the water. Oliver had his sunglasses on, hiding his distinctive blue eyes. Kat knew he wanted the anonymity today and the sun was high in the sky, reflecting brightly off the water, making sunglasses kind of mandatory, but she wished he'd take them off. She loved being able to look into his eyes.

Kat couldn't believe people actually lived like this—chauffeured cars, five-star hotels, sipping champagne on an ocean-side cliff-top. Oliver's future, legitimate fiancée would be a lucky woman.

She knew she couldn't avoid the topic any longer. He had been patient but she suspected Philippa would be less so. She knew she'd be expecting an answer the moment they arrived back at the hotel.

She'd spent many hours last night imagining what it would be like to be engaged to him. It was all too easy to imagine and that was when she knew she really couldn't agree to his proposal.

'We need to talk about your request,' she said.

'Have you made a decision?'

She nodded. 'I don't think I can do it.'

'Why not?'

She knew her feelings for him were all too real and she was terrified he'd see that. She couldn't act, and if she played her part convincingly he might figure out that she had fallen for him. She couldn't allow that to happen. They were too different. They had no future and it was best if she didn't get any more involved. She was starting to worry that she wouldn't get out with her heart intact, and playing the part of his fiancée would only make things harder. But she needed a reason that she could give him. 'What if I'm not convincing enough? If people see through me that won't help your case. It'll make us both look ridiculous. If I don't do it, will you be able to find someone else?'

'Yes. Philippa had some ideas. She'll pick someone. I told you it was totally your decision.'

She'd half hoped he'd try to talk her round. But she knew he'd only do that if this was real, not make-believe. She knew she was replaceable. She knew Philippa had several other possible candidates to put in front of Oliver. He'd said he wanted her, but that didn't mean he needed her. He just needed someone. He was smart enough to know there was no point in coercing a fake fiancée into playing the role. That would never work.

He accepted her decision without argument and Kat tried to hide her disappointment. It had been her choice after all.

The waitress had cleared their plates that now showed no traces of the freshly caught King George whiting they'd devoured. Oliver ordered coffee as Kat's mobile vibrated on the table. She glanced at it without intending to pick it up. It was Saskia. She'd call her back.

The phone stopped ringing but buzzed almost immediately with a text message.

Call me—urgent.

Her heart plummeted as icy fingers gripped it and tugged it lower in her chest. Waves of cold fear ran through her. Saskia knew where she was, she'd encouraged her to go with Oliver, and Kat knew she wouldn't interrupt without good reason.

'It's Saskia,' she said as she picked up her phone and showed Oliver the text message. 'I have to call her.'

Oliver nodded.

Kat took her phone outside. She was aware that Oliver stood as she did but he didn't follow her.

She pressed redial and stood on the cliffs at Port Willunga, facing the ocean but not seeing it as she waited for the call to connect and Saskia to answer. It was a glorious day but Kat couldn't focus on anything, her thoughts scrambling in her head as she tried to guess what was wrong. She was desperate for her call to be answered.

'Sas? What is it? Is it Papa?' she said the moment the call connected.

'He's OK.' Saskia immediately tried to quell Kat's rising panic. 'He's on his way to Port Augusta with the flying doctor.'

'What happened?'

'He had a heart attack.'

'What? When?'

'This morning.'

Oh, God. Why had she agreed to come away with Oliver? What was she doing in Adelaide? Her father needed her.

'How is he?' What if he didn't make it? What if she lost him too? Her family was everything to her.

'He's stable. But we'll know more when he gets to Port Augusta. I thought you might want to meet him there.'

'Of course I do. I'll go to the airport now. Has someone gone with him?'

'Rosa has.'

'Can you message Zia Rosa, tell her I'm on my way?'

'OK. Call me later. I love you.'

'Love you too...thanks, Sas.'

'On your way where? What's happened?' Oliver was beside her. She hadn't noticed him come out of the restaurant.

'It's my dad. He's had a heart attack.' Her voice caught on a sob. 'He's being flown to Port Augusta. I need to get there.'

The driver pulled up beside them as Kat finished speaking. Oliver held the car door open for her. 'Hop in. I've paid the bill—we can go straight to the airport.'

She didn't ask how he knew what needed to be done;

she was incapable of thinking logically. She was just grateful that he was there and was willing and able to sort things out. Someone needed to take control and her muddled brain wasn't capable of thinking of anything but getting to Port Augusta. The actual logistics of the trip were beyond her.

'Can you look up flights to Port Augusta for me? I have no idea when the next one will be.'

'I'll call the hotel. They can organise it for us.'

Oliver had his mobile phone in his hand. 'It's Frank Foster,' he said.

Kat was only half listening. She heard something about a plane and bags.

She kept her eyes locked onto her phone, waiting in vain for an update from someone. Anyone.

'How long does it take the flying doctor to reach Port Augusta?' Oliver asked her.

'An hour.'

'So, they're unlikely to be there yet,' he said gently, taking her phone and turning it face down in her lap. 'I'm sure your aunt will call you as soon as she can.'

'What if I don't get there in time?'

'I'll make sure you do. I have a plan. I'm sure everything will be all right.'

'But what if it's not?' Her voice wobbled. 'I was in Adelaide when my mum passed away. I can't go through that again.'

'Kat.' Oliver turned in his seat to face her. He picked up her hands and his touch calmed her, reassured her. 'Saskia said he was stable. He's in the hands of the flying doctors on his way to specialist care. You have to trust them to do their job and trust me to get you there. Do you?' He continued when she nodded. 'And is there anything else you could have done for him if you'd been there? Other than what is happening now?'

'No.' She shook her head.

'So, take a breath. I'll get you there as soon as I can.'

She took his advice and tried her best to relax. She was glad Oliver was with her. When she'd been in this position last time, when she'd received the phone call with the news that her mum had been in a car accident, she'd been alone. This was better.

The car called past the hotel where the concierge was waiting with Kat's bags, as Oliver had arranged, before continuing on to the airport. Kat grew more edgy as they approached the airport. She hoped there wouldn't be any delays with the flight to Port Augusta, no late passengers, no mechanical or security issues. Every minute counted.

The driver pulled to a stop well before the main terminal. Oliver had the door open almost before the wheels had finished turning.

'Why are we getting out here?' Kat asked. The entrance to the terminal was still several hundred metres ahead of them.

'I've booked us a private plane. We can go straight onto the apron. It's waiting for us. It'll take off as soon as we get there.'

'A private plane?'

'It's the fastest way of getting us there. Call your aunt—let her know you're on the way.'

Oliver took Kat's luggage from the driver as she nodded and brought her aunt's number up on the phone. She walked as she talked, disconnecting as Oliver introduced himself to the pilot and they walked out onto the tarmac.

'How is he?' Oliver asked as the pilot stowed Kat's luggage.

'Stable. My aunt will text any updates while I'm in the air.'

'Good news. Let's get going.'

'You're coming with me?' Kat asked as Oliver stepped onto the stairs behind her.

He nodded. 'I didn't think you were in any state to be sent off alone. You don't mind, do you? I didn't think you'd want to be alone with all your thoughts. I won't interfere at the hospital, I'll just see you safely there.'

Of course he wouldn't interfere at the hospital—he didn't do family.

'No, I don't mind. I'd love some company.'

'Good. I'll come back to Adelaide later, once I know you're OK, so that I'm back to accompany George when he's discharged, as promised.'

'I don't know how to thank you,' she said as she collapsed into the seat and felt the plane immediately begin to taxi.

Oliver handed her a bottle of water from the fridge. 'You don't need to thank me. I'm pleased I could do this for you.'

The leather seats were large and comfortable, the air-conditioning was just the right temperature and the bottled water refreshing. Oliver sat beside her and wrapped his arm around her shoulder, holding her close. Kat closed her eyes and finally let herself relax. She was on the way. Oliver had got her this far; there was nothing more she could do right now.

Kat hesitated at the entrance to the hospital emergency department. She could see her aunt Rosa in the waiting area. She didn't want to introduce her to Oliver. Not now. She didn't want to explain who he was and why she was with him. She didn't want distractions.

She turned to Oliver. 'Thank you for all your help. That's my aunt Rosa over there. I can manage from here.'

'You'll be OK?'

Oliver couldn't hide the look of disappointment on his face. She felt terrible for brushing him off but she couldn't deal with any introductions at the moment. He'd told her he didn't do family. He couldn't expect to meet any more of hers. Not now. Not today.

She nodded. She couldn't worry if she'd upset him. She didn't have room in her head to worry about his feelings.

Oliver's breath was coming in short, sharp bursts, keeping time with his fists as he punched into the boxing pads Chris held in front of him. Thwack, thwack, grunt, breathe.

'Take it easy, buddy, you've got to look after that strained rib muscle.'

Oliver could feel the muscle complain every time he landed a punch, but he welcomed the pain. It kept him focused on the exercise, it kept his mind off Kat. A solid session in the gym was the only way to exhaust him. It meant he could collapse into bed at the end of the day and hopefully get some sleep.

'I reckon that will do for today,' Chris said, allowing Oliver one more punch. 'You can cool down on the bike.'

Oliver wasn't ready to call it quits. Not on the session and not on Kat. He picked up his towel and wiped the sweat from his face and neck. He'd go for a run on the treadmill and then cool off.

He cranked the treadmill up, jogging at a pace to keep his heart rate elevated, but the exercise didn't require his full concentration and his mind, inevitably, turned to Kat. He hadn't seen her for three days. She was still in Port Augusta, with her father, who was recovering after heart surgery. She hadn't told Oliver when she'd be back. He hadn't asked.

They'd communicated via text message. He hadn't known what was expected of him. She'd refused to be his fake fiancée but he wasn't really sure why. He could only assume she didn't want to be associated with him and any rumours. He could only assume she was disappointed in him and the situations he found himself in.

She said she believed him, but what if she didn't? Her opinion was important to him. *She* was important to him but he didn't know what to do about that. She had shut him out and he knew he couldn't go after her. He had to move on. With a fake fiancée.

He'd offered to help get Kat to Port Augusta because he could and because he wanted to. He wanted to help her and he also wanted to prove to her that he was capable of thinking about someone other than himself. Something other than his career. But he knew his offer hadn't been completely altruistic. He had hoped it might help her to see past some of his mistakes. Had hoped it might help her to change her mind about him.

But it hadn't helped. She'd sent him away. She hadn't wanted to introduce him to her aunt or her father. He understood it was a stressful time for her but he'd mistakenly, stupidly, thought that he could help ease that stress. That his presence would provide some comfort.

He'd told her he understood her decision not to be his fake fiancée, but it had stung.

She had rejected him.

And now he had to choose someone else to 'propose' to but it was a decision he'd been delaying. Not only because he didn't want it to be someone else but also because it would mean the end of his time with Kat. Once he had a fiancée in the eyes of the world his time spent with Kat would be over. It would have to be.

Philippa had been hounding him to make a decision and he'd promised her an answer tomorrow, but he still couldn't see past Kat. If he needed a fiancée, he still wanted it to be her. It didn't matter how many times he told himself that he'd manage, that he could live without her, he couldn't get her out of his head.

He missed her.

He decreased the speed on the treadmill, slowing it to a walk. He'd go back to his room, shower and have another look at those photos from Philippa. He'd choose someone else and try to forget about Kat. He obviously had stronger feelings for her than she did for him.

He'd made a mistake.

He'd focus on the movie. On his career. Just as he'd always done. Only he knew he'd lost some of the enjoyment that he usually got from work. It was no longer enough to keep him satisfied. He needed Kat.

Kat looked out of the window of the plane at the ochre earth and pale mullock heaps that dotted the landscape. She was relieved to be coming home and relieved that her father was recovering well following surgery to insert a stent into his blocked artery. She had a lot to be grateful for.

Normally she'd be pleased to see the familiar landscape but she had other things on her mind today. She was eager for the plane to land, eager to be home, but more eager to see Oliver. She'd missed his company over the past few days and she intended to head straight to the film set once she'd picked up her car. She needed an Oliver fix and she had something to tell him.

He'd texted her asking after her dad but hadn't intruded. She hadn't asked if he was keeping his distance deliberately or whether a text message was the level of communication he was happy with when it came to discussing her family. She'd been pleased to hear from him but appreciated that he hadn't pushed her. She'd wanted to be able to concentrate on her father without distractions. But now she was keen to see him. Her father was being transferred by ambulance home to Coober Pedy and was going to make a full recovery; she didn't need to feel guilty about spending time with Oliver.

She thanked God for Oliver and his calm, unflappable personality when she'd needed to get to her father's side quickly. For someone who knew how to have a good time it was reassuring to see that it wasn't all about red carpets, private jets and five-star luxury. She'd known he had a good work ethic, she'd seen plenty of evidence of that, but to see such a compassionate side was something special. And it had made her rethink what he'd asked of her.

He had been there for her when she needed him. It was her turn to do the same for him.

She was excited to see him. She'd missed how he made her feel—beautiful, special and fun. He'd shown her there was more to life than working and living here. She didn't want to be disappointed by her life but she wondered how she would go back to normal once he'd left. There'd be no more five-star hotels, no more karaoke serenades, private jets or amazing sex. She suspected he would move on without a backward glance but she doubted she'd be able to do the same. She imagined things would never be quite the same for her again.

She drove out to the film set, the cluster of dusty trailers, marquees and huts in the desert a familiar sight to her now. She parked and headed straight to his trailer. If he wasn't there she'd search elsewhere.

She knocked on his door and was relieved when it opened, and her heart leapt in her chest when she saw him standing there. She'd almost forgotten how gorgeous he was.

'Kat! You're back!' He stepped towards her and she expected him to greet her with a kiss but he stopped in his tracks, stepped back and held the door open wider. 'Come in.'

She stepped inside and saw Philippa sitting on the couch. Was that why he'd held himself back?

'We're just in the middle of something.'

'Actually, I needed to see both of you.' She'd wanted to see Oliver first but her news did involve them both. She might as well tell them together.

Philippa was shuffling through some papers on the coffee table, her movements drawing Kat's eye. She could see pages of photos spread out on the table. Had he picked another fake fiancée? Of course he had.

'Have you chosen someone else?' she asked. She hadn't imagined this scenario. Why hadn't she? She should have known. She'd been stupid. He wouldn't need her now.

'Yes,' said Philippa.

'Why?' asked Oliver.

Oliver hadn't said yes. Maybe there was still a chance he needed her. 'I came to tell you I would do it.'

'Really?' Oliver was staring at her.

'If you still need me.'

'Yes! Definitely.' His smile stretched across his mouth, from one corner to the other, and Kat knew she'd made the right decision.

'I do have one condition,' she added. She waited for both Oliver and Philippa to nod, to show they were at least paying attention. 'I want you to donate any money that you were happy to pay me to the Coober Pedy drive-in, to go towards the upgrading of the facilities. It can be a donation on behalf of Oliver to the town.' She didn't want any remuneration but she had decided this was one thing she could do, one way she could make sure something else positive came out of this. It would be a win for the town and she could sell it as being a grand gesture on Oliver's part. Maybe it would get him some more positive publicity.

'Done.' Philippa didn't hesitate and Kat wondered if she should have named a price.

'And I want another donation to the flying doctor service too,' she said, hoping she hadn't overstepped the mark.

'No problem,' Philippa replied.

'Are you sure you're OK with this?' Oliver asked her. There was the smallest of creases between his blue eyes. He looked worried. She didn't think she'd seen him look worried before. He was normally so full of confidence, so carefree.

She wasn't sure she could pull it off but she knew she wanted to try. She wanted to help. 'Do you really think we can convince people to believe we're in love?'

'Oliver is an actor,' said Philippa. 'It's his job to make people believe.'

'But I'm *not* an actor—do you think I'll be able to do this?'

'I don't; you were Oliver's choice. If you think it's too much for you to handle then I have plenty of other potential fiancées for him.'

Kat was not about to let Philippa get the better of her. She remembered Oliver's words—he wasn't one to back down from a challenge. Neither was she. It wouldn't be hard to pretend to be in love with Oliver. Not too hard at all.

'I want it to be you, Kat.' Oliver reached for her and her body came alive at his touch. 'We can do this.' His blue gaze locked her in place. Their hips were touching. He ran his hands down her upper arms and Kat breathed in deeply as her insides trembled. 'I don't want to do this without you. Are we good?'

She nodded, incapable of speech while his eyes held her attention and his hands held her elbows.

He bent his head and Kat closed her eyes as his lips touched hers. Softly, lightly, a gentle caress.

'Thank you,' he said as he lifted his head, leaving Kat to wonder which kiss that was. It didn't matter, it had been just what she'd wanted. Exactly what she needed.

'I'll take you to dinner tonight,' he said, 'just the

two of us—we need some time to sort out how this is going to work—but now I have to get back on set. Can you meet me at the hotel at seven-thirty? I'll book a table in Mona's restaurant.'

She nodded. She could do this and she'd worry about the consequences later.

Kat dressed carefully, it wasn't every day she got engaged. Even if it was all a charade having dinner at Mona's was reason enough to dress up.

She stepped into the red trouser suit she'd bought in Adelaide. That Oliver had bought her. He'd seen it in a shop window on Jetty Road and had insisted she try it on. He'd said the colour red would always remind him of her. She'd protested that she had nowhere to wear it, it was far too smart for anywhere she went in Coober Pedy, *and* it was too expensive. Oliver had told her she looked beautiful and had bought it for her.

She zipped it up and looked in the mirror. She had to admit it fitted her well but if she hadn't been meeting Oliver she doubted she would have had the confidence to wear head-to-toe red. It was such a bold statement. But Oliver gave her confidence. She recalled the admiration in his eyes when he'd first seen her in this outfit and she crossed her fingers that he'd like it just as much tonight.

He was waiting for her in the hotel lobby. He smiled and took her hands, holding them wide apart as he looked at her. His eyes were bright as he said, 'You look sensational.'

He did too. He had also dressed up and wore pale cotton trousers, a pale blue dress shirt and a navy jacket. He had no tie and wore leather shoes, without socks. He looked as if he'd walked off the page of a fashion catalogue.

He stepped in close and let go of her hands. He put his fingers under her chin, tipping her face up to him and kissing her on the lips. Kat felt the now familiar flutters in her belly as the touch of his lips warmed her from the inside.

'Are you hungry?'

She nodded. He took her hand and she walked beside him towards the restaurant. It was only past the bar, further into the hotel, further underground, but it took them several minutes as several hotel guests requested selfies with Oliver. He asked Kat if she minded, which she didn't, before he posed happily with fans.

When they eventually made it into the restaurant he asked for the quietest table, away from curious ears but still within sight of other diners. He was acting as though he didn't have a care in the world.

'Aren't you worried about the lawsuit?' Kat asked after the waiter had taken their order.

Oliver shook his head. 'I feel sick when I think about what happened to Natalie; she shouldn't have died and I feel terrible that it happened in my house, but it wasn't my fault and I have confidence in my legal team. I admit I've had my fair share of headlines over the years and this is right up there in the scale of monumental disasters, but I know I did nothing wrong. I believe justice will be done. I can't imagine what it must be like for Natalie's parents and I feel for them, I really do, but I'm not going to be made the scapegoat.

'I am not going to let them ruin my reputation or my career. It's one thing to have a reputation as a playboy, another one entirely to be implicated in an accidental death.'

'I know I agreed to be your fake fiancée until you're off the hook,' she said as the waiter brought their meal and Oliver ordered more drinks, 'but do you have any idea how long that might take?' Kat didn't know how successful she'd be in pulling off the role of a fake fiancée, or, more to the point, she was worried that the longer their plan lasted, the more difficulty she'd have separating fact from fiction.

'I'm hoping not long. I want to get it settled and out of the papers. I've spoken to my lawyer. He's got several statements and photographs of Natalie which seem to contradict her parents' claim that she never touched drugs. I feel bad that he has investigators trawling through her private life but her parents instigated this and my lawyer thinks he will have enough evidence soon to get Natalie's parents to drop the lawsuit. I can't thank you enough for what you're doing for me but it shouldn't be for too long. Is that OK?'

She nodded.

'Thank you. I owe you a favour. Two probably.'

'I'll let you pay for dinner.' She smiled, relieved to hear him being so positive about the situation.

'I was going to, and that only takes care of one favour.'

'I'll think of something else,' she said, knowing exactly what she would ask for.

'Good,' Oliver said just as the waiter appeared with a bottle of champagne. 'I want to propose a toast.'

'What are we toasting?' Kat asked as Oliver handed her the glass that had been poured.

'To a successful partnership.' He smiled and touched

his glass to hers. 'I think we could make a good team,' he said as she sipped her champagne. 'Which brings me to another question for you.'

Before she could ask what it was Oliver had stood up from the table and dropped to one knee.

'What are you doing?' Kat almost choked on her champagne.

'Legitimising our agreement.'

Kat was aware of a lull in conversation as the other restaurant patrons all turned to watch them.

'From the moment I first saw you I was captivated but you have shown me so much more than your beauty. Not only are you beautiful, sexy and smart but you are also kind, generous, caring and loving and I need you in my life. I can only hope that you need me too and that I have some of the qualities you value in a part- ner. Kat, will you do me the honour of accepting my proposal of marriage?'

Kat's heart was racing and her hands were shaking but she still noticed that there was no declaration of love. There wasn't anything that could be construed any differently on her part than what it was—a fake proposal.

She knew the other patrons watching wouldn't notice. They'd only see Oliver, down on one knee, proposing. They wouldn't be listening to the words. They'd be caught up in the theatrics. After all, he was an actor. But no matter what they heard and how well Oliver played his role, she knew the engagement was fake and she needed to remember that was all it was. And she had a part to play.

CHAPTER EIGHT

OLIVER WAS STILL down on one knee, waiting. The restaurant was silent, the other patrons all waiting too.

Kat wasn't used to such a public display and the attention made her mind go blank. She had no idea what her lines were. She wasn't used to this at all. She felt tears in her eyes but, while they lent authenticity to the spectacle, she had no idea why she was crying.

Somehow, she managed to nod and suddenly applause rippled around them as Oliver sprang up from his knees and gathered her into his arms and kissed her. Despite her knowing his proposal was a sham, his kisses felt real and Kat took some comfort from that. Being kissed by Oliver was a memory no one could take away from her. That was something she could keep.

She was aware of a barrage of camera flashes as people recorded and photographed Oliver's proposal. She knew the pictures would be uploaded to social media, and perhaps it was all part of the plan—if not Oliver's then definitely Philippa's. She understood this was what she'd signed up for: Oliver needed the positive publicity.

The applause died down when they sat. Oliver

topped up their champagne glasses before reaching behind him, into the pocket of his jacket. When he turned back to Kat he held a small velvet box in the palm of his hand. He flipped open the lid.

Nestled inside was a diamond ring. Teardrop-shaped, in a high claw setting, it was enormous, stunning but totally impractical in the rough and tumble outback and seemed even more so to Kat when she considered her job. She needed something that was tough, that could withstand getting knocked and wouldn't tear into the rubber gloves she was always pulling on for work. She would have chosen a bezel setting and would have preferred an opal.

'Where did this come from?'

'Philippa picked it out this afternoon.'

His proposal might have felt real but it didn't take much to shatter the illusion. Six little words.

Someone else had chosen the ring.

He picked up her left hand and slid the ring onto her fourth finger. It was a perfect fit. The deal was done.

A final burst of camera flashes lit up the room.

Kat looked around nervously. 'The news will be well and truly out before I make it home tonight—you'd better hope my father doesn't hear about this before I have a chance to explain.' She needed to tell her family what was going on. She realised, too late, she should have warned them already.

'I would like to be there when you tell him.'

'Why?'

'Because it's the right thing to do. It's courteous and one thing I've never been accused of is having poor manners. And it's important that I meet your father if we're going to manage to sell this story to the media.'

He was right. Her whole family needed to meet him and she could use his support when she told them of the arrangement. She wasn't sure how they would react to this news. 'You could come to dinner tomorrow.'

'Your weekly family dinner?' He sounded worried.

'It's at Dean and Saskia's…but if you don't think you can handle it…'

'I'll be fine.'

Saskia greeted them at the door and Oliver relaxed slightly. Saskia was a familiar face at least.

He didn't do family but he knew he had to make an exception in this case. Even though he and Kat were only posing as a newly engaged couple, he knew it was important that he meet Kat's father and make sure he got him on side.

But the warm greeting he'd hoped for wasn't forthcoming. Saskia barely acknowledged either of them and if she said 'hello' he must have missed it. She pulled Kat inside and whispered, rather loudly, 'I can't believe you didn't tell us, Kat. It's all over the internet.'

Saskia was brandishing her mobile phone and, without pausing, tapped it and held it up so they could see the screen. A video of Oliver's proposal, recorded by a restaurant patron last night and uploaded to the internet, was running.

Kat's face went pale. 'Does Papa know? Has he seen this?'

Saskia shook her head. 'No.'

'It's not what you think.'

'What does that mean?'

'I'll tell you after we've spoken to Papa.'

Saskia picked up Kat's left hand. 'Where's the ring?'

Her hand was bare.

'In my purse. I was worried about damaging it.'

Oliver knew she was thinking the ring had to be returned. He was finding he was attuned to her thoughts and often knew what she was going to say before she spoke. He was an experienced observer of people, their mannerisms, gaits and habits—it all helped when he was trying to build a character. He was a good mimic of accents too but, while he listened to *how* people spoke, he didn't always listen to what they said. It was different with Kat. *He* was different with Kat.

Kat was definitely upset, obviously worried about her father's reaction to their news, and Oliver's own nerves intensified. He hoped he could pull this off. And he hoped it wasn't a mistake to be meeting Kat's family en masse. To be breaking this news to them collectively.

He was tense as Saskia led them into the house and Kat introduced him to her father. Tony did not look impressed. Kat had warned him on several occasions about her protective father. Oliver just hoped he gave him a chance.

'Papa, this is Oliver Harding. Oliver, this is my father, Tony.'

Oliver extended his hand. 'It's a pleasure to meet you, sir.'

Tony's handshake was firm, his palm rough. He looked Oliver up and down, taking in his neatly pressed clothes, his soft leather shoes, his manicured nails. Oliver was certain he didn't approve and it bothered him. He wanted Kat's father to like him. He knew Kat would be influenced by her family's perceptions of him and he didn't want anything they said or thought to make Kat think less of him.

'You're an actor.'

It was a statement, delivered as though Tony felt actors were on a par with axe murderers.

'Yes, I am.' He wasn't going to apologise for his career choice. He was good at his craft and he made a very good living. He was successful.

'And American.'

'Papa!'

'Settle down, Katarina; an American is as welcome for dinner as the next person. What would you like to drink, Oliver? Will you have a beer?'

'That sounds good, thank you.'

Maybe the night would go better than expected, Oliver thought as he accepted a drink and was introduced to Roger's wife, Maya, as well as Kat's aunt Rosa. Despite doing his best over the years to avoid families—both his own and anyone else's—he found it was nice to be able to put faces to the names that he'd heard so often from Kat.

The family gathered in the spacious living room; although Kat had described their underground houses to him, he was still surprised by the size of the rooms and the height of the ceilings. The room was large and airy with one window that looked out into the front 'garden', which was really just more bare earth with a couple of native eucalyptus trees, an outdoor seating area and a barbecue. Along with the adults, there were several children who ran in and out of the room, interested only in the food that was laid out on the coffee table, but even when Saskia sent them off with their own bowls of crisps the conversational noise level was still high.

Until Kat said, 'Papa, we have some news.'

The noise level in the room dropped immediately, almost as if someone had flipped a switch or pulled a plug. Five pairs of eyes swivelled in their direction. Even though Kat had spoken, Oliver was aware that a lot of the attention was focused on him. Kat had said 'we' and it was obvious her family were keen to hear what was coming next, and Oliver knew they would be gunning for him if they didn't like what they heard.

'It's nothing to get excited about but we wanted to tell you before you heard anything on the grapevine. Oliver and I are engaged.'

'What?' Tony was looking from Kat to Oliver as if he couldn't believe what he was hearing. Oliver and Kat were sitting on the same couch, not touching, and there was a good several inches between them, but even so, Oliver got the impression that Kat's father would very much like to pick him up and put him on another chair, far away from Kat, in another room even.

Oliver was watching Tony but out of the corner of his eye he could see both Roger and Dean. He noticed that they both sat up a little straighter in their chairs, waiting for Tony's reaction, waiting to see if they needed to spring into action. Pick Oliver up and throw him out of the house, perhaps? Oliver didn't doubt that between the two of them they'd have no trouble managing that.

'You're going to marry a man I've never met, and you,' he turned to Oliver, staring him down, 'you didn't have the decency to come to see me first.'

Oliver wondered if he was joking. His expression

suggested he wasn't. Did he really expect that a man would still ask his potential father-in-law for permission to marry his daughter? Did people still do that? Oliver prided himself on his manners but, he had to admit, he had no idea about proper proposal etiquette.

'Papa, calm down. We're not actually going to get married.'

'What on earth does that mean? People don't get engaged to *not* get married.'

'I'm doing this as a favour for Oliver. It's for publicity. It will help his career.'

Dean and Roger were still bristling but at least they'd stayed in their seats. Saskia had excused herself earlier and was busy in the kitchen, and the only person who seemed to be on their side, judging from the sympathetic looks she was sending Kat's way, was Maya. He wasn't sure about Aunt Rosa.

'Would you like to explain exactly *how* an engagement can help a career?' Tony was addressing Kat, completely ignoring Oliver.

'Oliver needs some positive publicity. The media have got hold of a story, a false accusation, and Oliver needs something to deflect attention, something to put a positive spin on things. His publicist thinks an engagement will do the trick. I've agreed to help, just until everything settles down again.'

'And what about you? What do you get out of this arrangement?'

'You know how the Cooper Pedy Residents' Association has been fundraising for improvements for the drive-in? Oliver is going to donate money towards the upgrades and also to the flying doctors. I'm doing this for the town.'

'That's all well and good but what about your reputation? You'll have two broken engagements, Katarina. No man will marry you after that!'

Two? What was he talking about? Oliver's head was spinning as he tried to follow the rapid-fire conversation—perhaps he'd misheard. But before he had a chance to clarify just what had been said Kat was responding to her father.

'Papa, don't be ridiculous. No one even needs to know about this one.'

'Everyone *will* know about this one though, won't they?' Aunt Rosa commented. 'Isn't that the point?' Perhaps she wasn't on their side.

'Kat,' Saskia interrupted as she re-entered the room, 'have you got any balsamic vinegar at your place? I seem to have run out.'

'I'll go and have a look.'

'We'll talk about this when you get back,' Tony muttered as Kat stood up.

'Oliver, why don't you give Kat a hand?' Saskia instructed with a nod.

Oliver didn't hesitate. Saskia had given him an excuse to escape the heat and maybe both he and Tony needed a chance to rein in their tempers and digest information. Tony that his daughter was engaged, and Oliver the news that Kat was engaged *again*. He couldn't believe Kat hadn't said anything.

He followed Kat next door, the heat of the afternoon assaulting him as he left the coolness of the underground dwelling to step outside.

'You've been engaged before?' he asked as the front door closed behind him. He'd wanted a chance to see

Kat's home, to be able to picture her there whenever he wanted to, but he was far too bewildered to take in his surroundings. There were other things occupying his thoughts.

'Yes.'

Oliver was astounded. He'd asked about an ex-husband, so she could have mentioned an ex-fiancé… she'd had plenty of time.

But then again, why would she have? They didn't have to know everything about each other. Even if he wanted to.

'When?'

'Six years ago. When I was in Adelaide.'

Six years! She would have been so young.

'What happened?'

He wanted to know everything, even though he was aware it wasn't really any of his business. It shouldn't matter but he was surprised to find he felt jealous. He'd wanted to be the first one to propose to her.

He knew he was being ridiculous. His proposal wasn't real, but part of him liked pretending it was.

'Mum died.' Kat's voice wobbled and Oliver felt terrible for hounding her. She'd told him about losing her mother a few years earlier. He should have remembered that and put two and two together. 'And I left Adelaide and came back here.'

'And he didn't?'

Kat shook her head and Oliver could see tears gathering on her lashes. Was she crying for her mum or for someone else?

He moved towards her, wanting to take her in his arms and comfort her, but she held up a hand. 'I'm OK,' she said and her words felt like a slap in the face.

'Adam came back with me initially but our plan was never to stay permanently. He was a vet. Is a vet. But there's no work here. Dad had his first heart scare when Mum died. Shortness of breath, difficulty breathing. We thought it was a panic attack but it was cardiac complications, so I didn't feel that I could leave him to cope with losing Mum alone. Even though he's got family living next door I didn't think it was the right thing to do and, to be honest, I didn't want to leave him. I didn't want to leave at all. I needed to have my family around me too. Adam stayed for a while but he didn't like it here. He was bored. He went back to Adelaide. I stayed.'

'For the past five years?'

'Yes.' Kat turned her back and walked into the kitchen. Oliver followed. 'In the beginning there was a lot going on. I was upset with him for leaving. I felt he didn't support me. I was struggling after Mum died and that was our first hurdle, and I figured if we couldn't get through that together there wasn't much hope for our future. Life isn't smooth sailing. I needed to know I could depend on him.

'When I needed him he wasn't there for me. He expected to be the most important person in my life, which he was, mostly, but my family needed me more, and I needed them. Adam wasn't the man I thought he was. Family comes first and there was no room in his life for my family.'

'Kat, I'm sorry, I had no idea.'

'Of course you didn't.'

'Are you sure about doing the whole engagement thing again?' Was she really prepared to have another broken engagement just to help him out, because they couldn't possibly make this work, could they? They came from two completely different worlds and he didn't intend to get married, ever. She was looking for her soulmate.

'It's fine.'

He wished she sounded more convincing but she was no actress. He could imagine how upset she would have been. He knew she wanted to find 'the one' and live happily ever after.

'Are you sure?' He really needed her to stick with the plan and, despite worrying that he might be adversely affecting her life, he really hoped she meant it. 'The whole western world will know about this, Kat. That's the point.'

'Well, it won't cause much of a ripple in Coober Pedy. You said yourself that the tabloids will move on eventually. They'll find another story. A bigger one. They won't be concerned about you, or us, for ever. It will be fine. *I'll* be fine.'

'And your father?'

'Don't worry about my father. I can handle him.'

'You shouldn't have to handle him.' He felt responsible and therefore obligated to help. Kat shouldn't have to handle her father. 'This is my fault. I've put you in an awkward position, and I need to fix it.' He was determined to win Tony over.

'He doesn't know you. I think it's just the shock. I probably should have told him in private; maybe I could have explained things better.'

'I don't want you to bear the brunt of this. That's not fair.'

'It'll be OK; my father can be a little protective of me but I'll get him on side. We should get back,' she said, holding up the bottle of vinegar, 'before they send out a search party.'

* * *

Kat's cousins and her father were in the front, and only, garden, standing around the barbecue. Oliver knew this was his opportunity to attempt to fix things.

He knew how important family was to Kat and, if he didn't, she'd just made it perfectly clear once again. Her family came first. Their opinion mattered to her. It mattered to him too but for different reasons. He wanted to make things easier for Kat but he also needed her family to support, at least publicly, this fake engagement.

Her father and cousins were polite, offering him another drink and making space for him at the grill, but it was clear it was going to have to be up to him to extend an olive branch. That wasn't a problem; he could do that.

'I can understand you have reservations,' he said, extending that branch, 'but I guarantee Kat won't be disadvantaged by helping me.' He wasn't expecting the barrage of questions that came flooding back to him.

'How can you be sure? You can't know her well.'

'You were obviously surprised to hear she'd been engaged before.'

'How do you expect to pull this off if you know nothing about her? How do you expect to convince everyone you're madly in love?'

'What's her favourite food? Her middle name? Her dream job?'

He was surprised to find he knew the answers. He had talked to Kat more than he'd ever talked to anyone. They'd shared plane journeys, car rides and dinners. They'd had hours alone together. She might have kept some secrets but he was convinced he knew the essence of her.

'Her favourite food is roast lamb but she will eat seafood any chance she gets, especially prawns. Her middle name is Maria, after her grandmother, and she always wanted to join the flying doctors but now, ultimately, she'd like to work with the air ambulance. Her favourite colour is red, her favourite movies are romantic comedies and her ex-fiancé's name is Adam.' They didn't need to know that he'd just learnt that but he'd give them what they want to hear even if it wasn't what they expected. 'She is kind and generous, warmhearted, loving.'

Kat was all the things he'd never really experienced in one person before. The people he was normally surrounded by all had an agenda. Even if they were pleasant and honest they all needed something from him—a job, a favour, a photograph. He enjoyed Kat's company all the more because she seemed to enjoy his. She didn't expect things of him and she seemed to like him, the real him, not the movie star.

'I was raised to be hard-working and respectful. I like Kat and I respect her.' He avoided mentioning that he had nothing to do with his father and very little to do with his mother—he suspected that wouldn't win him any fans. In his opinion his family dynamics were irrelevant; he'd worked hard to become the man he was today, to have confidence in his abilities.

'I am a good person.' He wanted to be even better. He wanted to be someone she would be proud of. He wanted to be someone who deserved someone like Kat in his life.

It was obvious Kat's family didn't think he was that person. They didn't think he was good enough and that bothered him. He would have to prove himself. To them and to Kat.

He wished Kat hadn't told her father the engagement was fake—maybe he'd be less hostile if he thought Oliver's intentions were honourable, but then again, maybe not. Either way, he doubted that Tony would be going to give a glowing recommendation of his new son-in-law-to-be if asked either.

'Family is the most important thing in her life,' Oliver said. 'She told me you and her mother were married for thirty-two years, and she wants that too.'

'And what if your little stunt stops her from getting that?'

'It won't. I promise this won't harm her reputation. I'll make sure that she is the one who calls off the engagement, that she comes out of this with her reputation intact.'

'How can you be sure?' Tony demanded. 'You're playing with her feelings. Her life. You should think carefully about what you are asking of her. Think about what she needs.'

He knew Tony was right. He needed to consider Kat's needs before his own but he didn't think that the fake engagement and Kat's needs were incompatible. They were both getting something out of the arrangement and he was positive they could do this without any repercussions.

Dinner was far from the relaxed Sunday night meal Kat was used to. The atmosphere was tense, everyone was on edge, and she wondered if she'd made a mistake agreeing to Oliver's request.

It was important to her that her family liked Oliver.

It shouldn't matter—they weren't going to have a future together—but still, she hadn't expected this level of disapproval.

She, Saskia and Maya tried hard to keep the conversation flowing but it was difficult and there were plenty of uncomfortable silences. When Roger's phone rang in the middle of dinner, Kat jumped, startled by the shrill sound.

Roger got up to take the call but everyone could hear his half of the conversation and the tension increased as they waited to hear what had happened. It was clear there was an emergency of some sort. Dean was out of his seat before Roger disconnected the call.

'That was Emilia,' Roger said. 'Jimmy was due home an hour ago and Emilia hasn't been able to get him on his cell phone.'

'What's going on?' Oliver asked Kat.

'Emilia's husband is a miner. Being late home and not answering his phone isn't unusual—phone reception can be dodgy out here—but he could have had an accident and she can't go and check on him because she doesn't know where he was working. That'll be why she called Roger. He knows where Jimmy's been working. He and Dean will go and take a look. Either Jimmy's phone has gone flat, is out of range, he's found opal or there's been a slide. An accident.'

'Is there anything I can do to help?'

'Not this time. The boys will raise the alarm if necessary. If there has been an accident the mine rescue team will be called in to help, and I need to be available. I'm going to have to take you back to the hotel, just in case.'

'Will you need your car?'

'No.'

'Why don't I borrow it? You don't need to drive me around. I can get myself home and that frees you up now. I will come back in the morning and pick you up—you're working on set tomorrow, right?'

Kat nodded. 'Are you sure?'

'Positive.'

'All right, I'll grab my keys.'

Kat waited while Oliver thanked Saskia and said goodbye to Rosa, Maya and her father. Her father was cool but at least he was acknowledging Oliver, although she was ashamed of the behaviour of the men in her family.

'I'm sorry about Papa—I didn't expect him to be quite so hostile,' she said as she and Oliver left the house.

'Don't worry about it. It doesn't matter if they don't like me as long as they don't make things difficult for you. Will you be OK?'

She nodded and stood outside the house and watched him drive away, wondering again if this would work out according to the plan.

She went inside to give Saskia and Maya a hand cleaning up.

'That went badly,' she said as she picked up a tea towel and started to dry the glasses.

'What did you expect?' Saskia asked.

'Why exactly did you agree to this?' asked Maya.

'He asked for my help.'

'And you couldn't refuse.'

'No, I couldn't. I owed him a favour. He got me back to Port Augusta after Papa's heart attack. He was amazing. So calm and in control. He did that for me and now I can do this for him.'

'What was so bad that he needed to create a good fake news story to deflect the bad news?'

Kat explained about the lawsuit. 'That's why I agreed to help him.'

'Your father will go ballistic if he hears about that.'

'That's why I'm not saying anything to Papa and the boys. Oliver is certain the lawsuit will be dropped and I believe him. They already don't trust him and I don't want to make things any worse.'

'You don't think they'll find out?'

'How? They never look at any entertainment news. They're only interested in three things—finding opal, the price of opal and the football.'

'And family,' Maya added as her phone beeped with a message. 'It's Roger,' she said. 'Jimmy's OK. He found a seam of opal and lost track of time.'

'Are you sure you're OK with this whole fake engagement?' Saskia asked; it was obvious she wasn't going to let this go. 'I know you like him. You don't feel like he's taking advantage of your generosity? Your feelings?'

'It's a business deal. It's not hurting anyone. I'm helping him. Just like he helped me and like he'll be helping the community with his donation to the drive-in and to the flying doctor.'

'It's one thing for him to help with a search or to donate money; it's another thing completely for him to get you involved in this publicity stunt. And what about going forwards? What's the plan then?'

'He'll win the lawsuit and then we'll call it off.'

'When will that be?'

'I'm not sure exactly.'

'And you're OK with that?'

Yes.' She'd have to be. It was the deal she'd made.

Kat scarcely had time to worry about her family's opinion of Oliver over the next week. Philippa had done her
job and the video footage of Oliver's proposal had gone
viral. The media had turned up in full force, clamour-
ing for a story, and Kat's life had become a whirlwind
of interviews and photo shoots interspersed between
her work on and off set. It left barely any time for the
two of them to be alone together and even less time for
her to dwell on all the reasons her family disapproved
of the 'engagement'.

She had explained Oliver's involvement in getting
her to Port Augusta from Adelaide to see her father,
and she thought that maybe her Papa was softening a
little, but it didn't really matter. It wasn't a real relationship. Her family didn't have to like him. It wouldn't
bother Oliver, he didn't do family, and she wouldn't
let it bother her.

They had done a couple of interviews early in the
week, all arranged by Philippa, for the Australian
media. Kat had been super-nervous but the journalists had been gentle and Oliver had been beside her
all the time. He was very relaxed in front of the camera and his experience and calmness helped to settle
Kat. Those interviews would be syndicated around
the world but today they were faced with several interviews on a much larger scale. These would be the
last of their joint interviews and first up was a panel
of print journalists from the States followed by an interview that would go to air on American television.

Philippa had organised hair and make-up for Kat and she'd flown in a selection of outfits for Kat to choose from. Kat had insisted on Australian designers but she'd never heard of half of the ones Philippa had chosen. To give her credit, all the outfits were gorgeous but that made it impossible to choose just one. In the end Kat had asked Oliver's advice and he'd chosen a sleeveless cobalt-blue trouser suit with a halter neckline. The colour of the outfit reminded her of Oliver's eyes.

She felt overdressed, and over-made-up, for the middle of the morning but Oliver had reminded her that the television interview would be screened in the evening and she would look perfect.

He had held her hand and led her to the couch for the interview. He'd insisted that they be seated on a couch, not two separate chairs, and Kat had been grateful for that; she'd needed him close.

The interview began with all the questions Kat had become used to. How they had met. What Kat did for a job. How she had found growing up in Coober Pedy.

Oliver was very attentive: he was constantly touching her, his hand on her thigh, around her shoulders or holding her hand. He made her feel beautiful and she almost believed his answers when he talked about how they'd met, what he had thought when he first saw her and how they'd fallen in love. He almost had her convinced that he had real feelings for her but then she remembered that he did this all the time—put on a show for the media. He would give them what they wanted to keep himself in the headlines. It was all just an act. Even when he held her hand, a move that appeared so relaxed and natural, she noticed that he made sure her engagement ring was on show.

She forced herself to concentrate. This was their last interview and she had a part to play.

'Have you set a date for your wedding?'

'Not yet.' Oliver fielded most of the questions but he looked at her before answering, giving the impression that they were a team.

'Where will you get married?'

'We haven't decided.' He squeezed her hand and smiled at her and Kat knew the audience would think they had decided but were keeping that information to themselves.

'Will it be a big celebrity wedding or something private?'

'I'd like a big wedding. I want to show Kat off to everyone but she hasn't met my friends yet. It might be a small wedding if she doesn't like them.' His blue eyes sparkled as he laughed.

'Will they like her?'

'They will love her.' He looked at Kat, holding her gaze, his expression now earnest.

'Have you met her family?'

'I have.'

'And what did they think of Oliver, Kat?'

'They found him charming.' That was true of Maya and Saskia at least. Kat didn't feel she needed to be any more specific—in fact, Oliver had coached her in what to say.

'What about this lawsuit? You're standing by your man while he fights these charges, Kat?'

'Of course.'

'Any comment, Oliver?'

'No comment. I have every faith in our justice system. I am extremely sorry for the Hanson family's loss but we are focusing on our own future.'

'And what does that future look like, Kat? Will you be starting a family?' The journalist moved quickly along. Kat knew from previous interviews that they had to ask the question but, as it was all based on supposition, they couldn't really continue with that line. 'Do you want children?'

'Of course,' she replied, keeping her gaze directed at the journalist. 'Very much.' She couldn't look at Oliver; she was afraid he'd see the truth in her eyes.

'Oliver?'

'Definitely.'

He was looking at her and Kat's heart flipped in her chest. He looked as if he meant every word.

'The movie is about to wrap on location and filming will move back to the States. Are you going to be moving too, Kat?'

'Kat will join me later. It won't be much fun for her in the States, away from her friends and family, while I'm working.'

Oliver was giving answers they hadn't discussed but Kat knew it didn't matter. None of this was real and by the time 'later' came around the lawsuit would be over and Oliver wouldn't need her any more. The idea was upsetting but there was nothing she could do.

Kat's heart sat like lead in her chest. It was supposed to be a party—it *was* a party—but she was miserable. The movie had wrapped on location and Oliver was leaving tomorrow. Filming would finish in the studio in the States. She knew she would miss him, she knew her life would never be the same without him. But she would cope, she'd have to.

She was talking to Julia when she saw him crossing the room towards them. It was getting late and she knew, at best, they only had a few hours left. She pasted a smile on her face, although her heart was breaking.

'Kat, could I borrow you for a second?'

He could have her for a lifetime if he wanted.

She nodded.

'I have something I want to give you,' he said as he took her arm and led her to a quiet corner. He sat her down and handed her a pile of beautifully wrapped gifts. A stack of box-shaped presents, but none small enough to be jewellery. They looked like books.

Kat swallowed her disappointment and opened the first one.

It was a photograph. He'd made copies of some of the publicity photos they had taken together. He'd framed them for her and included her favourite one. It captured her sitting on his lap. She was smiling and he was laughing. His head was thrown back, and they weren't looking at each other—she was leaning forwards away from him—but his arms were wrapped tightly around her waist, as if he was afraid to let her go. She wished that were the case.

Even though it was all an act she couldn't deny the photos were gorgeous. She looked happy; she glowed. She looked like a woman in love.

She hoped he didn't notice.

'These are gorgeous. Thank you.'

She knew she would treasure the pictures. One day. She wasn't sure if she was ready to display them just yet. She might need some time before she was ready to see his face every day, before she was ready to see the reflection of her unrequited love.

She hadn't meant to fall in love with him. She'd thought she'd be able to come out of this with her heart intact but it seemed fate had other ideas in store for her. It was time to bring this all to an end before she crumbled completely.

'Oliver?' she said as she wrapped the frames up again. She would look at them later. Alone. 'There's something I wanted to speak to you about. You're leaving tomorrow and I'm not sure what you and Philippa want me to do or say about our "engagement" once you're gone.'

'I thought maybe I'd say you're coming to visit me in a few weeks. What do you think?'

She didn't want to visit. She wasn't interested in a holiday. This was her chance to find out if he had genuine feelings for her at all. She wanted him to offer her a future. A life together. She wanted him to propose to her for real. But it seemed a few more days was all she could have. It wasn't enough, not nearly, and she wouldn't settle for that. 'Is that necessary? Don't you think the lawsuit might be resolved by then?'

'That wouldn't matter. You could still visit me.'

She shook her head. She'd hoped she wouldn't be faced with this scenario, the one where Oliver didn't profess his undying love, but she'd thought this through, just in case. 'We have to call the engagement off eventually. It will make our break-up more authentic if we don't see each other again after you leave. I thought we could go with the story that I am staying here while my dad recovers. When the lawsuit is over your life will go back to normal. You won't need me any more. You'll forget all about me.'

She waited for him to say that wasn't what he wanted.

'You don't want to visit me?' he said, which wasn't the same thing at all.

'I wouldn't want to leave Papa.'

'Kat, he's fine. He's recovered well from his surgery. You could leave for a few weeks.'

She felt guilty using her father as her excuse but she wanted more than a few weeks. She wasn't going to settle for less even if it meant suffering a broken heart. She knew that if he loved her they would find a way to work things out. But it looked as if she wasn't going to get her wish. 'I have to stay.'

'If that's what you want.'

No. It wasn't what she wanted at all. She wanted him to say he loved her, that he couldn't live without her, that he would stay with her. But she knew that was impossible. 'I should go,' she said. She didn't belong here. In his world.

'Now?'

She nodded. She loved him but she didn't expect him to love her back. She needed to make a clean break. She couldn't stand the thought of saying goodbye but she knew she had to. And she had to do it quickly.

They didn't speak as he walked with her to her car. There was nothing left to say.

He took her in his arms and spun her to face him. 'You are wrong, by the way,' he said as he lifted her chin and looked into her eyes. 'I'll never forget you,' he said as his lips came down onto hers.

The kiss was gentle. Sad. Kat didn't know that was even possible.

She knew it was a goodbye kiss but she thought it might be better called the 'break my heart' kiss.

'You have an open invitation to visit me any time, so let me know if you change your mind,' he said as she made herself let go of him.

She nodded and got into her car. She could feel tears threatening to spill and she didn't want to cry in front of him. She didn't want him to see how her heart was breaking.

She wiped away her tears with the back of her hand as she drove away. She didn't look back. She knew she'd turn right around if she did.

He watched her drive away. He could scarcely breathe and his heart ached in his chest. He wasn't ready to say goodbye. He wanted to chase after her, to beg her to reconsider but he knew he'd be wasting his time. She wasn't going to leave her father. Her family came first. It was what she had always told him but he'd hoped that maybe he would be worth the sacrifice on her part. But if she wouldn't leave for a few weeks, how could he ask her to leave for ever?

And how did he expect it to work? What would they do going forwards? Where did he see them? Did they have a future? Could he expect her to leave everything she loved behind to travel with him? To live his nomadic existence…his lonely, nomadic existence? He couldn't ask her to leave with him. Everything she loved was here. Her family, her career, her world. She was surrounded by people who loved her. And she had chosen to stay with them. He'd known she would but he'd hoped differently.

He wanted her to love him, to choose him, but was that fair? Did he love her?

He didn't know. He'd never been in love before. All he knew was that, watching her drive away, he felt as if she was taking his heart with her.

He stood and watched until her tail lights disappeared.

Leaving him alone again. As always.

CHAPTER NINE

'HOW ARE YOU? Have you heard from him?' Saskia asked as she sat on Kat's bed and watched her tidy her room.

'No.'

Oliver had been gone for a week. Kat had seen an interview he'd given at Sydney Airport as he left the country. He'd been asked about his fiancée and he had looked suitably upset when he'd replied that Kat was staying in Coober Pedy temporarily while her father was recovering from surgery but was planning to join him later.

She knew that wouldn't happen.

'You should have gone with him.'

'I can't leave Papa. I'm all he has.'

'It's not for ever, Kat. And that's not true. He has Rosa, me, the boys, Maya. We're all here. You could have gone.'

'What would be the point? It's not real, Sas. It's all make-believe.' Oliver had asked her to visit but Kat wanted more. She wanted for ever. She wanted true love.

Saskia picked up a framed photo. Kat's favourite. 'It looks pretty real.'

'It was all an act.' At least on his part. She wanted to believe they shared something real but she really wasn't sure. She'd fallen in love with him and their connection had felt real to her, but what if she'd fallen for Oliver because of a fantasy? Because she'd always dreamt of finding the one. What if he wasn't the one but was simply an option? 'He doesn't need me.'

'Are you sure? You could go and find out. What's the worst thing that could happen? You find it's not what you thought and you come home miserable. You're already miserable, so isn't it better to take a chance? What are you afraid of?'

She was afraid he wouldn't want her. That she wasn't sophisticated enough and wouldn't have anything in common with his life. His friends. His world. That she wouldn't belong. That she'd look out of place and he'd see she wasn't right for him.

She was afraid that their differences were bigger than their similarities because, after all, what did they really have in common? They had talked and laughed and loved. They had shared secrets and dreams, but those secrets and dreams were so different.

She felt as if she knew him but she was scared to take a chance. It was easier to stay than to take a risk. She liked to play it safe. She liked to follow rules. She liked routine. He was a rule-breaker, independent. She needed her family and friends. He was a loner. She could get past all those differences with the exception of family. She wasn't sure if she could be with someone who didn't value family.

'We are too different.'

'Don't be ridiculous.' Saskia wasn't holding back with her opinion. 'Since when do you think that every couple has to be exactly alike? Why should they think alike, act alike? Imagine how boring that would be. Think about how he makes you feel.'

He made her feel special. He made her feel beautiful. He made her happy. And now he'd made her miserable. She was lonely. She missed him.

'If you're not going to go to him maybe you just need to get away from here for a while. Away from the memories. We should have a girls' trip. Maya and I could leave the kids with our husbands and go with you. What do you think?'

'Maybe,' she said, but what she thought was, what if she was away and something else went wrong? Or, even worse, what if Oliver came back for her but she wasn't here?

She knew that was a ridiculous notion but she could admit, if only to herself, that it was what she was dreaming of.

She'd fallen in love with him but there was nothing she could do.

He was gone. It was over.

Kat looked at the clock. Fifteen minutes until the end of her shift.

Her life had been dragging on painfully slowly for the past four weeks since Oliver had left. Every morning she woke up hoping to feel better. Hoping she wouldn't feel as though part of her was missing. When would it end?

'Do you think it's safe to get changed now?' she asked Dave. 'Saskia and Maya are going to collect me from here.'

She was going out to dinner with her cousins' wives

to celebrate Maya's birthday. The other crew would be here to take over shortly and she wanted to be ready to go, but she knew how often a last-minute emergency would derail any plans for an on-time knock-off.

'Sure. It's been—'

'Don't say it!' Kat held up her hand in warning. She was superstitious enough to stop Dave from uttering the word. The minute you said a shift had been quiet, chaos would descend.

Dave laughed. 'Go and get changed. I'll hold the fort.'

Kat barely had time to get her boots off before Dave was knocking at the door. 'Kat, we've got a call-out. Are you still dressed?'

She sighed and stuffed her feet back into her boots, leaving her bag with her change of clothes behind.

'Take your bag with us,' Dave said. 'I might be able to drop you straight to dinner.'

She doubted that—it seemed as though everything that could go wrong did. Her life was a mess. 'Where are we going?' she asked as they climbed into the ambulance.

'Out towards Crocodile Harry's place,' he said as he handed her the GPS coordinates so she could punch them into the satnav as he drove. 'A couple of tourists; one's had a fall, a suspected fractured leg.'

Crocodile Harry's was only ten minutes out of town. It was where George had filmed the cave scenes and the mention of it made Kat immediately think of Oliver.

'Do we know what we're looking for?' Kat asked.

'A white Toyota Landcruiser.'

Lucky, then, they had the GPS details. Those vehicles were a dime a dozen out here.

Dave drove west into the setting sun. Kat flipped the sun visor down, the sun was low in the sky making visibility difficult, and her sunglasses weren't providing enough resistance against the glare as she searched the horizon.

'I see a car.' She pointed to their left, to where a four-by-four sat on top of a hill. It was approximately in the right position according to the satnav.

Dave turned off the main road and bumped his way over the rough terrain. As they approached Kat could see a table and chairs set up beside the vehicle. It looked as if someone had gone to a lot of trouble to set up a picnic to watch the sunset. Four tall posts had been erected and fairy lights were strung between them. Solar powered, they were just beginning to shine in the dusk. The table and two chairs sat beneath the lights.

Kat jumped out of the ambulance, swung open the back door and grabbed her kit. She headed for the vehicle.

A man appeared from below the crest of the hill. The way he moved reminded her of Oliver and she felt a pang of loss as she blocked that thought. She had been thinking of him on the drive out here and now her imagination was playing tricks on her.

The man came closer. He looked just like Oliver.

She held her hand up to shield her face from the setting sun. Surely it couldn't be him?

'Hello, Kat.'

It was him. The sound of his voice set her heart racing. He smiled his familiar smile; it started at one corner of his mouth, spreading across his lips and lighting up his eyes. Kat couldn't breathe. She felt dizzy and was afraid her legs would buckle.

'Oliver? What are you doing here?'

'Waiting for you.'

She looked around in confusion. 'Where's the patient?'

'There isn't one.'

She turned around to question Dave, unable to work out what was going on. Dave stood behind her holding the bag that contained her change of clothes. Clothes she had packed to wear to dinner with Saskia and Maya. He passed the bag to her, swapping it for the medical kit, and walked off without a word.

'I don't understand,' she said, turning back to Oliver. 'I'm supposed to be having dinner with Saskia.'

He was shaking his head. 'You don't have any other plans. Dave, Saskia, Maya—they're all part of this.'

'Part of what?'

'Come and sit down.' He took her hand and Kat clung to him, not sure she was going to be able to walk without help. Her brain had frozen. Nothing made sense.

Oliver pulled out a chair for her at the table and she almost collapsed into the seat. The table had been covered with a white tablecloth, and two champagne glasses, an ice bucket with a bottle of champagne and a vase of flowers had been laid out on top. She stared at the tableau.

'Did you do this?'

He nodded. 'I did it for you. There's something I need to discuss with you. It's about our engagement. There's something I need.'

'I'm sorry, I should have thought,' she said as she started to tug at her engagement ring. Her hands were hot and clammy, the ring tight on her finger. It wouldn't budge.

She wasn't sure why she was still wearing it. It was totally impractical in her job but she hadn't been able to make herself take it off. She pretended she was worried she might lose it but that wasn't true. She wore it because it was a reminder of him. She'd been surprised that he had never asked for it back, but then they'd never officially called off the engagement. She supposed this was it.

But that didn't explain the champagne, the flowers, the table under the lights. She was totally confused.

'What are you doing?' he asked her as she continued her futile attempt to remove the ring.

'Of course, you need this back.' She reached into the ice bucket and grabbed some ice cubes to cool down her finger.

'What? No! That's not what I came for. You can keep it.'

'I don't want it,' she said as she finally tugged it free. 'You need to give it back to Philippa.'

'I suppose I should,' he said as he took it and slipped it into his pocket. 'You never liked it anyway.'

He was right, she hadn't, not only because it was impractical but also because it had no meaning. It hadn't been given with love.

'It's a beautiful ring,' she said, 'but it was never mine to keep. I know we need to end our engagement but you didn't need to come all the way back here.' Oliver had been in touch a week ago to tell her the lawsuit had been dropped. She'd known then that he didn't need her any more. 'I could have sent the ring back to you.'

'I'm not here for the ring, Kat. I'm here for you.'

'For me?'

He nodded. 'I never should have left. I should have fought for you. For us. I should have told you I love you.'

'You love me?'

'I do.'

It was exactly what she'd wanted to hear but she couldn't understand why he hadn't told her this before. What had changed? What was going on? 'Why didn't you tell me this before?'

'I was scared.'

'Of what?'

'I didn't think I deserved you. I didn't think you would choose me. I thought you would choose your family. I know how important they are to you and I didn't know how I could compete with them, but then I realised I don't want it to be a competition. I don't want you to choose them or me. I want you to choose me as well. I want to be your family too. I just hope I'm not too late.

'I want to be the man you deserve, the man you love. I want you to be proud of me. You have given me a sense of purpose—you have made me want to be a better version of myself. A better person, a better son, a better man. But I had to work out who I was. Who I wanted to be.'

'I don't understand.'

'Let me explain.' He reached across the table and held her hand. 'I don't think I have ever really felt comfortable in my skin. I have never truly felt a part of something; I've always felt as though I'm a disappointment. I think that's why I love acting—it's a chance to escape from myself, from reality. It's a chance to be someone different, someone who isn't real, someone who won't disappoint real people. For years I've been searching, trying to find my place in the world, trying to work out what my purpose is, but it's been a lonely existence. But since I met you I can see myself as part of a bigger picture. Part of something special.

'I want to be part of something real. You exist in the real world and you've shared your world with me, you've shown me what is out there. I'm tired of make-believe— I want to be part of your world. Of your life. I love you and I want to marry you.'

'You want to marry me?'

'I do. I love you and I want to spend my life with you. Until I met you I didn't believe that there could be one person who was the right fit for me, or that I would be the right person for somebody either. I thought that sounded clichéd, boring, that there would be nothing left to look forward to, but you have shown me that with the right person I can have all of that and more. I can have someone to share that with. Something to look forward to together. I want to be part of something bigger than myself. I want to be part of us. Everything about you has made me change my mind. I'm a changed man. Trite maybe, clichéd certainly, but that doesn't mean it isn't true. I want to be the man you want to spend the rest of your life with. I need you.'

The sun had set now. It was nearing winter and the end of the day came quickly in the desert. The temperature was dropping as darkness fell. The sky was dark and clear and the fairy lights merged together with the stars.

'I wanted to bring you out here so it was just you and

me this time. This is about us. Just us. I want you to know this is real. There's no performance. No agenda. I know you think we are very different but there is one thing we have in common: we both want to be loved. I love you and I hope that, just maybe, you love me too.'

He stood and knelt in the red earth beside Kat. 'Katarina Maria Angelis, I love you, I adore you, I need you. I want to spend the rest of my life with you, as your husband. Please will you make my life complete? Will you marry me?'

'Yes,' she said as she pulled him to his feet. 'I do love you and I do adore you. I need you too and yes, I will marry you.'

She wound her arms around his neck and kissed him deeply, pouring all her emotions into the kiss, letting him know that she loved him, adored him and needed him.

'There's one more thing,' he said as he pulled a ring box from his pocket. He held it in the palm of his hand and flipped the lid open. A round black opal was nestled inside. Even in the semi-darkness it flashed with vibrant colours—red, blue and green. It was in a bezel setting, surrounded by diamonds. Kat didn't recognise the setting but she was sure she recognised the stone. Black opals were extremely rare.

'Is that my mother's opal?'

Oliver nodded. 'Your father said you've always loved it. He gave it to me and I got it reset today.'

'My father gave this to you?'

'Yes. Along with his blessing. I went to see him, to explain my intentions. I wanted him to believe that I deserve you. I wanted him to trust that I am worthy of marrying his daughter. That I will take care of you. That I love you.'

He slipped the ring onto her finger. It was perfect. He was perfect.

And, as he kissed her again, Kat knew they would be perfect together.

* * * * *

COMING SOON!

We really hope you enjoyed reading this book. If you're looking for more romance, be sure to head to the shops when new books are available on

Thursday 26th December

To see which titles are coming soon, please visit

millsandboon.co.uk/nextmonth

MILLS & BOON

Coming next month

THE MIDWIFE'S SECRET CHILD
Fiona McArthur

'Let us see where this leads us, Faith. I will not let you down again.'

Her barriers quivered under the strain but held. 'As you say. We'll see.'

She watched his eyes narrow at her less than trusting response.

He held out his palm and reluctantly she took his strong fingers in hers and his warmth seeped into her like it had from the first moment they'd met years ago and did again – until their hands separated, slowly.

She tucked her fingers behind her back. Instead of stepping away he stepped closer. His bulk blocking out the light from the open door. His male scent coated with the salt of the sea. His strong jaw coming closer as he leaned in and she turned her head until he kissed her cheek. His breath warm on her face, his mouth even warmer, and despite herself her body softened even with that light touch. His hand came up and caressed the other side of her cheek. Cupping her face with more warmth and such tenderness that slowly she turned her head towards him. Towards his full, sensuous mouth, until their lips were a breath apart. Inhaling the life force between them as they hovered on the brink of the kiss that shouldn't.

Yet, it was she who leaned forward and offered her mouth, her first sign of trust, her first forgiveness.

But it was he who propelled them slowly but surely into a kiss that buckled her knees and sent her hands up between them to clutch his shirt. His arms came around her with a certainty and possession that jammed them together until her breasts were hard against his rock like chest. She wanted to be lost like this so much.

She pushed him away.

He stilled at once. Nodded, turned and left before she could make her feet move. Her breath eased out. She sagged against the door she moved to shut. Phew.

Continue reading
THE MIDWIFE'S SECRET CHILD
Fiona McArthur

Available next month
www.millsandboon.co.uk

MILLS & BOON

THE HEART OF ROMANCE

A ROMANCE FOR EVERY KIND OF READER

MODERN

Prepare to be swept off your feet by sophisticated, sexy and seductive heroes, in some of the world's most glamourous and romantic locations, where power and passion collide.
8 stories per month.

HISTORICAL

Escape with historical heroes from time gone by. Whether your passion is for wicked Regency Rakes, muscled Vikings or rugged Highlanders, awaken the romance of the past.
6 stories per month.

MEDICAL

Set your pulse racing with dedicated, delectable doctors in the high-pressure world of medicine, where emotions run high and passion, comfort and love are the best medicine.
6 stories per month.

True Love

Celebrate true love with tender stories of heartfelt romance, from the rush of falling in love to the joy a new baby can bring, and a focus on the emotional heart of a relationship.
8 stories per month.

Desire

Indulge in secrets and scandal, intense drama and plenty of sizzli hot action with powerful and passionate heroes who have it all: wealth, status, good looks…everything but the right woman.
6 stories per month.

HEROES

Experience all the excitement of a gripping thriller, with an inten romance at its heart. Resourceful, true-to-life women and strong, fearless men face danger and desire - a killer combination!
8 stories per month.

DARE

Sensual love stories featuring smart, sassy heroines you'd want as best friend, and compelling intense heroes who are worthy of the
4 stories per month.

To see which titles are coming soon, please visit

millsandboon.co.uk/nextmonth